Y0-BZE-202

D

SRA
Connecting
Math Concepts

SRA

Columbus, Ohio

The **McGraw·Hill** Companies

Acknowledgments

The authors are grateful to the following people for their input in the field-testing and preparation of *Connecting Math Concepts, Level D:*

Lou Bradley
Jane Dougall
Marjorie Feyer
Debbi Kleppen
Amy Lindquist
Carolyn McFadden
Lori McGinty
Barbara Nielson
Juan Carlos Nolasco
Laurie Nowak
Mary Rosenbaum
Vicky Santos
Pam Sprute
Kathleen Taylor
Charlene Annette Tolles
Linda Van Hook
Roberta Weisberg
Bryan Wickman

www.sra4kids.com

**SRA
McGraw-Hill**

Copyright © 2003 by SRA/McGraw-Hill.

All rights reserved. Except as permitted under the United States Copyright Act, no part of this publication may be reproduced or distributed in any form or by any means, or stored in a database or retrieval system, without the prior written permission of the publisher, unless otherwise indicated.

Send all inquiries to:
SRA/McGraw-Hill
8787 Orion Place
Columbus, OH 43240-4027

Printed in the United States of America.

ISBN 0-02-684686-1

6 7 8 9 VHG 08

The McGraw-Hill Companies

Contents

Program Summary

Facts about *Connecting Math Concepts, Level D*

Children who are appropriately placed in Level D	Students who have completed Level C or who pass placement test
Placement criteria	Pass placement test (see page 9)
Format of lessons	Scripted presentations for all activities Program designed for presentation to entire class
Number of lessons	Maximum 120 (including 10 test lessons)
Content	Lessons 1–6: Review of Level C Lessons 7–120: New teaching, extensions of earlier-taught concepts, and projects
Scheduled time for math periods	45–50 minutes per period for teacher-directed activities Additional 15–25 minutes for independent work
Weekly schedule	5 periods per week
Teacher's material	*Teacher's Guide* *Presentation Book 1* (Lesson 1–Test 6) *Presentation Book 2* (Lesson 61–end of program) *Answer Key*

Student material	Program material:
	    Workbook (Lessons 1–120)
	    Textbook (Lessons 1–120)
	Additional materials:
	    calculator
	    ruler
	    small paper bags
	    blank cards
	    coins
	    dice
	    scissors
	    tape measures or yardsticks
	    colored pencils

In-program tests	Test Lessons 1–10 Following every 10th regular lesson (10, 20, 30, through 100)
Remedies	See page 38, Test Remedies

Scope and Sequence for
Connecting Math Concepts, Level D

Lessons

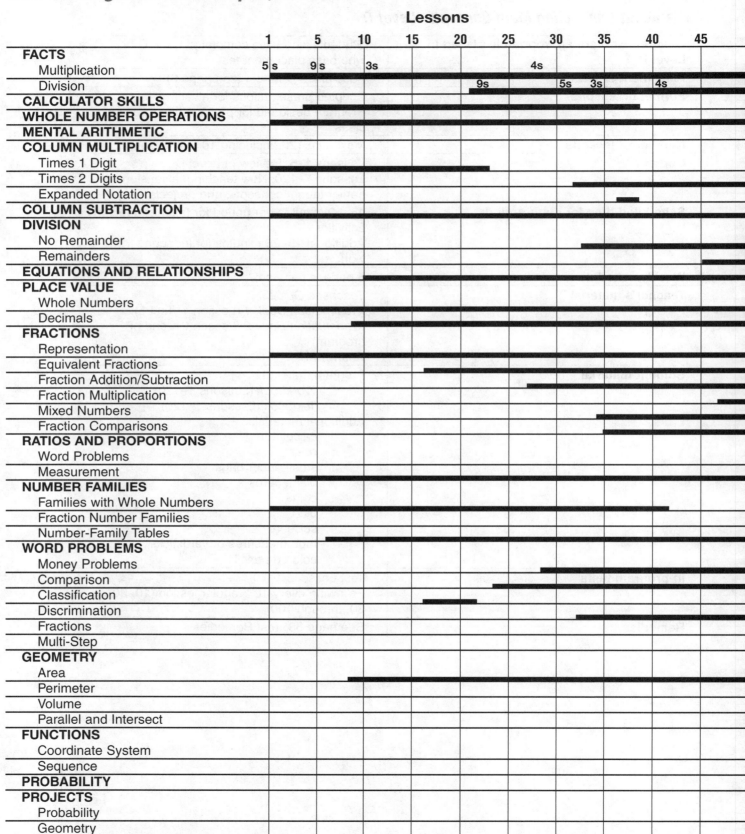

	1	5	10	15	20	25	30	35	40	45
FACTS										
Multiplication	5s	9s	3s				4s			
Division					9s		5s 3s		4s	
CALCULATOR SKILLS										
WHOLE NUMBER OPERATIONS										
MENTAL ARITHMETIC										
COLUMN MULTIPLICATION										
Times 1 Digit										
Times 2 Digits										
Expanded Notation										
COLUMN SUBTRACTION										
DIVISION										
No Remainder										
Remainders										
EQUATIONS AND RELATIONSHIPS										
PLACE VALUE										
Whole Numbers										
Decimals										
FRACTIONS										
Representation										
Equivalent Fractions										
Fraction Addition/Subtraction										
Fraction Multiplication										
Mixed Numbers										
Fraction Comparisons										
RATIOS AND PROPORTIONS										
Word Problems										
Measurement										
NUMBER FAMILIES										
Families with Whole Numbers										
Fraction Number Families										
Number-Family Tables										
WORD PROBLEMS										
Money Problems										
Comparison										
Classification										
Discrimination										
Fractions										
Multi-Step										
GEOMETRY										
Area										
Perimeter										
Volume										
Parallel and Intersect										
FUNCTIONS										
Coordinate System										
Sequence										
PROBABILITY										
PROJECTS										
Probability										
Geometry										

The Scope and Sequence Chart shows where each track or major topic begins and where it ends. The chart does not show various lessons on which activities are presented. For more details on the lessons in which particular skills are taught, see pages 174–183.

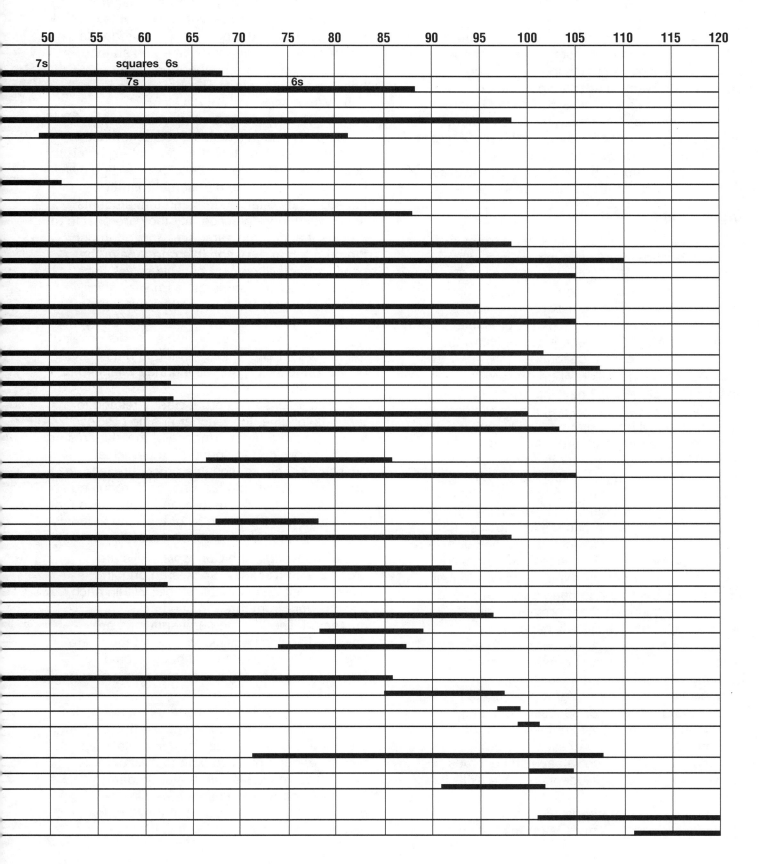

How the Program Is Different

Connecting Math Concepts differs from traditional approaches in the following ways:

Field Tested

Connecting Math Concepts has been shaped through extensive field testing and revising based on problems students and teachers encountered. This work was completed before the program was published. The development philosophy of *Connecting Math Concepts* is that, if teachers or students have trouble with material presented, the program is at fault. Revisions are made to correct the problems.

Organization

The organization of how skills are introduced, developed, and reviewed is unique. In traditional programs, the curriculum is called a spiral. The students work exclusively on a particular topic for a few lessons. Then a new topic (often unrelated to the preceding topic) is presented. *Connecting Math Concepts* does not follow this format for the following reasons:

a) During a period, it is not productive to work only on a single topic. If new information is being presented, it is very easy for students to become overwhelmed with the information. A more sensible procedure, and one that has been demonstrated to be superior in studies of learning and memory, is to distribute the practice, so that, instead of working 45 minutes on a single topic, students work each day for possibly 10 minutes on each of four topics.

b) When full-period topics are presented, it becomes very difficult for the teacher to provide practice on the latest skills that had been taught. Unless the skills that had been taught are used and reviewed, students' performance will deteriorate, and the skills will have to be retaught when they again appear. A more sensible organization is to present work on skills continuously (not discontinuously), so that students work on a particular topic (such as division) for part of 70 or 80 lessons, not for 5 or 6 entire lessons at a time. In this context of continuous development of skills, review becomes automatic, and reteaching becomes unnecessary because students use the skills in every lesson.

c) When skills are not developed continuously, students must learn a lot of new concepts during a short period and are also expected to become "automatic" in applying the new concepts and skills. For most students, adequate learning will not occur. A better method is to develop skills and concepts in small steps, so that students are not required to learn as much new material at a time and so they receive a sufficient amount of practice to become facile or automatic in applying it.

d) When skills are not developed continuously, students and teachers may develop very negative attitudes about mastery. Students may think that they are not expected to "learn" the new material, because it will go away in a few days. Teachers become frustrated because they often understand that students need much more practice, but they are unable to provide it and at the same time move through the program at a reasonable rate. Again, the continuous development of skills solves this problem, because students learn very quickly that what is presented is used, in this lesson, the next lesson, and many subsequent lessons. When the practice is sufficient, students develop the mind-set needed for learning to mastery because the skill is something they will need in the immediate future.

e) When lessons are not clearly related to "periods" of time, the teacher has no precise way to gauge the performance of the students or to judge how long to spend on a particular "lesson." A more reasonable procedure is to organize material into lessons, each requiring so much time to teach. The teacher then knows that the lesson has the potential of teaching students within a class period of 45–50 minutes.

In *Connecting Math Concepts*, skills are organized in **tracks.** A track is an ongoing development of a particular topic. Within each lesson, work from three to five tracks is presented. The teaching presentations are designed so it is possible to present the entire lesson in 45–50 minutes (although some lessons may run longer, and more time may be needed for lower performers).

From lesson to lesson, the work on new skills develops a small step at a time, so that students are not overwhelmed with new information and receive enough practice both to master skills and to become facile with them. Students, therefore, learn quickly about *learning new concepts* and realize that what they are learning has utility because they will use it.

Connections

The teaching and the design of the tracks in Level D permit all students to learn connections that are typically presented but not mastered by the students.

For the teacher and the student, the track design and the development of problem-solving skills means that anything introduced in one lesson will appear in later lessons. It will be further developed and integrated into a full range of problem types. It will later become a component skill in sophisticated applications.

Again, the range of problem types presented in Level D is impressive; however, the fact that students actually learn to process all these types of problems is even more impressive.

An example of the connections and problem-solving applications is the work with fractions.

Students learn to write fractions from pictures of separate units.

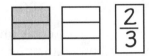

They also write fractions from number lines:

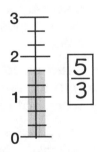

Then they write fractions for whole numbers:

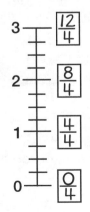

They write fractions from descriptions:

The numbers for a fraction are 12 and 15. The fraction is more than 1. $\boxed{\dfrac{15}{12}}$

There are 6 parts in each unit. 4 parts are shaded. $\boxed{\dfrac{4}{6}}$

The numbers for a fraction are 8 and 14. The denominator is 14. $\boxed{\dfrac{8}{14}}$

The numbers for a fraction are 33 and 100. The numerator is 100. $\boxed{\dfrac{100}{33}}$

Students learn to add and subtract fractions with like denominators. They also learn to work addition and subtraction problems that have a fraction and a whole number.

$$\frac{14}{7} - \frac{8}{7} = \boxed{\frac{6}{7}}$$

Students multiply fractions by fractions and multiply whole numbers by fractions.

$$\frac{2}{1} \times \frac{8}{7} = \boxed{\frac{16}{7}}$$

After students learn each of these operations, they work on problem sets that require them to discriminate between previously-taught types and apply the appropriate operation.

In addition to the discreet operations and discriminations, students learn about connections. They learn how addition is connected to multiplication, how fractions are related to other fractions, and how fractions expressed in one form, such as:

$$\frac{3}{100}$$

are expressed in other forms:

$$.03$$

and

$$100\overline{)3}$$

Many exercises in Level D focus on these relationships. One of the most important relationships involves equivalent fractions. Students learn a simple test to determine whether fractions are equivalent. They start with the fraction that has the smaller numbers and figure out what to multiply by (in the numerator and in the denominator) to get the other fraction. If the missing fraction equals 1, the fractions are equivalent. If the missing fraction does not equal 1, the fractions are not equivalent.

$$\frac{4}{5} \quad \frac{20}{25}$$

$$\frac{3}{8} \quad \frac{21}{32}$$

The first pair of fractions are equivalent because the first fraction is multiplied by 5/5 to get 20/25. The second pair are not equivalent because the first fraction is multiplied by 7/4 to get 21/32.

Students compare fractions such as 3/8 and 21/32 by applying a basic rule about multiplication that they learn. If 3/8 is multiplied by more than 1, the answer is more than 3/8. If 3/8 is multiplied by less than 1, the answer is less than 3/8. 21/32 is more than 3/8 because 3/8 is multiplied by more than 1 to get 21/32.

A variation of this procedure permits students to compare fractions that are quite difficult to compare by inspection only.

For instance:

$$\frac{15}{32} \text{ and } \frac{5}{9}$$

Students simply apply the rule about equivalent fractions. They start with the fraction that has the smaller numbers. Students then take one of the numbers from the other fraction (the number they can reach by multiplying):

$$\frac{5}{9} = \frac{15}{}$$

Now they do the multiplication:

$$\frac{5}{9} \times \frac{3}{3} = \frac{15}{27}$$

The two fractions are equivalent. That means that the comparison fraction (15/32) is less than 15/27. Pictures of the two fractions would show the same number of parts shaded. However, the circle for 15/32 would have more parts; therefore, 15 parts would be a smaller area than 15 parts in the other fraction.

Using the same procedure, students can compare selected fractions with decimal numbers.

For instance:

$$\frac{4}{5} \text{ and } .85$$

Students write the decimal number as a fraction:

$$\frac{85}{100}$$

Then they select the number from 85/100 that can be reached by multiplication:

$$\frac{4}{5} = \frac{}{100}$$

They complete the pair of equivalent fractions:

$$\frac{4}{5} \times \frac{20}{20} = \frac{80}{100}$$

And compare:

$$\frac{80}{100} \text{ with } \frac{85}{100}$$

Fractions that equal 1 also play an important part in working word problems that involve addition and subtraction of fractions.

Level D introduces several types of these problems. One mentions numbers but asks about a fraction.

There were 6 red birds. There were 11 birds in all. What fraction of the birds were not red?

Students apply the rule that **all,** or the whole group, is 1. They then make a number family that shows the two small numbers that are added and the big number, which is 1:

	not	
red	red	all
6		11

birds

Since **all** is 1, students show the fraction for **all** as 11/11. The fraction for **red** birds must be 6/11.

	not	
red	red	all
$\frac{6}{11}$		$\frac{11}{11}$

birds

The fraction for **not red** is the difference between 11/11 and 6/11.

A similar type of problem gives information about fractions (not numbers):

> **3/8 of the workers are men. What fraction of the workers are not men?**

The names for this problem are: **men, not men,** and **all.** The fraction is given for men.

The fraction for **all** must have the same denominator. Therefore, the fraction for **all** is 8/8.

$$\underset{\text{workers}}{\overset{\displaystyle\text{men}\quad\overset{\text{not}}{\text{men}}\quad\text{all}}{\dfrac{3}{8}\longrightarrow\dfrac{8}{8}}}$$

The fraction of workers who are not men is the difference between 8/8 and 3/8.

Problems of this type are closely connected to basic statements of probability. **If there are 7 cards in a hat and 3 of the cards are red,** we can make a number family that shows all the cards in the hat. And we can answer basic questions about the probability of drawing a red card from the hat. Given that drawing any card is equally probable, and given that 3/7 of the cards are red, the fraction 3/7 tells about the composition of the set and about our chances:

$$\underset{\text{cards}}{\overset{\displaystyle\text{red}\quad\overset{\text{not}}{\text{red}}\quad\text{all}}{\dfrac{3}{7}\quad\dfrac{4}{7}\longrightarrow\dfrac{7}{7}}}$$

The numerators show that if we took 7 trials, we would expect to draw **red** cards on 3 of the trials and **not red** cards on 4 of the trials.

This kind of relationship is very puzzling in traditional sequences but is articulated clearly in the Level D sequence because all the components are taught before they are integrated.

A version of probability involves ratios. Before students learn this variation, however, they work on a broad range of ratio and proportion problems that involve equivalent fractions.

The wording of some problems tells about the proportions for a smaller unit. For instance:

> **3 workers build 4 houses.**

The fraction:

$$\dfrac{\text{workers}}{\text{houses}}\quad\dfrac{3}{4}$$

Other problems tell about ratios.

> **The ratio of bass to perch is 8 to 7.**

The fraction:

$$\dfrac{\text{bass}}{\text{perch}}\quad\dfrac{8}{7}$$

To work a ratio problem, students construct a pair of equivalent fractions.

For instance:

> **The ratio of bass to perch is 8 to 7. If there are 56 perch, how many bass are there?**

The problem:

$$\dfrac{\text{bass}}{\text{perch}}\quad\dfrac{8}{7}\quad=\dfrac{\Box}{56}$$

Students figure out the number to multiply 7 by to reach 56. That tells about the fraction that equals 1:

$$\dfrac{\text{bass}}{\text{perch}}\quad\dfrac{8}{7}\times\dfrac{8}{8}=\dfrac{\Box}{56}$$

By multiplying on top, students determine that there are 64 bass.

After students work with different variations of wording (including sentences that tell about *per* and *each*), measurement problems are introduced. These often involve a fraction that has 1 as the numerator.

> **How many inches are in 5 yards?**

Students refer to the table of measurement facts and confirm that **1 yard is 36 inches.**

The larger unit is yards. The smaller is inches.

Students write an equation with the larger unit on top.

$$\dfrac{\text{yards}}{\text{inches}}\quad\dfrac{1}{36}=\dfrac{5}{\Box}$$

To work the problem, students multiply by the fraction 5/5. The answer is 180 inches.

Students connect what they know about ratios and fractions that equal 1, to probability.

In a bag, there are 7 cards. Three of them are winners. The rest are not winners. If you took trials until you got 18 winners, about how many trials would you expect to take?

Students write the ratio of winners to trials. For the first fraction, that's the ratio of winners to the things in the set.

$$\frac{\text{winners}}{\text{trials}} \quad \frac{3}{7} = \frac{18}{\square}$$

Students determine that the fraction that equals 1 is 6/6. So they would expect to take about 42 trials to get 18 winners.

Students learn to plot lines on the coordinate system, and they learn to **plot lines for equivalent fractions.** The X axis is the denominator and the Y axis is the numerator. By plotting the line for the fraction 3/7, students show the full range of relationships between winners and trials.

Here is the line for finding fractions that are equivalent to 3/7:

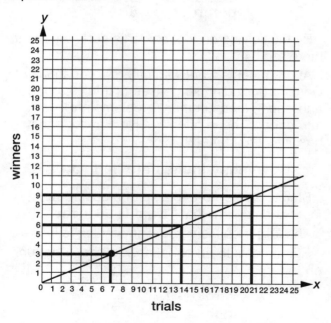

The dot shows that there are 3 winners in 7 cards. The line shows if you took 14 trials, you'd expect 6 winners. If you took trials until you got 9 winners, you'd expect to take about 21 trials.

The final application of connections between probability, fractions that equal 1, and equivalent fractions is a project format in which students figure out the composition of a set.

For this kind of experiment, students are given basic information about the number of things in a bag:

There are 5 cards in the bag. You have to figure out how many of them are winners. There's either 1 winner, 2 winners, or 5 winners.

To solve the problem, students figure out the number of trials that would be suggested by different numbers of winners.

For 1 winner: $\quad \dfrac{1}{5} = \dfrac{10}{\boxed{50}}$

For 2 winners: $\quad \dfrac{2}{5} = \dfrac{10}{\boxed{25}}$

For 5 winners: $\quad \dfrac{5}{5} = \dfrac{10}{\boxed{10}}$

Each of the equations shows the number of trials that would be expected to get 10 winners.

Students do an experiment in which they take trials until they get 10 winners. Then they compare their fraction with the closest possibility. For instance, the students require 18 trials to get 10 winners. They compare the number of trials they took with the denominators of the different fractions. The fraction with the closest value tells them about the composition of the set. The fraction 10/25 is the closest.

Students infer that there are 2 winners in the set. Similar connections occur with all components and ideas that are logically connected. Students learn to use the information they receive about mathematical entities to solve narrowly defined problems and to connect the new to the familiar.

Placement

Level D of *Connecting Math Concepts* is appropriate for students who complete Level C or students who pass the placement test. A reproducible copy of the placement test appears on page 10.

Administering the Placement Test

Try to test students on the first day of instruction.

Pass out a test form to each student. Present the wording in the test administration script.

Note: What you say is shown in **blue** type.

When observing the students, you should make sure that they are working on the correct part or correct item of the test. Do not prompt them in a way that would let them know the answer to the item.

If the class is particularly weak on parts of the placement test, work on these skills before starting with Level D. Present items similar to those of the test.

TEST ADMINISTRATION SCRIPT

- Find part 1.
  These are multiplication facts. You have one minute to finish these problems. Read them carefully. Get ready. Go.
- (At the end of one minute, say:) Stop writing. Pencils down.
- Find part 2.
  You're going to write numerals that I dictate. You can see three hundred twenty-four is already written. That shows where you'd begin a hundred numeral.

Numeral A. Seven hundred forty-eight. Write it.
Numeral B. Six hundred two. Write it.
Numeral C. 17. Write it.
Numeral D. 300. Write it.

- You'll work the rest of the parts on your own. For part 3, read each problem. Write the number problem and the answer.
- For the rest of the parts, just write the answer to each problem. Raise your hand when you're finished.
- (Collect test forms.)

Placement Criteria

The criteria for passing the test are:

	Pass	Fail
Part 1	0–2 errors	3 or more errors
Part 2	0 errors	1 or more errors
Part 3	0 errors	1 or more errors
Part 4	0–1 errors	2 or more errors
Part 5	0–1 errors	2 or more errors
Part 6	0 errors	1 or more errors
Part 7	0–1 errors	2 or more errors
OVERALL	Students pass 5–7 parts.	Students pass 4 or fewer parts.

Is Level D appropriate for your classroom? A rule of thumb is that three-fourths or more of the students in the class should pass the placement test. If more than one quarter of the students fail the placement test, it may be difficult to present Level D to the entire class. A recommendation is to place the lower performers in Level C.

Placement Test

Name _____ **Score** _____

Part 1

a. $5 \times 4 =$ ___   e. $4 \times 0 =$ ___   i. $8 \times 5 =$ ___

b. $2 \times 6 =$ ___   f. $9 \times 1 =$ ___   j. $1 \times 2 =$ ___

c. $7 \times 2 =$ ___   g. $4 \times 4 =$ ___   k. $3 \times 2 =$ ___

d. $8 \times 10 =$ ___   h. $3 \times 5 =$ ___   l. $0 \times 10 =$ ___

Part 2

a.

b.

c.

d.

Part 3

a. Hiro Moto had 47 nuts. Somebody ate 30 of his nuts. How many did he end up with?

b. A man had 23. Then he got 16 more. How many did he end up with?

Part 4

a. $\begin{array}{r} 14 \\ + 79 \\ \hline \end{array}$ b. $\begin{array}{r} 370 \\ + 98 \\ \hline \end{array}$

c. $\begin{array}{r} 39 \\ + 95 \\ \hline \end{array}$ d. $\begin{array}{r} 12 \\ 46 \\ + 599 \\ \hline \end{array}$

Part 5

a. $2 \overline{)14}$ b. $5 \overline{)30}$ c. $9 \overline{)27}$

d. $8 \overline{)8}$ e. $1 \overline{)8}$

Part 6

a. $\begin{array}{r} 54 \\ \times 2 \\ \hline \end{array}$ b. $\begin{array}{r} 43 \\ \times 5 \\ \hline \end{array}$

Part 7

a. $\begin{array}{r} 360 \\ - 218 \\ \hline \end{array}$ b. $\begin{array}{r} 37 \\ - 18 \\ \hline \end{array}$ c. $\begin{array}{r} 647 \\ - 134 \\ \hline \end{array}$ d. $\begin{array}{r} 409 \\ - 136 \\ \hline \end{array}$

Copyright © SRA/McGraw-Hill. Permission is granted to reproduce for school use.

Placement Test Answer Key

Part 1

a. $5 \times 4 = \underline{20}$ e. $4 \times 0 = \underline{0}$ i. $8 \times 5 = \underline{40}$

b. $2 \times 6 = \underline{12}$ f. $9 \times 1 = \underline{9}$ j. $1 \times 2 = \underline{2}$

c. $7 \times 2 = \underline{14}$ g. $4 \times 4 = \underline{16}$ k. $3 \times 2 = \underline{6}$

d. $8 \times 10 = \underline{80}$ h. $3 \times 5 = \underline{15}$ l. $0 \times 10 = \underline{0}$

Part 2

	3	2	4
a.	7	4	8
b.	6	0	2
c.		1	7
d.	3	0	0

Part 3

a. Hiro Moto had 47 nuts. Somebody ate 30 of his nuts. How many did he end up with?

$$\square \xrightarrow{\;30\;} 47 - \begin{array}{r} 47 \\ 30 \\ \hline \end{array}$$
$$17 \text{ nuts}$$

b. A man had 23. Then he got 16 more. How many did he end up with?

$$23 \; 16 \longrightarrow \square + \begin{array}{r} 23 \\ 16 \\ \hline 39 \end{array}$$

Part 4

a. $\begin{array}{r} \overset{1}{14} \\ + 79 \\ \hline 93 \end{array}$ b. $\begin{array}{r} \overset{1}{370} \\ + 98 \\ \hline 468 \end{array}$

c. $\begin{array}{r} 39 \\ + 95 \\ \hline 134 \end{array}$ d. $\begin{array}{r} \overset{1}{12} \\ 46 \\ + 599 \\ \hline 657 \end{array}$

Part 5

a. $2\overline{\smash{)}14}$ → 7   b. $5\overline{\smash{)}30}$ → 6   c. $9\overline{\smash{)}27}$ → 3

d. $8\overline{\smash{)}8}$ → 1   e. $1\overline{\smash{)}8}$ → 8

Part 6

a. $\begin{array}{r} 54 \\ \times 2 \\ \hline 108 \end{array}$ b. $\begin{array}{r} \overset{1}{43} \\ \times 5 \\ \hline 215 \end{array}$

Part 7

a. $\begin{array}{r} \overset{5}{3}\overset{1}{6}0 \\ - 218 \\ \hline 142 \end{array}$ b. $\begin{array}{r} \overset{2}{3}\overset{1}{7} \\ - 18 \\ \hline 19 \end{array}$ c. $\begin{array}{r} 647 \\ - 134 \\ \hline 513 \end{array}$ d. $\begin{array}{r} \overset{3}{4}\overset{1}{0}9 \\ - 136 \\ \hline 273 \end{array}$

Cumulative Tests

CMC Level D has cumulative tests following Lessons 30, 60, 90, and 120. The tests sample the various key skills and discriminations taught in the previous 30-lesson period, as well as important skills taught since the beginning of the level.

The tests appear in Appendix A, *Cumulative Tests:*

Each test has between 45 and 70 items, and requires about 55 minutes to complete. The teacher presentation for each test appears first, followed by the reproducible blackline masters.

The Percent Summary and Scoring Chart for each cumulative test is presented immediately after the teacher presentation and blackline masters in Appendix A. The Answer Key and Test Remedy Charts follow the Scoring Chart for each test. The last pages in Appendix A, after the Test Remedy Chart for the Final Cumulative Test, are the Remedy Summaries for the Cumulative Tests.

Scoring

Here is the Percent Summary and Scoring Chart for Cumulative Test 2. (Cumulative Test 2 follows Lesson 60.)

CUMULATIVE TEST 2 PERCENT SUMMARY					
SCORE	%	SCORE	%	SCORE	%
96	100	86	90	76	79
95	99	85	89	75	78
94	98	84	88	74	77
93	97	83	86	73	76
92	96	82	85	72	75
91	95	81	84	71	74
90	94	80	83	70	73
89	93	79	82	69	72
88	92	78	81	68	71
87	91	77	80	67	70

CUMULATIVE TEST 2 SCORING CHART				
PART	SCORE		POSSIBLE SCORE	PASSING SCORE
1	1 for each item		22	18
2	2 for each item		10	8
3	EACH ITEM — Problem 2 / Answer 1 / Total 3		6	5
4	2 for each item		6	Parts 4, 5 combined
5	2 for each item		6	10
6	EACH ITEM — Problem 1 / Answer and unit name 1 / Total 2		4	Parts 6, 7 combined
7	2 for each item		6	8
8	2 for each item — Each correct fraction 3 / Total 6 / Deduction for incorrect fraction 1		6	Parts 8, 9 combined
9	2 for each item		6	10
10	3 for each item		9	Parts 10, 11, combined
11	EACH ITEM — Problem 2 / Answer 1 / Unit Name 1 / Total 4		8	14
12	1 for each item		3	3
13	2 for each item		4	4
	TOTAL		96	

The scoring chart shows how to score each item, the possible score for the part, and the passing score for the part. This test has 13 parts and a total possible score of 96.

Remedies

Remedies are to be provided for each part that is not passed. Students do not pass a part if they score less than the number of points indicated in the column "Passing Score."

A summary table provides information on the exercises in the program that are to be presented to students who do not pass a particular part. Below is the remedies summary that appears with Cumulative Test 2.

CUMULATIVE TEST 2 REMEDIES	
PART	LESSON and (EXERCISE)
1 a–l	21 (5), 22 (6), 23 (4), 24 (4), 25 (3), 26 (8), 27 (1), 28 (1), 31 (2), 32 (2, 3), 33 (4), 34 (3, 6), 35 (5), 36 (2),
1 m, p, r	38 (1), 42 (2), 43 (6), 44 (5), 45 (7), 58 (5), 59 (7)
1 n, o, q, s, u	28 (5), 29 (1), 31 (1), 32 (5), 36 (5), 37 (7), 56 (5)
1 t, v	48 (4), 50 (2), 49 (5), 51 (5), 52 (1), 55 (2), 56 (5), 57 (1), 58 (3), 59 (3) 13 (6), 14 (7), 15 (4), 16 (3), 18 (5), 19 (7)
2	1 (2), 2 (4), 3 (3), 4 (3), 5 (2), 6 (4), 7 (1), 8 (1), 9 (4), 22 (5), 23 (2), 24 (6), 34 (4), 35 (7), 36 (4), 37 (6, 8), 38 (3), 39 (6), 41 (4), 46 (6), 47 (6), 48 (7)
3	16 (1), 17 (1), 18 (4), 19 (6), 22 (4)
4	33 (7), 34 (7), 35 (6), 36 (3), 37 (3), 38 (4), 39 (1), 41 (6), 42 (6), 44 (6), 45 (3, 4), 49 (3), 50 (3), 51 (1, 6), 52 (6), 53 (5), 54 (2), 55 (7), 56 (7)
5	16 (6), 17 (6), 18 (7), 19 (1), 20 (2), 21 (1), 22 (3), 23 (6), 24 (3), 25 (1), 26 (7), 28 (6), 35 (4), 36 (7), 39 (4), 40 (3), 41 (1), 43 (1)
6	29 (7), 31 (4), 35 (9 part 10), 39 (8 part 9), 45 (8 part 4), 51 (7 part 9)
7	10 (3), 14 (1, 3), 15 (3, 5), 16 (2), 18 (2), 27 (6), 29 (5), 31 (5), 32 (4), 45 (5), 46 (4), 47 (4), 48 (5), 49 (7), 52 (7), 53 (4), 56 (9), 58 (6)
8	1 (2), 2 (4), 3 (3), 4 (3), 5 (2), 6 (4), 7 (1), 8 (1), 9 (4), 16 (6), 17 (6), 18 (7), 19 (1), 20 (2), 21 (1), 22 (3), 42 (4), 43 (5), 44 (3)
9	1 (5), 2 (3), 3 (2), 4 (6), 5 (4), 6 (2, 7), 7 (3, 7), 11 (4), 12 (6), 13 (1), 14 (8), 17 (5), 18 (6), 19 (2), 21 (8), 22 (7), 23 (3), 25 (5)

PART	LESSON and (EXERCISE)
10	34 (8), 35 (8), 36 (1), 38 (7), 41 (5), 42 (5), 43 (4), 44 (4), 45 (6), 46 (5), 47 (5), 48 (1)
11	9 (2), 12 (3), 13 (9), 14 (5), 15 (7), 16 (5), 18 (3)
12	21 (6), 22 (8), 23 (8 part 4), 28 (7 part 3)
13	1 (3), 2 (6), 3 (1), 4 (1), 8 (8), 9 (3), 11 (5)

For each part of the test that some students don't pass, you would present some or all of the exercises listed. (Present the exercises in the order they are listed. Present them only to the students who did not pass the part. Try to present the remedies at a time other than the regularly scheduled math period.) If students perform perfectly on a remedy, skip to the next new type of remedy exercise. The objective for that exercise will be bold-faced.

The goal of each remedy is to teach students well enough so they can work items of that type in the context presented in the CMC program.

PLACING STUDENTS WHO FAIL 3 OR MORE PARTS OF THE TEST:

As a rule of thumb, if a student fails three or more parts of the test, the student is not placed properly in the program, which means that they will continue to have problems with the material. The ideal remedy would be to place students at a lesson in which they would be successful on about 90% of the tasks in each exercise.

PLACING MID-YEAR STUDENTS:

The tests may be used to place students who come in after the school term has started. Here are the steps:

(1) Present the Final Cumulative Test for CMC Level D.

(2) Use the scoring chart to determine which of the parts the students passed.

(3) Placement for further testing:

If the student passed no more than five parts, place the student at the beginning of Level D, or test the student for placement in CMC Level C.

If the student passed seven to twenty parts, give the student another cumulative test:

Cumulative Test 1, if student passed seven to ten parts

Cumulative Test 2, if student passed eleven to sixteen parts
Cumulative Test 3, if student passed seventeen to twenty parts.

If the student passed twenty-one to twenty-five parts of the Final Cumulative Test, place student in CMCE.

(4) If you give the student another cumulative test, use the scoring chart for that test to determine which of the parts the student passed and which parts the student failed.

(5) Place students so they need remedies for no more than two skills.

Here's an example:

A teacher gave a student the Final Cumulative Test (step 1).

The test was graded and the student passed only thirteen parts of it (step 2).

Then, the teacher gave the student the Lesson 60 Cumulative Test 2 (per step 3).

According to the scoring chart for Cumulative Test 2 (above), the student failed Parts 1, 4, 5, 6, and 10. The student missed problems a, d, e, f, and h of Part 1.

The remedies table divides the problems for Part 1 into 4 sections—problems a through l; problems m, p, and r; problems n, o, q, s, and u; and problems s, t, and v. The problems the student in our example missed were in the section a through l.

According to the remedies table for Cumulative Test 2 (above), the remedies for: Part 1, a through l begins on Lesson 21; Part 4 begins on Lesson 33; Part 5 begins on Lesson 16; Part 6 begins on Lesson 29; and Part 10 begins on Lesson 34.

Placing the student on or before the beginning of Lesson 29 would be an acceptable placement because the student would need remedies for no more than two parts of the Cumulative Test (step 5). The student would need remedies for only Part 1, a through l, and Part 5. The other "remedies" would be included in the upcoming instruction.

Placing the student beyond Lesson 29 wouldn't be acceptable because the student would need remedies for at least three parts— Part 1, a through l, Part 5, and Part 6.

Test Preparation Materials

Level D contains seventeen Test Preparation lessons that acquaint students with some of the formats and contents of standardized achievement tests. The material appears at the end of *Presentation Book 1*. It is placed there as a reminder that the time for test preparation work may be near.

Reproducible blackline masters for all seventeen Test Preparation lessons follow the teacher presentation for the test preparation lessons.

For each of the seventeen Test Preparation lessons, students need (1) a copy of the Multiple-Choice Response Sheet, and (2) specific pages from the test preparation student booklet.

The blackline master for the Multiple-Choice Response Sheet appears immediately following the teacher presentations for the seventeen Test Preparation lessons (page 429).

Connecting Math Concepts, Level D

Multiple-Choice Response Sheet

TEST PREPARATION LESSON ☐   NAME _____

Sample A: A○ B○ C○ D● E○
Sample B: F○ G○ H○ I○ J○

1. A○	B○	C○	D○	E○	29. A○	B○	C○	D○	E○
2. F○	G○	H○	I○	J○	30. F○	G○	H○	I○	J○
3. A○	B○	C○	D○	E○	31. A○	B○	C○	D○	E○
4. F○	G○	H○	I○	J○	32. F○	G○	H○	I○	J○
5. A○	B○	C○	D○	E○	33. A○	B○	C○	D○	E○
6. F○	G○	H○	I○	J○	34. F○	G○	H○	I○	J○
7. A○	B○	C○	D○	E○	35. A○	B○	C○	D○	E○
8. F○	G○	H○	I○	J○	36. F○	G○	H○	I○	J○
9. A○	B○	C○	D○	E○	37. A○	B○	C○	D○	E○
10. F○	G○	H○	I○	J○	38. F○	G○	H○	I○	J○
11. A○	B○	C○	D○	E○	39. A○	B○	C○	D○	E○
12. F○	G○	H○	I○	J○	40. F○	G○	H○	I○	J○
13. A○	B○	C○	D○	E○	41. A○	B○	C○	D○	E○
14. F○	G○	H○	I○	J○	42. F○	G○	H○	I○	J○
15. A○	B○	C○	D○	E○	43. A○	B○	C○	D○	E○
16. F○	G○	H○	I○	J○	44. F○	G○	H○	I○	J○
17. A○	B○	C○	D○	E○	45. A○	B○	C○	D○	E○
18. F○	G○	H○	I○	J○	46. F○	G○	H○	I○	J○
19. A○	B○	C○	D○	E○	47. A○	B○	C○	D○	E○
20. F○	G○	H○	I○	J○	48. F○	G○	H○	I○	J○
21. A○	B○	C○	D○	E○	49. A○	B○	C○	D○	E○
22. F○	G○	H○	I○	J○	50. F○	G○	H○	I○	J○
23. A○	B○	C○	D○	E○	51. A○	B○	C○	D○	E○
24. F○	G○	H○	I○	J○	52. F○	G○	H○	I○	J○
25. A○	B○	C○	D○	E○	53. A○	B○	C○	D○	E○
26. F○	G○	H○	I○	J○	54. F○	G○	H○	I○	J○
27. A○	B○	C○	D○	E○	55. A○	B○	C○	D○	E○
28. F○	G○	H○	I○	J○	56. F○	G○	H○	I○	J○

Copyright © SRA/McGraw-Hill. Permission is granted to reproduce for school use.

The blackline masters for the student booklet corresponding to each Test Preparation lesson appear on pages 317–418 of *Presentation Book 1*. This material presents the items to which students respond. They respond by filling in the appropriate bubble on their Multiple-Choice Response Sheet. Students should not write on the pages of the test-taking booklet.

The pages for each student's test-taking material may be assembled into a reusable booklet that contains the Multiple-Choice Response Sheet items for all seventeen lessons.

Each test-preparation lesson has teacher-directed activities. Students learn test-taking strategies in Lessons 6 through 15. Exercise 7 in Lessons 6 through 10 and 12 through 14, Exercise 9 in Lesson 11, and Exercise 8 in Lesson 15 present the test-taking strategies and provide students practice applying them. Exercise 8 in Lessons 6 through 10 and 12 through 14 present independent work.

Worksheets

For Lessons 1 through 3, students perform some of their work on worksheets. These worksheet blackline masters appear immediately following the Multiple-Choice Response Sheet. Students write directly on their worksheets, so the worksheets, unlike the pages for the test-taking booklet, are not reusable.

Sample Lesson

Here is the teacher and student material for Lesson 9.

Test Preparation

LESSON 9

Materials Note

Each student will need:
- lined paper for Exercises 2, 4, 5, and 8
- test booklet and Multiple-Choice Response Sheet for Exercises 1 through 6.

EXERCISE 1
Identifying Numerals

a. (Direct students to find lesson 9 in their test booklet and write their names and the lesson number on their answer sheets.)

b. Find item 1 on lesson 9 of your test booklet. √
- I'll read the problem: If you rounded this number to the nearest hundred, you'd round it to 200. If you rounded this number to the nearest ten, you'd round it to 180. Which of these could be the number?
- Look for a number that rounds to 180. Mark the choice for item 1. √
- What letter did you mark? (Signal.) *E.*
- Yes, the choices are 276, 283, 186, and 174. None of those choices rounds to 180, so the answer is: none of these.

c. Work items 2 and 3.
- Raise your hand when you're finished.
- (Observe students and give feedback.)
- Item 2: What number rounds to 500 and rounds to 520? (Signal.) *524.*
- What letter did you mark? (Signal.) *G.*
- Item 3: What number rounds to 100 and has an 8 in the tens and a 7 in the ones? (Signal.) *87.*
- What letter did you mark? (Signal.) *C.*

d. Work items 4 through 6. They describe numbers in different ways.
- Raise your hand when you've marked answers through item 6.
- (Observe students and give feedback.)

e. Check your work.
- Item 4: What number rounds to 400, rounds to 440, and has a 9 in the ones place? (Signal.) *439.*
- What letter did you mark? (Signal.) *I.*
- Item 5: What number is between 600 and 700, has a zero in the tens place, and has a one in the ones place? (Signal) *601.*
- What letter did you mark? (Signal.) *D.*
- Item 6: What number is between 300 and 400, and has a 7 in the tens place? (Signal.) *374.*
- What letter did you mark? (Signal.) *F.*

EXERCISE 2
Division

a. Find item 9. √
- Items 9 and 10 are division problems written with the divide-by sign. Remember, write the bigger number under the division sign. Then figure out the answer and mark the choice.
- Item 9. Read it. (Signal.) *12 divided by 2.*
- What number goes under the division sign? (Signal.) *12.*
- Work the problem and mark the correct choice.
- Raise your hand when you've finished item 9. Don't mark an answer for items 7 and 8.
- (Observe students and give feedback.)
- (Write on the board:)

> **9.** $\dfrac{6}{2\overline{)12}}$

- Here's the problem you should have worked: 12 divided by 2. What's the answer? (Signal.) *6.*
- What letter did you mark? (Signal.) *E.*
b. Item 10. Read it. (Signal.) *360 divided by 9.*
- Work item 10.
- Raise your hand when you're finished.
- (Observe students and give feedback.)
- (Write on the board:)

> **10.** $\dfrac{40}{9\overline{)360}}$

- Here's what you should have.
- Item 10: 360 divided by 9. What's the answer? (Signal.) *40.*
- What letter did you mark? (Signal.) *H.*

EXERCISE 3
Edges

a. Find item 11. √
- (Teacher reference:)

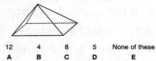

11 How many edges does this figure have?

12	4	8	5	None of these
A	B	C	D	E

12 How many edges does this figure have?

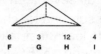

6	3	12	4
F	G	H	I

13 How many edges does this figure have?

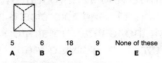

5	6	18	9	None of these
A	B	C	D	E

14 How many edges does this figure have?

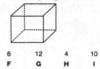

6	12	4	10
F	G	H	I

- The edges of the figure are shown with solid lines or dotted lines. The dotted lines show the edges that are farther away from you. Count the number of edges for the figure in 11 and mark the answer.
- Raise your hand when you've finished.
- Item 11: How many edges are there? (Signal.) *8.*
- What letter did you mark? (Signal.) *C.*
- The figure has 4 edges along the base and 4 more edges that come to a point.

b. Your turn: Work items 12 through 14.
- Raise your hand when you're finished.
- **(Observe students and give feedback.)**
- Item 12: How many edges does this figure have? **(Signal)** *6.*
- What letter did you mark? **(Signal.)** *F.*
- The base has 3 edges. Then there are 3 edges that come to a point.
- Item 13: How many edges does this figure have? **(Signal.)** *9.*
- What letter did you mark? **(Signal.)** *D.*
- The base has 3 edges. There are 3 edges going from the base to the top and the top has 3 edges.
- Item 14: How many edges does this figure have? **(Signal.)** *12.*
- What letter did you mark? **(Signal.)** *G.*
- The base has 4 edges. There are 4 edges going from the base to the top, and the top has 4 edges.

EXERCISE 4
Products/Sums

a. Find item 15. √
- Items 15 through 20 tell about sums and products. The items that ask about the sum **don't** ask about the sum of the digits in a numeral. They ask about the sum of two numbers. You get the sum by adding. How do you find the sum of two numbers? **(Signal.)** *By adding.*
- The rule in the box tells about the product. The product is the number you get when you multiply. You get the product of two numbers by multiplying. How do you get the product? **(Signal.)** *By multiplying.*
- Remember, you get the sum by adding; you get the product by multiplying.

b. Answer items 15 and 16.
- Raise your hand when you're finished.
- **(Observe students and give feedback.)**
- Item 15. Everybody, what operation do you use to get a sum? **(Signal.)** *Add.*
- What letter did you mark? **(Signal.)** *A.*
- Item 16. What operation do you use to get a product? **(Signal.)** *Multiply.*
- What letter did you mark? **(Signal.)** *H.*
c. Item 17. The product of two numbers is 6. The sum of the numbers is 5. That means that when you multiply the two numbers together, you get 6. When you add the numbers you get 5. Find the numbers.
- Raise your hand when you've marked an answer for item 17. √
- Item 17. What letter did you mark? **(Signal.)** *B.* The numbers are 3 and 2. 3 times 2 equals 6, and 3 plus 2 equals 5.
d. Work item 18.
- Raise your hand when you're finished.
- **(Observe students and give feedback.)**
- Item 18: The product of the numbers is 14. The sum of the numbers is 9. What are the numbers? **(Signal.)** *7 and 2.*
- What letter did you mark? **(Signal.)** *I.*
  7 times 2 equals 14. 7 plus 2 equals 9.
e. Work items 19 and 20.
- Raise your hand when you're finished.
- **(Observe students and give feedback.)**
- Item 19: The product of the numbers is 30. The sum of the numbers is 11. What are the numbers? **(Signal.)** *6 and 5.*
- What letter did you mark? **(Signal.)** *D.*
  6 times 5 equals 30. 6 plus 5 equals 11.
- Item 20: The sum of the numbers is 10. The product is 9. What are the numbers? **(Signal.)** *9 and one.*
- What letter did you mark? **(Signal.)** *F.*
- 9 plus 1 equals 10. 9 times 1 equals 9.

EXERCISE 5
Order of Numbers

a. Find the numbers in the box above item 23. √
- To answer items 23 through 25, you have to put the numbers for the box in order from smallest to largest. On your lined paper, write in a row the largest number first, then write the next largest number. Keep writing the next largest number until you've written all of the numbers.
- Raise your hand when you've written the numbers in a row from smallest to largest.
- (Observe students and give feedback.)
- Everybody, what's the smallest number? (Signal.) *4781.*
- What's the next largest? (Signal.) *4807.*
- What's the next largest? (Signal.) *4870.*
- What's the next largest? (Signal.) *4871.*
- What's the largest number? (Signal.) *4880.*

b. Item 23 asks: If you put the numbers in order from smallest to largest, what would be the fifth number? Find the fifth number in your row and mark the answer. Don't mark an answer for items 21 and 22. √
- Everybody, what's the fifth number in order from smallest to largest? (Signal.) *4880.*
- What letter did you mark? (Signal.) *B.*

c. Work items 24 and 25.
- Raise your hand when you're finished.
- (Observe students and give feedback.)
- Item 24. What's the second number in order from smallest to largest? (Signal.) *4807.*
- What letter did you mark? (Signal.) *I.*
- Item 25. What's the fourth number from smallest to largest? (Signal.) *4871.*
- What letter did you mark? (Signal.) *E.* 4871 was not one of your choices. "None of these" was the correct choice.
- Find the numbers in the box above item 26. To answer items 26 through 28, you have to write these numbers in order from **largest** to **smallest.** Write the numbers from largest to smallest, then mark your answers.
- Raise your hand when you've marked the answers through item 28.

- (Observe students and give feedback.)
- Everybody, you'll read the numbers you wrote from largest to smallest. What's the first number you wrote? (Signal.) *1019.*
- Yes, 1019 is the largest number.
- What's the next number? (Signal.) *705.*
- What's the next number? (Signal.) *260.*
- What's the next number? (Signal.) *81.*
- What's the next number? (Signal.) *12.*
- What's the last number? (Signal.) *Zero.*
- Item 26. What's the third number in order from largest to smallest? (Signal.) *260.*
- What letter did you mark? (Signal.) *F.*
- Item 27. What's the first number in order from largest to smallest? (Signal.) *1019.*
- What letter did you mark? (Signal.) *B.*
- Item 28. What's the fifth number in order from largest to smallest? (Signal.) *12.*
- What letter did you mark? (Signal.) *I.*

EXERCISE 6
Estimation Problems

a. Find item 29. √
- The problem shown is: 68 minus 31. You're going to indicate the correct estimation problem. That's the problem that shows the rounded value for 68 and the rounded value for 31. Mark the correct choice.
- Raise your hand when you're finished.
- (Observe students and give feedback.)
- Item 29. What letter did you mark? (Signal.) *B.* The problem with the rounded values is 70 minus 30.

b. Work items 30 through 32.
- Raise your hand when you're finished.
- (Observe students and give feedback.)
- Item 30: 38 plus 13. What's the correct problem with rounded values? (Signal.) *40 plus 10.*
- What letter did you mark? (Signal.) *I.*
- Item 31: 73 minus 49. What's the correct problem with rounded values? (Signal.) *70 minus 50.*
- What letter did mark? (Signal.) *B.*
- Item 32: 47 plus 52. What's the correct problem with rounded values? (Signal.) *50 plus 50.*
- What letter did you mark? (Signal.) *H.*

EXERCISE 7
Test-Taking Rules
What to Do When You're Running Out of Time

a. There are three rules that help you do well when you're taking a test.

b. Who can tell me rule 1? (Call on a student. Praise close responses to the rule: *Work the problems that you can work.*)

- Yes, rule 1 is: Work the problems that you can work.
- Everybody, what's rule 1? (Signal.) *Work the problems that you can work.*

c. What does the rule mean if you're working a hard problem? (Call on a student. Idea: *Write the problem on your paper and work it.*)

- Yes, don't try to do hard problems in your head. Work them on paper.

d. Who can tell me rule 2? (Call on a student. Praise close responses to the rule: *If you can't work a problem, skip it and come back to it.*)

- Yes, rule 2 is: If you can't work a problem, skip it and come back to it.
- Everybody, what's rule 2? (Signal.) *If you can't work a problem, skip it and come back to it.*

e. Who can tell me rule 3? (Call on a student. Praise close responses to the rule: *Make sure that each problem has one and only one answer.*)

- Yes, rule 3 is: Make sure that each problem has one and only one answer.
- Everybody, what's rule 3? (Signal.) *Make sure each problem has one and only one answer.*

f. Look at your answer sheet and find the first item you'd mark if there was only one minute left.

- Everybody, what's the number of the first item you'd mark? (Signal.) *7.*
- Find the next item you'd mark. What's the number of the next item? (Signal.) *8.*
- What's the number of the next item you'd mark? (Signal.) *21.*
- What's the number of the next item you'd mark? (Signal.) *22.*
- What's the number of the next item you'd mark? (Signal.) *33.*
- What's the number of the **last** item you'd mark? (Signal.) *56.*

g. (Repeat step f until firm.)

h. We're going to pretend you're taking a test, and there's not much time left. You haven't answered items 7, 8, 21, 22, and 33 through 56. So, when I tell you there's only one minute left, you'll mark one and only one answer for each of those items.

i. Get ready to mark the answers. After you're finished, we'll find out how many more points you scored by following the rules for doing well on tests.

j. Here we go. There is only one minute left. Finish up your paper.

k. (Reinforce students who quickly fill in one and only one answer for all of the problems on the answer sheet.)

- (Prompt students who don't fill answers in quickly to start marking answers more quickly.)
- (Alert students who have more than one answer filled in on any item to make sure that there's only one answer per item.)

l. (After one minute, direct students to correct their answer sheet.)

m. Check your work.

- For the items you just marked, I'll tell you the make-believe answer. Mark it with a **C** if you marked the correct answer and an **X** if you didn't mark it. Raise your hand after I say each answer if you guessed the right one.
- Item 7. The answer is **D.** (Acknowledge students who raise their hands.)
- Item 8. The answer is **H.** (Acknowledge students who raise their hands.)
- (Repeat for items: 21, B; 22, I; 33, A; 34, F; 35, D; 36, F; 37, C; 38, I; 39, D; 40, I; 41, C; 42, H; 43, B; 44, J; 45, E; 46, G; 47, D; 48, F; 49, C; 50, G; 51, D; 52, H; 53, A; 54, J; 55, B; 56, F.)

n. Count the **C**s you wrote next to the numbers.

- Raise your hand if you got eight or more of them correct. (Students respond.)
- Raise your hand if you got seven of the items correct. (Students respond.)
- Raise your hand if you got six of the items correct. (Students respond.)

o. (Repeat for five, four, three, two, one, and zero of them correct.)

- Most of you got four to six of the items correct. You wouldn't have gotten any of these problems correct if you hadn't filled answers in for those items.

EXERCISE 8
Independent Work

a. Find the independent work for lesson 9. √
b. Work items 1 through 19 on your lined paper.
• Raise your hand when you're finished.
• (Observe students and give feedback.)
• (Write on the board:)

• Here are the answers you should have for the problems.
d. Make an X next to any problem you got wrong.

1. $\frac{4}{3}$ or $1\frac{1}{3}$

2. $\frac{30}{49}$

3. $\frac{4}{4}$ or 1

4. $\frac{28}{10}$ or $2\frac{8}{10}$ or $2\frac{4}{5}$

5. 28

6. 9724

7. $17\frac{4}{5}$ or 17 R4

8. $17\frac{2}{3}$ or 25 R2

9. 1

10. 117

11. $12.48

12. $1.60

13. $0.34 or 34¢

14. 88

15. 266

16. 23 stamps

17. 39 stamps

18. 16 stamps

19. 62 stamps

Test Preparation

1 If you rounded this number to the nearest hundred, you'd round it to 200. If you rounded this number to the nearest 10, you'd round it to 180. Which of these could be the number?

276	283	183	174	None of these
A	**B**	**C**	**D**	**E**

2 A certain number when rounded to the nearest hundred is 500. The same number when rounded to the nearest ten is 520. Which of these could be the number?

418	524	492	513	None of these
F	**G**	**H**	**I**	**J**

3 A certain number when rounded to the nearest hundred is 100. The same number has an 8 in the tens place and a 7 in the ones place. Which of these could be the number?

287	187	87	147	178
A	**B**	**C**	**D**	**E**

4 A certain number when rounded to the nearest hundred is 400. The same number has a 3 in the tens place and a 9 in the ones place. Which of these could be the number?

339	493	593	439	393
F	**G**	**H**	**I**	**J**

5 A certain number is between 600 and 700. The same number has a 0 in the tens place and a 1 in the ones place. Which of these could be the number?

610	710	701	601	None of these
A	**B**	**C**	**D**	**E**

6 A certain number is between 300 and 400. The same number has a 7 in the tens place. Which of these could be the number?

374	327	471	382	276
F	**G**	**H**	**I**	**J**

9 $12 \div 2 = \square$

14	10	2	24	6
A	**B**	**C**	**D**	**E**

10 $360 \div 9 = \square$

90	30	40	45	27
F	**G**	**H**	**I**	**J**

© SRA/McGraw-Hill. Permission is granted to reproduce for school use.

11   How many edges does this figure have?

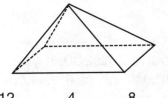

12	4	8	5	None of these
A	**B**	**C**	**D**	**E**

12   How many edges does this figure have?

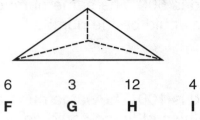

6	3	12	4
F	**G**	**H**	**I**

13   How many edges does this figure have?

5	6	18	9	None of these
A	**B**	**C**	**D**	**E**

14   How many edges does this figure have?

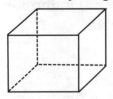

6	12	4	10
F	**G**	**H**	**I**

© SRA/McGraw-Hill. Permission is granted to reproduce for school use.

The **product** is the number you get when you multiply.

15 What operation do you use to get a sum?

   A add

   B subtract

   C multiply

   D divide

16 What operation do you use to get a product?

   F add

   G subtract

   H multiply

   I divide

17 The product of two numbers is 6. The sum of the two numbers is 5. What are the numbers?

   A 2 and 2

   B 3 and 2

   C 4 and 3

   D 6 and 5

   E None of these

18 The product of two numbers is 14. The sum of the two numbers is 9. What are the numbers?

   F 3 and 7

   G 9 and 1

   H 3 and 9

   I 7 and 2

   J None of these

19 The product of two numbers is 30. The sum of the two numbers is 11. What are the numbers?

   A 3 and 7

   B 10 and 3

   C 8 and 3

   D 6 and 5

   E None of these

20 The product of two numbers is 9. The sum of the two numbers is 10. What are the numbers?

   F 9 and 1

   G 8 and 2

   H 7 and 3

   I 4 and 6

   J None of these

© SRA/McGraw-Hill. Permission is granted to reproduce for school use.

Study the numbers in the box. Then answer items 23 through 25.

4781	4871	4807	4880	4870

23 If you put the numbers in order from smallest to largest, what would be the fifth number?

4781	4880	4807	4870	None of these
A	**B**	**C**	**D**	**E**

24 If you put the numbers in order from smallest to largest, what would be the second number?

4781	4880	4871	4807	None of these
F	**G**	**H**	**I**	**J**

25 If you put the numbers in order from smallest to largest, what would be the fourth number?

4781	4880	4870	4807	None of these
A	**B**	**C**	**D**	**E**

Study the numbers in the box. Then answer items 26 through 28.

0	705	81	12	1019	260

26 If you put the numbers in order from largest to smallest, what would be the third number?

260	81	705	12	1019
F	**G**	**H**	**I**	**J**

27 If you put the numbers in order from largest to smallest, what would be the first number?

260	1019	12	0	None of these
A	**B**	**C**	**D**	**E**

28 If you put the numbers in order from largest to smallest, what would be the fifth number?

0	1019	705	12	None of these
F	**G**	**H**	**I**	**J**

© SRA/McGraw-Hill. Permission is granted to reproduce for school use.

29 Here is a problem: 68
                            − 31

Which estimation problem shows the correct rounded values?

70	70	80	8	None of these
− 40	− 30	− 30	− 4	
A	**B**	**C**	**D**	**E**

30 Here is a problem: 38
                            + 13

Which estimation problem shows the correct rounded values?

30	30	38	40	None of these
+ 13	+ 10	+ 10	+ 10	
F	**G**	**H**	**I**	**J**

31 Here is a problem: 73
                            − 49

Which estimation problem shows the correct rounded values?

70	70	80	80	None of these
− 40	− 50	− 40	− 50	
A	**B**	**C**	**D**	**E**

32 Here is a problem: 47
                            + 52

Which estimation problem shows the correct rounded values?

40	50	50	40	None of these
+ 50	+ 60	+ 50	+ 60	
F	**G**	**H**	**I**	**J**

© SRA/McGraw-Hill. Permission is granted to reproduce for school use.

Independent Work

<u>Lesson 9</u>

Write items 1 through 15 on lined paper and work them.
Rewrite problems in a column if they need to be worked that way.

1 $\dfrac{10}{3} - 2 = \dfrac{4}{3}, 1\dfrac{1}{3}$ **2** $\dfrac{10}{7} \times \dfrac{10}{7} = \dfrac{30}{49}$

3

$$\begin{array}{r} \dfrac{7}{4} \\[4pt] -\dfrac{3}{4} \\[2pt] \hline \dfrac{4}{4}, 1 \end{array}$$

4 $\dfrac{10}{7} + 2 = \dfrac{28}{10}, 2\dfrac{8}{10}, 2\dfrac{4}{5}$

5 $56 \div 2 = 28$ **6** $286 \times 34 = 9724$ **7** $5\overline{)89} \; 17\dfrac{4}{5}, 17\,R4$ **8** $3\overline{)77} \; 25\dfrac{2}{3}, 25\,R2$

9 $27 \div 27 = 1$ **10** $468 \div 4 = 117$ **11** $\$3.12 \times 4 = \$12.48$

12 $\$0.54 + \$1.06 = \$1.60$ **13** $\$0.88 - \$0.54 = \$0.34$

14 $184 - 96 = 88$ **15** $55 + 3 + 208 = 266$

Read the story. Then answer items 16 through 19.

Cindy had 36 stamps. Jim had 23 stamps. Bob had 42 stamps, and Sue had 39 stamps.

16   How many stamps did Jim have?   23 stamps

17   How many stamps did Sue have?   39 stamps

18   How many fewer stamps did Jim have than Sue?   16 stamps

19   How many stamps did Jim and Sue have together?   62 stamps

Any of the answers listed for items 1, 3, 4, 7, and 8 is acceptable.

STOP

© SRA/McGraw-Hill. Permission is granted to reproduce for school use.

Test-Taking Strategies

The Test Preparation material teaches three critical test-taking strategies, in addition to acquainting students with some of the formats and content of standardized achievement tests. In Lesson 6, Exercise 7, the three strategies are introduced:

(1) Work the problems that you can work.

(2) If you don't know how to work a problem, skip it and come back to it.

(3) Make sure that each problem has one and only one answer.

Students are taught what each rule means, and they are taught to apply the rules. The first rule, "Work the problems that you can work," means that students should write down the problems that they can't work in their head and work them to figure out the answer. Exercise 5 of Test Preparation Lesson 9 shows an example of problem types students are trained to work on paper. Students are directed to write the numbers in order in a row on paper before answering the items.

Students who are not taught this strategy often perform poorly on standardized tests because they incorrectly answer problems that they know how to work. These students don't write down and work those problems because the test directions don't tell them to, and consequently, they get the answer wrong.

Throughout the remaining lessons, students are trained to apply this strategy and work various types of problems.

Students are taught that the second rule, "If you don't know how to work a problem, skip it and come back to it," means that they should not spend a lot of time on problems that they don't know how to work. Students should skip problems that they can't work and come back to them if they have time. Sometimes students who take standardized tests spend too much time on one problem and don't have time to answer many problems that they are capable of answering correctly. The practice students receive in the CMC Test Preparation program teaches them how to avoid spending too much time on problems they can't work quickly.

The last rule, "Make sure that each item has one and only one answer," means that when there is only one minute remaining in the test, students should guess on the items that aren't filled in and mark one answer for each of them. Exercise 7 of Lesson 6 teaches students to look over their answer sheet and identify the items that are not filled in. In Exercises 1–6 of Test Preparation Lesson 6, students are directed to skip items 7, 8, 17, and 18. These items were omitted to provide students practice in identifying items that are not filled in.

On Exercise 7 of Lessons 7–15, the teacher tells students to pretend that there is only one minute left and they are to mark answers for all items that don't have answers. Students mark an answer for each item. At the end of the exercise, the teacher indicates the correct answers for items that students did not mark. Students mark the correct answers and tally the number of "correct" guesses for those items to see how much their score improved by guessing.

Lessons 16 and 17 are primarily a 2-part mock test, providing students practice in applying everything they've learned about standardized test formats, content, and test-taking strategies.

Teaching the Program

Level D is designed to be presented to the entire class. You should generally be able to teach one lesson during a 45–50 minute period. Students' independent work requires another 15–25 minutes. The independent work can be scheduled at another time during the day.

Organization

The program will run far more smoothly if you follow these steps:

• Arrange seating so you can receive very quick information on high performers and lower performers. A good plan is to organize the students something like this:

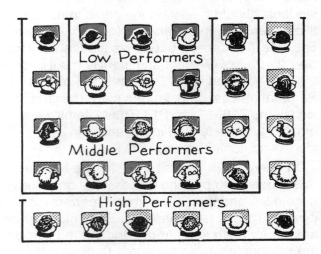

Front of Classroom

Low Performers

Middle Performers

High Performers

The lowest performers are closest to the front of the classroom. Middle performers are arranged around the lowest performers. Highest performers are arranged around the periphery. With this arrangement, you can position yourself so that, by taking a few steps during the time that students are working problems, you can sample low, average, and high performers.

While different variations of this arrangement are possible, be careful not to seat low performers far from the front-center of the room. The highest performers, understandably, can be farthest from the center because they attend better, learn faster, and need less observation and feedback.

• Arrange permanent pairs of students to work together in the team games. The pairings should be based on performance. Each low performer should be paired either with an average performer or a high performer.

Teaching

When you teach the program, a basic rule is that you shouldn't present from the front of the room unless you're showing something on the board.

For most of the activities, you direct students to work specified problems. For these activities, you should present from somewhere in the middle of the room (in no set place) and, as students work the problem; observe a good sample of students. Although you won't be able to observe every child working every problem,

you can observe at least half a dozen students in possibly 15 seconds.

Rehearse the lesson before presenting it to the class. Don't simply read the text, but act it out. When you are to write something on the board, look at the shaded cells that show what's going to happen and how you'll change the display. If you keep the changes in mind, you'll be much more fluent in presenting the activity.

Watch your wording. With the non-board activities, it's much easier than it is with board activities. The board formats are usually designed so they are manageable if you have an idea of the steps you'll take. If you rehearse each of the early lessons before presenting them, you'll soon learn how to present efficiently from the script. In later lessons, you should scan the list of skills at the beginning of each lesson. New skills are in boldface type. If a new skill is introduced in that lesson, rehearse it. Most of what occurs in the lesson will not be new, but a variation of what you've presented earlier, so you may not need to rehearse these activities.

Remind students about the two important rules for doing well in this program: Always work problems the way they are shown. And: No shortcuts are permitted.

Remember that everything introduced will be used later. Reinforce students who apply what they learn. Do not provide extensive help for those who don't. But require them to rework problems so they are appropriate.

Using the Teacher Presentation Scripts

The script for each lesson indicates precisely how to present each structured activity. The script shows what you say, what you do, and what the students' responses should be.

What you say appears in **blue** type:

You say this.

What you do appears in parentheses:

(You do this.)

The responses of the students are in italics.

Students say this.

Follow the specified wording in the script. While wording variations from the specified script are not always dangerous, you will be assured of communicating clearly with the students if you follow the script exactly. The reason is that the wording is controlled, and the tasks are arranged so they provide succinct wording and focus clearly on important aspects of what the students are to do. Although you may feel uncomfortable "reading" from a script (and you may feel that the students will not pay attention), follow the scripts very closely; try to present them as if you're saying something important to the students. If you do, you'll find after a while that working from a script is not difficult and that students indeed respond well to what you say.

A sample appears on page 30.

The arrows show the seven different things you'll do that are not spelled out in the script. You'll signal to make sure that group responses involve all the students. You'll "firm" critical parts of the exercises. You'll also use information based on what the students are doing to judge whether you'll proceed quickly or wait a few more seconds before moving on with the presentation. For some exercises, you'll write things on the board, and you'll often change the board display.

ARROW 1: GROUP RESPONSES (Signal.)

Some of the tasks call for group responses. If students respond together with brisk unison responses, you receive good information about whether "most" of the students are performing correctly. The simplest way to signal students to respond together is to adopt a timing practice—just like the timing in a musical piece.

A signal follows a question, a command, (as shown by arrow 1) or the words, "Get ready."

You can signal by nodding, clapping one time, snapping your fingers, or tapping your foot. After initially establishing the timing for signals, you can signal through voice inflection only.

Students will not be able to initiate responses together at the appropriate rate unless you follow these rules:

a) Talk first. Pause a standard length of time (possibly 1 second), then signal. Never signal when you talk. Don't change the timing for your signal. Students are to respond on your signal?not after it or before it.

b) Model responses that are paced reasonably. Don't permit students to produce slow, droning responses. These are dangerous because they rob you of the information that can be derived from appropriate group responses.

When students respond in a droning way, many of them are copying responses of others. If students are required to respond at a reasonable speaking rate, all students must initiate responses; therefore, it's relatively easy to determine which students are not responding and which are saying the wrong response. Also, don't permit students to respond at a very fast rate or to "jump" your signal.

To correct mistakes, show students exactly what you want them to do.

- I'm good at answering the right way. Watch: Read the numeral for 6 tens. 60. Wasn't that great?
- Let's see who can do it just that way: Read the numeral for 6 tens. (Signal.) *60.*

c) Do not respond with the students unless you are trying to work with them on a difficult response. You present only what's in blue. You do not say the answers with the students, and you should not move your lips or give other spurious clues about what the answer is.

Think of signals this way: If you use them correctly, they provide you with much diagnostic information. A weak response suggests that you should repeat a task and provides information about which students may need more help. Signals are, therefore, important early in the program. After students have learned the routine, the students will be able to respond on cue with no signal. That will happen, however, only if you always give your signals at the end of a constant time interval after you complete what you say.

ARROW 2: FIRMING (Repeat until firm.)

When students make mistakes, you correct them. A correction may occur during any part of the teacher presentation that calls for the students to respond. It may also occur in connection with what the students are writing. Here are the rules for corrections:

- You correct a mistake as soon as you hear it.
- A mistake on oral responses is saying the wrong thing or not responding.

To correct: Say the correct answer. Repeat the task the students missed. For example, "Read the numeral for 6 tens." (Signal.)

a. (Write **60**:)

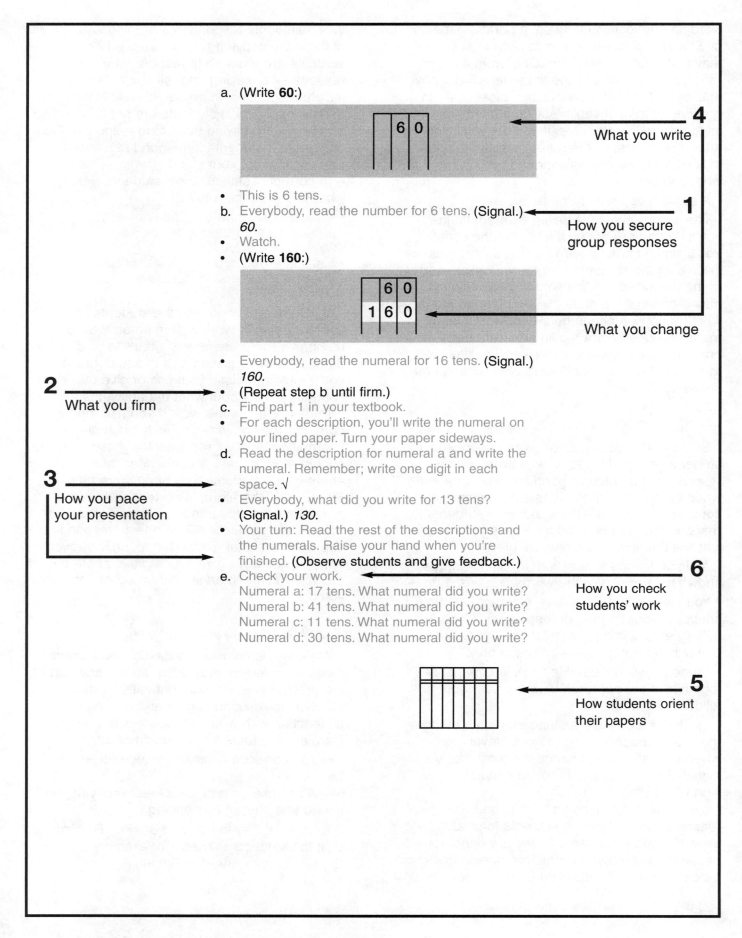

- This is 6 tens.
b. Everybody, read the number for 6 tens. (Signal.) ◄──── **1**
  60.
- Watch.
- (Write **160**:)

4 ──► What you write

1 How you secure group responses

What you change

- Everybody, read the numeral for 16 tens. (Signal.)
  160.

2 ──► • (Repeat step b until firm.)

What you firm

c. Find part 1 in your textbook.
- For each description, you'll write the numeral on your lined paper. Turn your paper sideways.
d. Read the description for numeral a and write the numeral. Remember; write one digit in each space. √

3 ──► • Everybody, what did you write for 13 tens? (Signal.) *130.*

How you pace your presentation

- Your turn: Read the rest of the descriptions and the numerals. Raise your hand when you're finished. **(Observe students and give feedback.)**
e. Check your work. ◄──── **6**
  Numeral a: 17 tens. What numeral did you write?
  Numeral b: 41 tens. What numeral did you write?
  Numeral c: 11 tens. What numeral did you write?
  Numeral d: 30 tens. What numeral did you write?

6 How you check students' work

5 ──► How students orient their papers

If some students do not respond, respond late, or say anything but 60, there's a mistake. As soon as you hear the mistake, you correct it.

Say the correct answer. "It's 60."

(Repeat the task.)

"Listen again: Read the numeral for 6 tens." (Signal.)

Remember, wherever there's a signal, there's a place where students may make mistakes. You correct mistakes as soon as you hear them.

A special correction is needed when correcting mistakes on tasks that teach a relationship. This type of correction is marked with the note:

(Repeat step ___ until firm.)

The note **(Repeat step until firm)** occurs when students must produce a series of responses (as in counting) and where they may not understand a relationship that is structured so it involves answering more than one question (as in step b).

When you "repeat until firm," you follow these steps:

1) **Correct the mistake**. (Tell the answer and repeat the task that was missed.)

2) **Return to the beginning of the specified step and present the entire step.**

In step b, you present two different tasks. If the students make any mistakes in step b, you repeat step b after you have corrected the mistakes. When you hear a mistake, you say the correct answer and repeat the question or task. However, you make sure that students are firm in **both** the tasks you present in step b. You can't be sure that students are firm unless you repeat the entire step.

Here's a summary of the steps you follow when repeating a part of the exercise until firm.

1) **Correct the mistake.**

Students make a mistake in reading **160.** Tell the correct answer, "It's 160."

Repeat the task:

"Listen again. Read the numeral for 16 tens."

2) **Repeat the step.** (Change display to **60.**)

"Let's see who remembers how those problems work."

Start at the beginning of step b and present the entire step.

"Read the numeral for 6 tens."
"Read the numeral for 16 tens."

Repeating until firm is based on the information you need about the students.

You present the context in which the mistake occurred, and the students can show you through their responses whether or not the correction worked, whether or not they are firm.

The repeat-until-firm direction appears only in the most critical parts of new-teaching exercises. It usually focuses on knowledge that is very important for later work. As a general procedure, follow the repeat-until-firm directions. However, if you're quite sure that the mistake was a "glitch" and does not mean that the students lack understanding, don't follow the repeat-until-firm direction.

ARROW 3: PACING YOUR PRESENTATION (Observe students and give feedback and √.)

You should pace your verbal presentation at a normal speaking rate—as if you were telling somebody something important.

> **Note:** The presentation works much better and the inflections are far more appropriate if you pretend that you're talking to an **adult,** not a young child. But make your message sound important.

The most typical mistake teachers make is going too slowly or talking as if to preschoolers.

The arrows for number 3 on the diagram show two ways to pace your presentation for activities where students write or get involved in touching or finding parts of their workbook or textbook page. The first is a √. The second is a note to **(Observe students and give feedback).**

A √ is a note to check what the students are doing. It requires only a second or two. If you are positioned close to several "average performing" students, check whether they are performing. If they are, proceed with the presentation.

The **(Observe students and give feedback)** direction implies a more elaborate response. You sample more students and you give feedback, not only to individual students, but to the group. Here are the basic rules for what to do and not to do when you observe and give feedback:

a) Make sure that you are not at the front of the class when you present the directions for the tasks that involve observing students' performance. For the textbook activity, you assign problems for the students to work (step d). When presenting the textbook activity, move from the front of the room to a place where you can quickly sample the performance of low, middle, and high performers.

b)   As soon as students start to work, start observing. As you observe, make comments to the whole class. Focus these comments on students who are following directions, working quickly, and working accurately. "Wow, a couple of students are almost finished. I haven't seen one mistake so far."

c)   When students raise their hands to indicate that they are finished, acknowledge them. When you acknowledge that they are finished, they should put their hands down.

d)   If you observe mistakes, do **not** provide a great deal of individual help. Point out any mistakes, but do not work the problems for the students. For instance, if a child gets one of the problems wrong, point to it and say, "I think you made a mistake." If students don't line their numerals up correctly, say, "You'd better erase that and try again. Your numerals are not lined up." If students are not following instructions that you gave, tell them, "You're supposed to write the answer under the other two numbers. You have to listen very carefully to the instructions."

e)   Do not wait for the slowest students to complete the problems before presenting the workcheck during which students correct their work and fix up any mistakes. A good rule early in the program is to allow a reasonable amount of time. You can usually use the middle performers as a gauge for what is reasonable. As you observe that they are completing their work, announce, "Okay, you have about 10 seconds more to finish up." At the end of that time, continue in the exercise.

f)   During the workcheck, continue to circulate among the students and make sure that they are checking their work. They should fix up any mistakes. Praise students who are following the procedure. Allow a reasonable amount of time for them to check each problem. Do not wait for the slowest students to finish their check. Try to keep the workcheck moving as quickly as possible.

g)   If you observe a serious problem that is not unique to the lowest performers, tell the class, "Stop. We seem to have a serious problem." Repeat the part of the exercise that gives them information about what they are to do. *Note:* Do not provide new teaching or new problems. Simply repeat the part of the exercise

that gives them the information they need and reassign the work. "Let's see who can get it this time."

h)   When higher-performing students do their independent work, you may want to go over any parts of the lesson with the students who had trouble with the structured work (such as, they made mistakes or didn't finish). Make sure that you check all the problems worked by the lower performers and give them feedback. Show them what they did wrong. Keep your explanations simple. The more you talk, the more you'll probably confuse them. If there are serious problems, repeat the exercise that presented difficulties for the lower performers.

If you follow these procedures very closely, your students will work faster and more accurately. They will also become facile at following your directions.

If you don't follow these rules, you may think that you are helping students, but you will actually be reinforcing them for behaviors that you are trying to change.

If you wait far beyond a reasonable time period before presenting the workcheck, you punish the higher performers and the others who worked quickly and accurately. Soon, they will learn that there is no payoff for doing well—no praise, no recognition—but instead a long wait while you give attention to lower performers.

If you don't make announcements about students who are doing well and working quickly, the class will not understand what's expected. Students will probably not improve much.

If you provide extensive individual help on independent work, you will actually reinforce students for not listening to your directions, or for being dependent on your help. Furthermore, this dependency becomes contagious. If you provide extensive individual guidance, it doesn't take other students in the class long to discover that they don't have to listen to your directions, that they can raise their hand and receive help, and that students who have the most serious problems receive the most teacher attention. These expectations are the opposite of the ones you want to induce. You want students to be self-reliant and to have a **reason** for learning and remembering what you say when you instruct them. The simplest reason is that they will use what they have just been shown and that those who remember will receive reinforcement.

If you provide wordy explanations and extensive reteaching to correct any problems you observe, you run the serious risk of further confusing the students. Their problem is that they didn't attend to or couldn't perform on some detail that you covered in your initial presentation. So tell them what they didn't attend to and repeat the activity (or the step) that gives them the information they need. This approach shows them how to process the information you already presented. A different demonstration or explanation, however, may not show them how to link what you said originally with the new demonstration. So go light on showing students another way.

Because Level D is carefully designed, it is possible to teach all the students the desired behaviors of self-reliance, following instructions, and working fast and accurately. If you follow the management rules just outlined, by the time the students have reached Lesson 15, all students should be able to complete assigned work within a reasonable period of time and have reasons to feel good about their ability to do math. As they improve, you should tell them about it. "What's this? Everybody's finished with that problem already? That's impressive. . . . " That's what you want to happen. Follow the rules, and it will happen.

ARROW 4: BOARD WORK

What you write on the board and how you change it is indicated with display boxes. In the sample exercise, you first write a problem (What you write). Then you write a second problem (What you change). The convention used in the display boxes is that what you initially present is shown in a gray box.

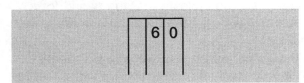

Any changes in that display (additions or alterations) are shown with parts that are in white.

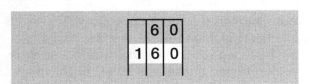

Scanning the boxes shows both what you'll write and how you'll change the display.

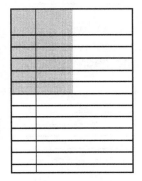

ARROW 5: LINED-PAPER ICON

For some textbook activities, an icon in the student material shows the student how to orient their lined paper to write or copy specified material. For work that involves working column problems or writing numerals, students turn their paper sideways. For other tasks, students orient their paper so lines are horizontal.

Different plans for using paper are workable. The biggest problem to solve is that students write problems on different parts of the page, and it is sometimes very difficult to find their work for any given part or problem. Another problem is that some students tend to cramp their work into a very small space, making it very difficult to read what they've written or see whether they have correctly gone through the problem-solving steps (such as writing the digits that are "carried" in a column-addition problem).

Here's a workable plan:

Direct students to fold their paper into four parts. (Fold from top to bottom and then fold from side to side.)

Students write their name on top of the front side. They use the front side for tasks that require orienting the paper so lines are horizontal. They use the backside for work that requires the paper to be turned sideways.

For the first part that requires work on the front side (lines horizontal), students work in the upper left part and write one equation or problem per line:

The next part that is to be written on the front side of the paper would go in the upper right quadrant:

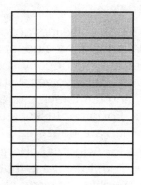

For parts that are to be written on the back, the first would go in the upper left (note the margin is at the top of the page):

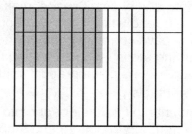

If more than one quadrant on the back is required, the next part would go in the upper-right quadrant.

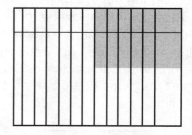

If there is a problem with finding student answers, one procedure is to require students to **box** the answer to each problem:

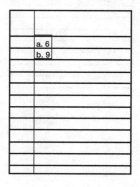

Other organizations are possible, such as requiring students to copy the answer to each problem in the margin.

ARROW 6: WORKCHECKS (Check your work.)

It is important to observe what students are doing and to make sure that they are both attending to workchecks and are correcting their mistakes.

The simplest procedure is to use a pencil/pen or colored-pencil plan. Students should write their work in pencil so they can erase and make any corrections that are necessary as they work. When you indicate that it is time to "Check your work," they put down their writing pencil and pick up their marking pencil or pen. If their work or answer is correct, they mark a **C** for the problem. If their work is wrong, they mark an **X**.

Later, students correct any mistakes. They do not hand in their work until mistakes are corrected.

If you establish the organization procedures at the beginning of the program, students will learn more and learn faster because they will be far more likely to learn from their mistakes. They will not be as tempted to cheat. Instead they will be more likely to read what they have written on their paper, and they will more easily learn that what is introduced in the program is used.

Grading Papers

The teacher material includes a separate *Answer Key* booklet. The answers usually indicate everything that students need to do to work problems appropriately. When children are taught a particular method for working problems, they should follow these steps, which means that you should indicate that the "work" for a problem is wrong if the procedure is not followed.

After each lesson, look at every student's work, especially the independent work. You can skim the pages of the higher performers; however, you should look more closely at the papers of lower performers—the structured activities and the independent work.

You can often provide this check while students are doing their independent work. Go to each student, look over their work, and mark any uncorrected mistakes with an **X.** Tell the student something like, "You had better do that problem again. I think you forgot to carry." Then go to the next student. (Typically, it takes no more than 15 seconds to look over a worksheet and identify any problems.)

When you look over the independent work, put a little check mark after the last problem the child has completed. That mark shows how much of their work you've already checked.

A good procedure for independent work is for students to raise their hands when they are finished. As students raise their hands, look over the independent work problems you haven't checked and write a comment if the work is good. (The comment shows that you've checked it.)

Students who have mistakes on their worksheet should correct the mistakes and show the corrected work to you at a specified time.

Different procedures are possible; however, a lot of the "paper grading" and feedback can be provided while the students do their independent work. If grading and feedback are not provided during this time, they should be completed before the presentation of the next lesson.

Unacceptable Error Rates

During structured activities, you should firm the students and make sure that students can run each activity quickly and accurately (if not on the first trial, after the firming has been provided).

Students' independent work should also be monitored. Specifically, no more than 30 percent of the students should make mistakes on any independent activity. On the first lesson that a recently-taught skill is perfectly "independent," error rates may exceed the ideal (more than 30 percent of the students making mistakes). However, if an excessive error rate continues, there is a problem that should be corrected.

Consider whether the preceding steps you've taken are adequate. High error rates on independent practice may be the result of the following problems:

a) The students may not be appropriately placed in the program.

b) The initial presentation may not have provided adequate firming. The students made mistakes that were not corrected. The parts of the teacher presentation in which errors occurred were not repeated until firm.

c) Students may have received inappropriate help. When they worked structured problems

earlier, they received too much help and became dependent on the help.

d) Students may not have been required to follow directions carefully. (If students do not learn early in the program that they are to follow directions precisely, serious problems may result later.)

Consider these possibilities if students tend to have many problems with the materials. If you look at their work as feedback about the way you are presenting material, the mistakes can be a source of information that is useful to you in showing you how to teach more effectively. Also make sure that you do not permit high error rates to continue. The simplest procedure is to show the students the types of mistakes they are making and give them information about what they should be doing. Then award bonus points (or some other form of reward) for doing well in independent parts of the worksheet.

Test Lessons

Following every tenth lesson, from Lesson 10 through 100, are **test lessons.** A test lesson includes some teaching activities as well as the 10-lesson test. The test is designed to assess the most important skills mastered in the previous 10 lessons. Those skills will be elaborated on during the next 10 lessons. The 10-lesson test, therefore, provides you with information about how well prepared students are to proceed in the program.

The 10-lesson tests can also be used to help place students who are new to *Connecting Math Concepts, Level D.* (See **Cumulative Tests, Placing mid-year students,** page 13). Several of the 10-lesson tests include content unique to CMC. Holding students accountable who haven't received instruction on content unique to CMC isn't appropriate. To alert teachers and students to material that is unique, parts of the test are gray screened. Teacher presentation that is gray screened should not be presented to students who have not received the preceding 10 lessons of instruction in the program. Students new to the program should ignore material in their textbooks or workbooks that is gray screened on the 10-lesson tests.

On Test 1, Part 3 tests number families, which are unique to CMC. The teacher presentation for Part 3 is gray screened, and Part 3 of the student material is also gray screened. The gray screen indicates that Part 3 should not be presented to or completed by students who have not received the first 10 lessons of instruction in CMC D. On 10-lesson Test 3, a segment of the teacher script for Part 5 refers to number families. This part of the script is gray screened, indicating that students who have not received the instruction from Lessons 21 to 30 should not be presented the gray-screened wording. Those students are expected to work the problems in Part 3, but they don't receive the specific instructions relating to number families. On 10-lesson Test 10, Part 2 shows different bags containing figures. Students are to write the probability for drawing a specific element from each bag and are then to complete a sentence telling about the probability. The sentences are unique to CMC and are gray screened in the student material, indicating that students who have not received instruction in CMC D from Lessons 91 to 100 should not complete them. Students are expected to complete the fractions for that part, however.

Sometimes, students copy from their neighbors. A good method of discovering who is copying is to spread students out during the test if it's physically possible to do so. Discrepancies in the test performance and daily performance of some students pinpoint which students may be copying.

If copying is occurring, reassign seating so that the students who tend to copy are either separated from those who know the answers or seated near the front-center of the room where it is easier for you to monitor them.

Here's the answer key for Test 9.

TEST ANSWER KEY

The teacher's answer key provides the correct answers for each lesson and 10-lesson test. The answer key for each test shows the correct work for each item, and a table for assigning percent grades based on the number of points earned.

TEST 9 PERCENT SUMMARY

SCORE	%	SCORE	%	SCORE	%
99	100	88	89	78	79
98	99	87	88	77	78
97	98	86	87	76	77
96	97	85	86	75	76
95	96	84	85	74	75
94	95	83	84	73	74
93	94	82	83	72	73
92	93	81	82	71	72
91	92	80	81	70	71
90	91	79	80	69	70
89	90				

TEST 9 SCORING CHART

PART	SCORE			POSSIBLE SCORE	PASSING SCORE
1	1 for each item			9	8
2	2 for each item			8	8
3	4 for each item			12	8
4	Each Cell 1	Each Point 2	Line 1	13	10
5	2 for each item			8	8
6	Perimeter 4	Area 4		8	8
7	5 for each item			10	10
8	EACH ITEM			15	12
	Answer 3	Unit Name 2	Total 5		
9	4 for each item			8	Parts 9, 10 combined 12
10	4 for each item			8	
	TOTAL			**99**	

Here's the answer key for Test 9:

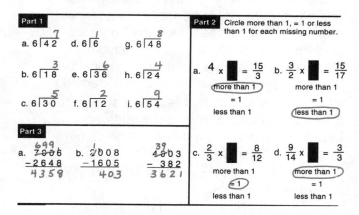

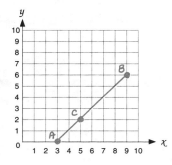

The percent-conversion table shows the percentage grade you'd award for students who have a perfect score of 99, a score of 98, and so on. For several of the 10-lesson tests, the total score possible is 100 points. For these tests no percent-conversion table is provided, as the point score is also the percent score.

The scoring chart for each part of the test indicates the possible points for each item, the possible points for the part and the passing criterion.

Note that points are sometimes awarded for working different parts of the problem. For example, for Part 4, students earn one point for each cell, two points for each point on the graph, and 1 point for the line. For Part 6, students earn four points for the perimeter and four points for the area. For Part 8, students earn three points for the answer and two points for the unit name. Each problem is worth a total of five points. The Test 9 Scoring Chart indicates that the passing score for Parts 9 and 10 combined is twelve points. If a student earns less than twelve points for those parts, the student fails the part(s) in which the student made errors. If the student missed one problem in each of the parts, the student fails both parts. If a student missed two problems in Part 9, and didn't make any errors in Part 10, the student fails only Part 9.

Test 9 Textbook

Part 5

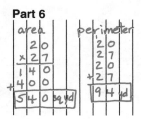

a. $\frac{8}{6}$ b. $\frac{12}{17}$

c. $\frac{50}{26}$ d. $\frac{100}{13}$

Part 6

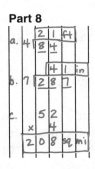

Part 7

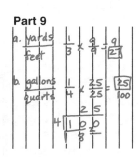

Part 8

Part 9

Part 10

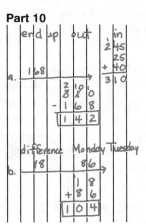

Use the criteria in the *Answer Key* for marking each student's test. Record the results on the Group Summary of Test Performance (provided on page 184 of the *Teacher's Guide.*)

Here's how the results could be summarized following Test 9:

Remedy Summary—Group Summary of Test Performance

Note: Test remedies are specified in the *Answer Key*. Percent Summary is also specified in the *Answer Key*.

Name	Test 9 Check parts not passed										Total %
	1	2	3	4	5	6	7	8	9	10	
1. Amanda Adams			✓		✓						84%
2. William Alberts			✓								92%
3. Henry Bowman	✓		✓					✓	✓		70%
4. Phillip Caswell											89%
5. Zoë Collier	✓										87%
6. Chan Won Lee			✓								83%
Number of Students Not Passed = NP	2	0	4	0	1	0	0	1	1		
Total number of students = T	6	6	6	6	6	6	6	6			
Remedy needed if NP/T = 25% or more	Y	N	Y	N	N	N	N	N	N		

The summary sheet provides you with a cumulative record of each student's performance on the 10-lesson tests.

Summarize each student's performance.

• Make a check in the appropriate columns to indicate any part of the test that was failed.

• At the bottom of each column, write the total number of failures for that part, and the total number of students in the class. Then divide the number of failures by the number of students to determine the failure rate for each part.

• Provide a remedy for each part that has a failure rate of 25 percent (.25) or more.

TEST REMEDIES

The presentation book specifies remedies for each test. Any necessary remedies should be presented before the next lesson (Lesson 91).

Here are the remedies for Test 9:

TEST 9 PERCENT REMEDIES				
PART	LESSON	EXERCISE	TEXTBOOK PART	EXTRA PACTICE TEST 9 WORKBOOK PART
1	66	6	3	4
	67	5	–	2
	76	3	3	–
	78	6	2	–
2	71	3	3	1
	74	7	–	3
	75	5	–	2
3	82	5	–	2
	84	4	4	–
4	77	5	5	1
	83	7	–	3
	85	4	4	1
5	16	4	4	–
	74	2	1	–
	81	6	5	–
6	85	1	1	–
	86	5	5	–
7	77	4	4	–
	79	4	3	–
	84	6	6	–
8	79	8	2	–
9	83	4	4	–
10	88	2	1	–

If the same students predictably fail parts of the test, it may be possible to provide remedies for those students as the others do a manageable extension activity. The program is designed so students use everything that has been taught. If individual students are weak on a particular skill, they will have trouble later in the program when that particular skill becomes a component in a larger operation or more complex application.

If students consistently fail tests, they are probably not placed appropriately in CMC D.

On the completed Group Test Summary for Mastery Test 9 (above), Henry Bowman failed several parts. If Henry receives the remedies for Parts 1, 3, 8, and 9, passes the retest for Test 9, but then later fails Mastery Test 10, he should probably be placed in a less challenging group.

If you are developing skills profiles based on each student's progress, reproduce the summary starting on page 173 for each student and circle the appropriate test score (+ or −).

Additional Information

LESSON OBJECTIVES

The lessons begin with objectives that show the various skills that are being taught and the order of activities in the structured teaching part of the lesson.

Here are the objectives for Lesson 6:

Materials

- Each student will need a calculator for Exercise 1.

Objectives

- **Use a calculator to check answers to addition problems that have more than two addends.** (Exercise 1)
- **Write and solve addition and subtraction problems from vertical number families.** (Exercise 2)
  Note: These families are like the horizontal families, except the big number is at the bottom and the small numbers are above, i.e.:

  $$56$$
  $$12$$

  $$68$$

- Use number maps to organize multiplication facts that involve 5. (Exercise 3)
- **Write fractions for separate groups and for number lines.** (Exercise 4)

Note: Number lines are similar to other figures; however, they may be more difficult for some students because the units are merged. The end of the first unit is the beginning of the second unit.

- Solve column multiplication problems. (Exercise 5)
- Use a number map to organize the multiplication facts that involve 9. (Exercise 6)
- **Compute the missing number in each row of a 3-by-3 table.** (Exercise 7)

Note: The rows of the table are like number families. A value is missing in each row:

10	15	
	36	70
44		75

To find the missing value, students add or subtract. They add if the total is missing. They subtract if one of the small numbers is missing.

Some of the objectives are in regular type.

- Use number maps to organize multiplication facts that involve 5. (Exercise 3)

These are objectives for exercises that are just like exercises from the preceding lesson, except that the instances or examples are changed.

Some of the objectives are in bold type:

- **Write and solve addition and subtraction problems from vertical number families.** (Exercise 2)
  Note: These families are like the horizontal families, except the big number is at the bottom and the small numbers are above, i.e.:

  $$56$$
  $$12$$

  $$68$$

These objectives signal a new activity or variation that is more difficult than what the students have done earlier. The bold objectives give you information for activities that are new. It's a good idea to rehearse these activities before presenting them to the students.

The note explains what is new about the exercise. Students are learning to find the missing numbers in vertical number families.

Tracks

The Scope and Sequence Chart (pages 2 and 3) shows the major skills that are taught. In *Connecting Math Concepts*, major skills are developed in tracks. Each lesson presents work from different tracks. A particular track, such as Number Families or Place Value, continues from lesson to lesson with progressively more difficult activities presented.

Multiplication-Division Facts

Connecting Math Concepts teaches facts. The justifications for teaching facts are:

a) Fact learning familiarizes students with the details of equations—signs and the relationship of the "big number" to the other numbers that constitute the fact.

b) Fact learning acquaints students with number patterns. By understanding the pattern for multiplying by 5, 3, and other numbers, students study very legitimate patterns.

c) Fact learning reinforces binary logic.

d) For much of the estimation and testing that is needed for working division problems and problems with unlike denominators, students need factual information.

e) Fact knowledge reinforces understanding of geometric relationships such as squares and cubes.

f) Knowledge of facts simplifies the student's task in working with functions and factoring.

The work on multiplication facts begins in Lesson 1 and continues through Lesson 68. The work on division facts begins in Lesson 21 and continues through Lesson 87.

Here's a schedule of facts that are reviewed:

Lessons	Multiplication by
1–10	5
5–13	9
11–19	3
28–37	4
48–57	7
58–59	Squares
63–68	6

Lessons	Division by
23–48	9
31–48	5
34–48	3
42–56	4
58–87	7
76–87	6

In Level C, students learned the following multiplication and division facts:

Multiplication:	Divison:
× 1	1⌐
× 2	2⌐
× 3	3⌐
× 4	4⌐
× 5	5⌐
× 9	9⌐
× 10	10⌐

These facts are reviewed in Level D. For each series of facts, students work from a unique number map. Each map is designed to facilitate learning the pattern for that particular series.

Here are the number maps for 5s, 4s, 3s, and 9s.

Each of these maps shows the unique pattern. For 9s, the second digit decreases by 1: **9, 18, 27**, etc., while the first digit increases by 1: **09, 18, 27**, etc. For 5s, the last digit of the numbers in the first column is 5. The last digit of the numbers in the second column is zero. For 4s, the second digits repeat after 20 (4, 8, 2, 6, 0).

The pattern for 3s shows that all values below the top row have a second digit 1 less than the digit above it.

The strategy for teaching facts is to provide students with a lot of practice with the number maps. Students write missing digits; write missing numbers; complete blank maps; work orally-presented problems by referring to the numbers on the map; and work with parallel maps, one of which shows the number of times and sets the stage for mastery of division facts.

Following the review of the facts, they are used in the full range of word problems and other problem-solving activities.

The new facts presented in Level D are 6s, 7s, and 8s. 7s are introduced in Lesson 48.

Here's the introduction:

> This number map shows the numbers for counting by 7. The second digit of each red number is 1 more than the digit above it.

7	14	21
28	35	42
49	56	63
70		

a. Find part 4 in your textbook. This number map shows the numbers for counting by 7. The numbers in the top row are 7, 14 and 21.
• In the next row, the second digit of each number is 1 more than the digit above it.
• The digit below 7 is 8. The digit below 4 is 5.
b. Touch the number that ends in 8.
• Everybody, what number are you touching? (Signal.) *28.*
• What's the second digit of the number below 28? (Signal.) *9.*
c. Your turn: Say the first three numbers for counting by 7. (Signal.) *7, 14, 21.*
• Say the next three numbers. (Signal.) *28, 35, 42.*
• Say the next three numbers. (Signal.) *49, 56, 63.*
• Say the last number. (Signal.) *70.*
• Don't look at your book.
d. Listen: Say the first three numbers. (Signal.) *7, 14, 21.*
• The number below 7 starts with 20. What number? (Signal.) *28.*
• The number below 14 starts with 30. What number? (Signal.) *35.*
• The number below 21 starts with 40. What number? (Signal.) *42.*
(Repeat step d until firm.)
e. My turn to say the numbers 7 through 42: 7, 14, 21, 28, 35, 42.
• Your turn: Say those numbers. (Signal.) *7, 14, 21, 28, 35, 42.*

Teaching Notes

The pattern for 7s is based on groups of three numbers at a time. The second digit of each number is 1 more than the digit above it on the map.

When you direct students to say the numbers through 42, pause at the end of each number group: 7, 14, 21 (pause) 28, 35, 42.

Also tell students: Remember this map. You'll use it to learn facts and solve lots of problems.

Following the introduction of a series, students practice the series as part of many lessons.

In Lesson 51, students complete a blank number map.

a. Find part 5. This is a number map for counting by 7. You know the rule for the second digits on the number map for sevens. The second digits are 1 more than the digits above them.
b. The first digits also follow a rule.
• All the first digits in the second row and the third row are 2 more than the digits above them. You can see those digits in green.
c. Touch **28.** What's the first digit? (Signal.) *2.*
• That's 2 more than zero.
• Touch **35.** The digit above 3 is 1. 3 is 2 more than 1.
• Touch **49.** What's the first digit of 49? (Signal.) *4.*
• What's the first digit above the 4? (Signal.) *2.*
• What's the first digit above the 4? (Signal.) *2.*
• Remember, in the second row and the third row, the first digit is 2 more than the digit above it. If you remember that rule, you can learn your sevens facts the fast way. Get a picture of that map in your mind.

_	1_	2_
2_	_	_
_	_	_
_		

WORKBOOK PRACTICE

a. Open your workbook to lesson 51 and find part 1. √
b. Numbers and digits are missing in this number map for counting by 7. Complete the map. Raise your hand when you're finished.
(Observe students and give feedback.)
c. Everybody, read the numbers in the top row. (Signal.) *7, 14, 21.*

Read the numbers in the next row. (Signal.) *28, 35, 42.*

Read the numbers in the next row. (Signal.) *49, 56, 63.*

Read the last number. (Signal.) *70.*

d. Write A through G on your lined paper. Raise your hand when you're finished.

e. I'll say problems that have 7. You'll write the answers. Remember, the number of **times** is just like the number of times for threes.

f. Problem A: 2 times 7. 2 times 7. Write the answer. (Quickly tap your foot 3 times.)

• Problem B: 7 times 7. 7 times 7. Write the answer. (Quickly tap your foot 3 times.)

• Problem C: 4 times 7. 4 times 7. Write the answer. (Quickly tap your foot 3 times.)

• Problem D: 6 times 7. 6 times 7. Write the answer. (Quickly tap your foot 3 times.)

• Problem E: 3 times 7. 3 times 7. Write the answer. (Quickly tap your foot 3 times.)

• Problem F: 8 times 7. 8 times 7. Write the answer. (Quickly tap your foot 3 times.)

• Problem G: 5 times 7. 5 times 7. Write the answer. (Quickly tap your foot 3 times.)

g. Check your work. I'll say each problem. You tell me the answer.

• Problem A: 2 times 7. (Signal.) *14.*
• Problem B: 7 times 7. (Signal.) *49.*
• Problem C: 4 times 7. (Signal.) *28.*
• Problem D: 6 times 7. (Signal.) *42.*
• Problem E: 3 times 7. (Signal.) *21.*
• Problem F: 8 times 7. (Signal.) *56.*
• Problem G: 5 times 7. (Signal.) *35.*

Starting in Lesson 56, students write division facts on lined paper, turning the paper so the lines are vertical. An example of this occurs in Lesson 34, part 2. They copy problems so that one digit occupies one space between the lines. This procedure permits students to write problems in a way that does not cramp the digits and to write the answer above the appropriate digit of the dividend.

$$\text{a.} \ 5\overline{\smash{)}3\,5}^{\ 7} \qquad \text{b.} \ 9\overline{\smash{)}2\,7}^{\ 3}$$

After students have practiced multiplication facts that involve 7, students begin a series of exercises starting in Lesson 58 that prepare them for using the number map to learn division facts. To learn these facts, students must associate each number on the map with the appropriate **number of times:** 35 is 5 times; 56 is 8 times.

Here's the exercise from Lesson 58:

1	2	3
4	5	6
7	8	9
10		

a. $7\overline{)21}$ d. $7\overline{)28}$ g. $7\overline{)7}$
b. $7\overline{)35}$ e. $7\overline{)42}$ h. $7\overline{)49}$
c. $7\overline{)56}$ f. $7\overline{)63}$ i. $7\overline{)0}$

a. Open your workbook to lesson 58 and find part 1. √

• You're going to use this number map to work problems that divide by 7. You touch the space for the number under the division sign. The number in that space is the answer.

b. I'll say some problems.

• Listen: 42 divided by 7. Touch the space where 42 would be on the map. Everybody, what number are you touching? (Signal.) *6.*

• That's what 42 divided by 7 equals.

• New problem: 63 divided by 7. Touch the space where 63 would be on the map.

• Everybody, what number are you touching? (Signal.) *9.*

• What does 63 divided by 7 equal? (Signal.) *9.*

• New problem: 14 divided by 7. Touch the right space.

• Everybody, what number are you touching? (Signal.) *2.*

• Say the fact for 14 divided by 7. (Signal.) *14 divided by 7 equals 2.*

• New problem: 56 divided by 7. Touch the right space.

• Everybody, what number are you touching? (Signal.) *8.*

• Say the fact for 56 divided by 7. (Signal.) *56 divided by 7 equals 8.*

c. Look at the problems beside the number map.

d. Problem A: 21 divided by 7. Touch the space for 21 and write the answer. Raise your hand when you're finished. (Observe students and give feedback.)

• Everybody, what does 21 divided by 7 equal? (Signal.) *3.*

e. Your turn: Write the answers to the rest of the problems in part 1. Raise your hand when you're finished. (Observe students and give feedback.)

f. Check your work. Read each division fact.

• Fact A. (Signal.) *21 divided by 7 equals 3.*
• Fact B. (Signal.) *35 divided by 7 equals 5.*
• Fact C. (Signal.) *56 divided by 7 equals 8.*
• Fact D. (Signal.) *28 divided by 7 equals 4.*
• Fact E. (Signal.) *42 divided by 7 equals 6.*
• Fact F. (Signal.) *63 divided by 7 equals 9.*
• Fact G. (Signal.) *7 divided by 7 equals 1.*
• Fact H. (Signal.) *49 divided by 7 equals 7.*
• Fact I. (Signal.) *Zero divided by 7 equals zero.*

Teaching Notes

Here's the procedure that students follow: If the number under the division sign is 35, students touch the space on the number map where 35 would be. Students have filled in number maps and know where 35 would be. Students read the number of times for that space. That's the answer to the division problem.

In the following lessons, students practice this procedure with fewer and fewer prompts until they divide reliably without referring to the number map.

In Lesson 58, the multiplication facts for the squares are practiced. (6×6 and 8×8 are the only square facts that are new to students.)

This same process used for teaching 7s is repeated for 6s, starting in Lesson 68 with multiplication and in Lesson 76 with division.

6	12
18	24
30	36
42	48
54	60

Mental Arithmetic

Oral exercises are presented to review addition-subtraction relationships and to prepare students for multiplication with renaming. One type of problem takes the form: 36 plus 5. What's the answer?

This practice prepares students for carrying. (For example, they work the problem 9×4 plus the remainder of 5. The oral exercise firms the component: $36 + 5$.)

Other oral exercises prepare students for division with a remainder. These exercises are of the form: 56 plus what number equals 62?

The oral practice relates to problems such as:

$$7\overline{\smash{\big)}62}^{8}$$

The last step in working this problem involves the component practiced orally. 56 plus what number equals 62? The answer gives the remainder.

Work on mental addition begins in Lesson 49 and continues through Lesson 64.

Here's the mental addition exercise from Lesson 49:
a. You're going to do some mental arithmetic.
b. Listen: 45 plus 3.
• Think of 5 plus 3.
• Everybody, what's 45 plus 3? (Signal.) *48.*
• Listen: 63 plus 4.
• Think of 3 plus 4.
• Everybody, what's 63 plus 4? (Signal.) *67.*
c. Listen: 81 plus 7.
• Everybody, what's the answer? (Signal.) *88.*
• Listen: 36 plus 3.
• Everybody, what's the answer? (Signal.) *39.*
• Listen 27 plus 2.
• Everybody, what's the answer? (Signal.) *29.*
• (Repeat step c until firm.)
d. You're going to write answers to problems. Write A through E on your lined paper. √
• Don't write the problems, just the answers.
e. Problem A: 42 plus 5. 42 plus 5. Everybody, write the answer.
• Problem B: 54 plus 4. 54 plus 4. Write the answer.
• Problem C: 64 plus 5. 64 plus 5. Write the answer.
• Problem D: 32 plus 6. 32 plus 6. Write the answer.
• Problem E: 24 plus 3. 24 plus 3. Write the answer.
f. Check your work.
• Problem A. What's 42 plus 5? (Signal.) *47.*
• Problem B. What's 54 plus 4? (Signal.) *58.*
• Problem C. What's 64 plus 5? (Signal.) *69.*
• Problem D. What's 32 plus 6? (Signal.) *38.*
• Problem E. What's 24 plus 3? (Signal.) *27.*
g. Raise your hand if you got everything right.

Teaching Notes

You prompt attention to the ones problem. What's 2 plus 5? If students tend to make mistakes, refer to the test when you check their work: What's 42 plus 5? Remember, 2 plus 5 is 7. So 42 plus 5 is 47.

A more difficult variation of mental addition is introduced in Lesson 55. This variation requires students to "turn the corner." 56 plus 5 equals what number? Here's the format from Lesson 57:
a. You're going to write answers to mental addition problems. Write A through F on your lined paper. Raise your hand when you're finished.
b. Problem A: 27 plus 5. Everybody, write the answer. (Quickly tap your foot 3 times.)
• Problem B: 42 plus 3. Write the answer. (Quickly tap your foot 3 times.)
• Problem C: 56 plus 4. Write the answer. (Quickly tap your foot 3 times.)
• Problem D: 64 plus 7. Write the answer. (Quickly tap your foot 3 times.)

- Problem E: 56 plus 2. Write the answer. **(Quickly tap your foot 3 times.)**
- Problem F: 28 plus 6. Write the answer. **(Quickly tap your foot 3 times.)**

c. Check your work. I'll say the problem and you tell me the answer.

- Problem A: 27 plus 5. What's the answer? **(Signal.)** *32.*
- Problem B: 42 plus 3. What's the answer? **(Signal.)** *45.*
- Problem C: 56 plus 4. What's the answer? **(Signal.)** *60.*
- Problem D: 64 plus 7. What's the answer? **(Signal.)** *71.*
- Problem E: 56 plus 2. What's the answer? **(Signal.)** *58.*
- Problem F: 28 plus 6. What's the answer? **(Signal.)** *34.*

d. Raise your hand if you got everything right.

Beginning in Lesson 62, the missing addend variation is introduced. Here is the exercise from Lesson 64:

a. You're going to write answers to problems. Write A through F on the front of your lined paper. √
b. Here's problem A: 35 plus some number equals 39. Write the missing number.
- Problem B: 35 plus some number equals 41. Write the missing number.
- Problem C: 35 plus some number equals 45. Write the missing number.
- Problem D: 38 plus some number equals 46. Write the missing number.
- Problem E: 38 plus some number equals 40. Write the missing number.
- Problem F: 73 plus some number equals 80. Write the missing number.
c. Check your work.
- Problem A: 35 plus what number equals 39? **(Signal.)** *4.*
- Problem B: 35 plus what number equals 41? **(Signal.)** *6.*
- Problem C: 35 plus what number equals 45? **(Signal.)** *10.*
- Problem D: 38 plus what number equals 46? **(Signal.)** *8.*
- Problem E: 38 plus what number equals 40? **(Signal.)** *2.*
- Problem F: 73 plus what number equals 80? **(Signal.)** *7.*

Teaching Notes

If students have trouble keeping up with your pace, repeat the exercise during the next lesson. Remember, students will have trouble with remainders if they are not perfectly firm in the mental operation.

The standard procedure for multiplying a value by a 2-digit value is to do two separate multiplication problems. To multiply 64 times 28, we multiply:

$$\begin{array}{r} 64 \\ \times\ 8 \\ \hline \end{array} \quad \text{and} \quad \begin{array}{r} 64 \\ \times\ 20 \\ \hline \end{array}$$

and add the answers together. This procedure makes sense to students if they understand that $28 = 20 + 8$. If this understanding is weak, students don't realize that they are multiplying by 20 (not 2). Mental calculations involving place-value addition firms the concept that 2-digit values can be expressed as addition facts.

Work on **place-value addition** starts in Lesson 37. Students are told to write the place-value addition for reaching 28. Students write: $20 + 8 = 28$.

In Lesson 39, students work on equations that present the number first and then give the place-value addition: $28 = 20 + 8$.

Here is the exercise from Lesson 39:

a. Find part 2.
   You've written place-value addition facts. The problems in part 2 are a little different. The numerals are shown. You're going to write an equal sign after the numeral and then the two values you add to reach that numeral.
b. Numeral A. What numeral is shown? **(Signal.)** *46.*
- My turn: 46 equals 40 plus 6.
- Listen again: 46 equals 40 plus 6.
c. Your turn: Complete equation A. √
   (Write on the board:)

> **a. 46 = 40 + 6**

- Here it is.
d. Numeral B. What numeral is shown? **(Signal.)** *36.*
- Write an equal sign. Then show the place-value addition for 36. Raise your hand when you're finished. √
   (Write on the board:)

> **b. 36 = 30 + 6**

- Here's what you should have: 36 equals 30 plus 6.
e. Your turn: Write equations for the rest of the numerals. Remember, first write the equal sign. Then write the place-value addition. Raise your hand when you're finished.
   (Observe students and give feedback.)

f. Check your work.
- Read the equation for C. Get ready. (Signal.) *39 equals 30 plus 9.*
- Read the equation for D. Get ready. (Signal.) *59 equals 50 plus 9.*
g. Raise your hand if you got all of the equations right.

Teaching Notes

Make sure that students are quite facile in reading the equations accurately. The more familiar they are with the "sound" of these equations, the easier they will find the logic and the work with place-value addition. Students must master place-value addition to be successful at column multiplication. Repeat step f if student responses are weak.

Skill with missing addends also sets the stage for borrowing from more than one digit. Beginning in Lesson 78 and continuing through Lesson 82, students solve problems of the type:

What number plus 1 equals 600? and, **What number plus 1 equals 60?**

Working these problems provides students with strong reinforcement for understanding the recursive nature of the counting system. It also enables them to have a better understanding of why the original value of the top number in this problem is conserved by the renaming:

$$\begin{array}{r} \overset{5\ 9}{6\ 0\ \overset{1}{0}} \\ -\ \ 4\ 2 \end{array}$$

Here's the exercise from Lesson 78:

a. Find part 2.
   For all these problems, the first number is missing.
b. Problem A: Some number plus 1 equals 70. Here's the fact. 69 plus 1 equals 70.
- Say the fact. (Signal.) *69 plus 1 equals 70.*
- Problem B: Some number plus 1 equals 40. Say the fact. (Signal.) *39 plus 1 equals 40.*
- Problem C: Some number plus 1 equals 90. Say the fact. (Signal.) *89 plus 1 equals 90.*
   (Repeat step b until firm.)
c. Problem D: Some number plus 1 equals 600. My turn to say the fact: 599 plus 1 equals 600.
- Your turn: Say the fact. (Signal.) *599 plus 1 equals 600.*

- Problem E: Some number plus 1 equals 800. Say the fact. (Signal.) *799 plus 1 equals 800.*

Teaching Notes

Make sure that students are very firm on the verbal work. If they make mistakes in step b, repeat step b before presenting step c.

Column Subtraction

A review of column subtraction begins in Lesson 1 of Level D and continues through Lesson 17.

The test of whether renaming is required begins by **reading the problem** in a column, then identifying whether that problem can be worked the way it is written. If the answer is **no,** renaming or "borrowing" is needed.

To borrow, students rewrite the top number. Here's the review exercise from Lesson 1:

- For some subtraction problems, you have to borrow.
- You have to borrow when you can't work a subtraction problem in a column.
- You start with the ones column and read the problem. If it begins with a smaller number, you can't work it.
- And if you can't work it, you borrow.

- Here's a problem:
- The problem in the ones column is 0 – 4.

$$\begin{array}{r} 5\ 7\ 0 \\ -1\ 0\ 4 \end{array}$$

- You can't work it, so you borrow 1 ten from the tens digit of 570.

$$\begin{array}{r} 5\overset{6}{7}\overset{1}{0} \\ -1\ 0\ 4 \end{array}$$

- Now you have a new problem in the ones column: 10 – 4. You also have a new problem in the tens column: 6 – 0. You can work both those problems and the problem in the hundreds column.

$$\begin{array}{r} 5\overset{6}{7}\overset{1}{0} \\ -1\ 0\ 4 \\ \hline 4\ 6\ 6 \end{array}$$

- Sometimes you have to borrow to work the problem in the tens column. You borrow from the **hundreds.**

- Here's a problem with the ones column already worked. The problem in the tens column is 7 – 8.

$$\begin{array}{r} 6\ 7\ 0 \\ -4\ 8\ 0 \\ \hline 0 \end{array}$$

- You can't work it, so you borrow from the hundreds digit of 670.

$$\begin{array}{r} \overset{5}{6}\overset{1}{7}0 \\ -4\ 8\ 0 \\ \hline 0 \end{array}$$

- The new problem in the tens column is 17 – 8. The new problem in the hundreds column is 5 – 4. You can work both those problems.

$$\begin{array}{r} \overset{5}{6}\overset{1}{7}0 \\ -4\ 8\ 0 \\ \hline 1\ 9\ 0 \end{array}$$

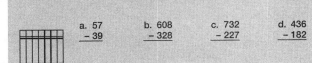

a. 57	b. 608	c. 732	d. 436
– 39	– 328	– 227	– 182

a. Find part 3.
I'll read what it says in the box. Follow along: For some subtraction problems, you have to borrow. You have to borrow when you can't work a subtraction problem in a column.

- You start with the ones column and read the problem. If it begins with a smaller number, you can't work it. And if you can't work it, you borrow.
- Here's a problem: 570 minus 104. The problem in the ones column is zero minus 4.
- Everybody, can you work that problem? **(Signal.)** *No.*
- You can't work it; so you borrow 1 ten from the tens digit of 570.
- Now you have a new problem in the ones column: 10 minus 4.
- You also have a new problem in the tens column: 6 minus zero.
- You can work both those problems and the problem in the hundreds column.
- Sometimes you have to borrow to work the problem in the tens column. You borrow from the **hundreds.**
- Here's a problem with the ones column already worked. The problem in the tens column is 7 minus 8.
- You can't work it; so you borrow from the hundreds digit of 670.
- Now you have a new problem in the tens column and a new problem in the hundreds column.
- The new problem in the tens column is 17 minus 8. The new problem in the hundreds column is 5 minus 4. You can work both those problems.

b. Find part 4.
For all these problems you have to borrow.
c. Problem A. Read the problem in the ones column. **(Signal.)** *7 minus 9.*
- Can you work that problem? **(Signal.)** *No.*
- So you borrow 1 ten from the tens digit of 57. Do it and work problem A. Remember the rules for working column problems. Turn to the back of your paper. Then turn it sideways. Keep the digits separated by the lines of your paper. Don't crowd your problems together. Raise your hand when you're finished working problem A.
(Observe students and give feedback.)
d. (Write on the board:)

$$\begin{array}{r} \overset{4}{\cancel{5}}\,{}^{1}7 \\ -\ 3\ 9 \\ \hline 1\ 8 \end{array}$$

a.

- Check your work. Here's what you should have. You borrowed 1 ten from the tens digit of 57. You wrote the ten you borrowed in front of the 7.

- The new problem in the ones column is 17 minus 9. The answer is 8.
- The new problem in the tens column is 4 minus 3. The answer is 1.
- 57 minus 39 equals 18.
e. Problem B. Everybody, read the problem in the ones column. **(Signal.)** *8 minus 8.*
- Can you work that problem? **(Signal.)** *Yes.*
- Read the problem in the tens column. **(Signal.)** *Zero minus 2.*
- Can you work that problem? **(Signal.)** *No.*
- So you borrow 1 hundred from the hundreds digit of 608. Do it and work problem B. Raise your hand when you're finished.
(Observe students and give feedback.)
f. (Write on the board:)

$$\begin{array}{r} \overset{5}{\cancel{6}}\,{}^{1}0\ 8 \\ -\ 3\ 2\ 8 \\ \hline 2\ 8\ 0 \end{array}$$

b.

- Check your work. Here's what you should have for problem B. The new problem in the tens column is 10 minus 2. The answer is 8. The new problem in the hundreds column is 5 minus 3. The answer is 2.
- 608 minus 328 equals 280.

Teaching Notes

Students sometimes fail to see the relationship between the problem in a column and whether or not borrowing is required. Present these tasks: Read the problem in the _s column. Can you work that problem without going off the number line?

If students answer incorrectly, tell them they are wrong. If problems are persistent, make a number line on the board and demonstrate whether or not a problem can be worked.

For example:

$$\begin{array}{r} 57 \\ -\ 39 \\ \hline \end{array}$$

Start at 7 on the number line and attempt to minus 9. Say the numbers you minus as you move toward zero.

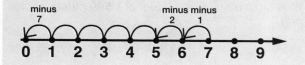

"I can't minus any more than 7 without going off the number line."

Repeat the demonstration with different problems until students understand that they must read the problem **as written** and consider **that** problem, not merely work a problem with those same values. Students often assume that because 7 plus 9 and 9 plus 7 gives the same answer, it's permissible to work 7 minus 9 the same way 9 minus 7 would be worked. Stress the idea: **Read the problem** in the ones column. . . . Can you work **that** problem? After several demonstrations, students will understand the logic.

After the review of subtraction, students work a variety of problems that require renaming, but problems that require "borrowing from zero" are not included in the set. In Lesson 82, the work on borrowing from zero begins. The first exercises build on the task: What number plus 1 equals 60? This is a component of the renaming operation.

Here's the exercise from Lesson 82:

a. (Write on the board:)

$$6\ 0\ 1$$
$$-\quad\ \ 9$$

- Everybody, read the problem. (Signal.) *601 minus 9.*
- You have to borrow to work this problem.

b. Here's a rule: You can't borrow from a zero. So you have to go to the first digit that is not a zero.

- I have to borrow to work the problem in the ones column. The tens digit of 601 is zero. I can't borrow from zero, so I go to a **digit that's not zero.** That's 6. I'll underline 60 because I have to borrow from 60.

(Underline 60:)

$$\underline{6\ 0}\ 1$$
$$-\quad\ \ 9$$

- Listen: I cross out the 6 **and** the zero. Then I rewrite 60 as 59, plus the 1 I borrow. Watch:
- (Write to show:)

$$\overset{5\ 9}{\underline{6\ 0}}{}^{1}1$$
$$-\quad\ \ 9$$

- Remember, 59 plus 1 equals the 60 we started with.

c. (Write on the board:)

$$4\ 0\ 0\ 1$$
$$-\qquad\ \ 9$$

- Here's a new problem. I have to borrow to work the problem in the ones column. I can't borrow from a zero. So I cross out the first digit that is not a zero and all the zeros. Watch:
- (Write to show:)

$$\cancel{4\ 0\ 0}\ 1$$
$$-\qquad\ \ 9$$

- I'm borrowing from 400. I rewrite the 400 as 399, plus the 1 I borrow. Watch.
- (Write to show:)

$$\overset{3\ 9\ 9}{\cancel{4\ 0\ 0}}{}^{1}1$$
$$-\qquad\ \ 9$$

- Remember, 399 plus 1 equals the 400 we started with. Now I can work the problem.

a. 706	b. 302	c. 6001
− 29	− 26	− 247

WORKBOOK PRACTICE

a. Find part 2 in your workbook.
For all these problems, you have to borrow to subtract in the ones column. Remember, you can't borrow from a zero. So you go to the first digit that is not a zero. Cross it out and cross out any zeros. Then rewrite the number.

b. Problem A. The problem in the ones column is 6 minus 9. You have to borrow, but you can't borrow from zero. Underline the two digits you'll borrow from. Raise your hand when you're finished. **(Observe students and give feedback.)**

- Everybody, what 2-digit value are you going to borrow from? (Signal.) *70.*
- Cross out 70 and rewrite it. Write it as 69 plus the 1 you borrow. Raise your hand when you're finished. **(Observe students and give feedback.)**
- (Write on the board:)

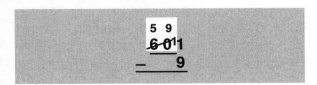

- Here's what you should have for the top number.

c. Problem B. The problem in the ones column is 2 minus 6. You have to borrow. Underline all the digits you'll borrow from. Then rewrite the top number. Don't work the problem. Just fix up the top number. Raise your hand when you're finished. (Observe students and give feedback.)

• (Write on the board:)

$$\begin{array}{c} {\scriptstyle 2\ 9} \\ \text{b. } \underline{3\,0}{}^{1}2 \end{array}$$

• Here's what you should have for the top number.
d. Problem C. The problem in the ones column is 1 minus 7. You'll have to borrow. Underline all the digits you'll borrow from. Then rewrite the top number. Raise your hand when you're finished. (Observe students and give feedback.)

• (Write on the board:)

$$\begin{array}{c} {\scriptstyle 5\ 9\ 9} \\ \text{c. } \underline{6\,0\,0}{}^{1}1 \end{array}$$

• Here's what you should have for the top number.
e. Now you can work the problems in part 2. Do it and raise your hand when you're finished. (Observe students and give feedback.)
f. Check your work.
• Problem A: 706 minus 29. Everybody, what's the answer? (Signal.) *677.*
• Problem B: 302 minus 26. What's the answer? (Signal.) *276.*
• Problem C: 6001 minus 247. What's the answer? (Signal.) *5754.*

Teaching Notes

For all these problems, students borrow. The steps are:
 a) Underline the part that will be rewritten.
 b) Rewrite the underlined part.
 The problem that students will have is remembering to go to the first digit that is not zero, but not underlining the entire number. Sometimes students underline the entire top number. Point out: "The part you'll rewrite can't end in the column you cannot work. If you can't work the problem in the ones column, you can't underline the ones column of the top number. If you can't work the problem in the tens column, you can't underline the tens column of the top number."

Make sure you observe students when they first work these problems in Lesson 82. If you correct student's misconceptions in this lesson, work in later lessons will be simplified.

Starting in Lesson 84, students discriminate which zero they must borrow from. The problem types are:

$$
\begin{array}{r}{\scriptstyle 5\ 9}\\[-2pt]\underline{6\,0}{}^{1}0\\ -1\,3\,1\\ \hline 4\,6\,9\end{array}
\qquad
\begin{array}{r}{\scriptstyle 5\ 9\ 9}\\[-2pt]\underline{6\,0\,0}{}^{1}0\\ -1\,3\,1\\ \hline 5\,8\,6\,9\end{array}
\qquad
\begin{array}{r}{\scriptstyle 5\ 9}\\[-2pt]\underline{6\,0}{}^{1}0\,3\\ -1\,3\,1\\ \hline 5\,8\,7\,2\end{array}
$$

Students tend to have the most trouble with the last type of problem. They tend to borrow to work in the ones column, although no borrowing is needed.

Anticipate this mistake. Remind students: "Remember, read the problem in the ones column and ask if you can work that problem the way it is written. If you can work it, work it. If you can't work it, borrow. But don't get fooled."

If you correct the mistakes in Lessons 82 and 83, students should proceed smoothly.

Operations Involving Number Facts

The work with facts sets the stage for work with operations that involve subtraction, multiplication, and division.

The work with place-value addition (36 = 30 + 6) sets the stage for multiplying by a 2-digit value.

The work with problems of the form **35 plus what number equals 38?** sets the stage for working division problems with remainders:

$$\begin{array}{r}7\\5\,\overline{)\,3\,8_{\,3}5}\end{array}$$

The work with problems of the form **What number plus 1 equals 600?** sets the stage for borrowing from more than one digit:

$$\begin{array}{r}6\,0\,0\\ -\ 2\,4\\ \hline\end{array}$$

Column Multiplication

The first thirty lessons provide a review of multiplication problem types taught in Level C. All these problems multiply by a 1-digit number. They may have as many as five digits in the top number and may involve carrying in any column. The facts incorporated in these problems are either facts that had been taught in Level C or facts that are being taught in Level D.

Multiplying by a 2-digit value begins in Lesson 32 and continues through Lesson 51. In Lesson 32, students work problems of the form:

$$2 \times 40 = \underline{\quad}$$

The rule that students apply is that you're multiplying by 40, so the answer ends in zero. The answer is not 8, but 80.

After working problems of this type for two lessons, students work the same type of problems when they are written in column form:

$$\begin{array}{r} 2 \\ \times\ 40 \\ \hline \end{array}$$

When you (or students) indicate the problem for specific digits, the problem always names the top value first.

$$\begin{array}{r} 56 \\ \times\ 8 \\ \hline \end{array}$$

The problem for the ones digit of 56 is 6×8 (not 8×6). The problem for the tens is 5×8 (not 8×5). This convention is introduced so that students see that working problems with 2-digit values is a simple extension of work with 1-digit values.

Before being introduced to more elaborate types, students discriminate between these problem types in Lesson 35:

$$\begin{array}{r} 5 \\ \times\ 40 \\ \hline \end{array} \qquad \begin{array}{r} 8 \\ \times\ 5 \\ \hline \end{array}$$

For both types there is a zero in the answer. For the type that multiplies by 40, however, there is an additional zero which is not part of the answer to the multiplication "fact" problem. Students are reminded that they are multiplying by 40, not 4. Therefore, there must be a zero in the ones column.

Starting in Lesson 36, students work problems that multiply a 2-digit value by a tens number:

$$\begin{array}{r} 34 \\ \times\ 20 \\ \hline \end{array}$$

The procedure is to first write zero in the answer. Then work the multiplication problem 34 $\times$ 2. The first digit of the answer to this problem goes right below the 2. Here's the first part of the introduction from Lesson 36:

$$\textbf{a.}\ \begin{array}{r} 34 \\ \times\ 20 \\ \hline \end{array} \qquad \textbf{b.}\ \begin{array}{r} 42 \\ \times\ 30 \\ \hline \end{array}$$

a. Open your workbook to lesson 36 and find part 1. √
b. (Write on the board:)

$$\textbf{a.}\ \begin{array}{r} 3\,4 \\ \times\ 2\,0 \\ \hline \end{array}$$

- Here's a new kind of problem that multiplies by a tens number.
- You're multiplying by a tens number, so the answer will have a zero in the ones column.
- (Write to show:)

$$\textbf{a.}\ \begin{array}{r} 3\,4 \\ \times\ 2\,0 \\ \hline 0 \end{array}$$

- Now we work the problem just like any other problem. 4 times 2 equals 8. (Write to show:)

$$\textbf{a.}\ \begin{array}{r} 3\,4 \\ \times\ 2\,0 \\ \hline 8\,0 \end{array}$$

- 3 times 2 equals 6. (Write to show:)

$$\textbf{a.}\ \begin{array}{r} 3\,4 \\ \times\ 2\,0 \\ \hline 6\,8\,0 \end{array}$$

- Here's what you should have. 34 times 20 equals 680.
- Remember, if you multiply by a tens number, you write a zero in the ones column. Then you work the problem for the first digit of the tens number.

c. Your turn: Write the answer to problem A. That's 34 times 20. Remember, write only one digit in each column. The answer is 680. It starts in the hundreds column.
Raise your hand when you're finished.

d. Now work problem B. Remember, write a zero in the ones column. Then work the problem for the first digit of 30. Raise your hand when you're finished.
(Write on the board:)

$$\begin{array}{r} b. \quad 4\,2 \\ \times\,3\,0 \end{array}$$

- What's the first thing you wrote in the answer? (Signal.) *A zero.*
- (Write to show:)

$$\begin{array}{r} b. \quad 4\,2 \\ \times\,3\,0 \\ \hline 0 \end{array}$$

- Then you multiplied 3 times 2. What's the answer? (Signal.) *6.*
- Then you multiplied 3 times 4. What's the answer? (Signal.) *12.*
- (Write to show:)

$$\begin{array}{r} b. \quad 4\,2 \\ \times\,3\,0 \\ \hline 1\,2\,6\,0 \end{array}$$

- Here's what you should have for problem B: 42 times 30 equals 1260. Raise your hand if you got everything right.

Teaching Notes

Some students tend to "crowd" the answer because, when they work a problem like:

$$\begin{array}{r} 3\,4 \\ \times\,2 \end{array}$$

they write the answer in the ones column.
When working the new type, they try to get their answer as close as possible to the ones column (something like a borrowed 10). Remind them: "One digit in a column. You're not carrying or borrowing." If their work is sloppy, have them erase their work and start over.

Next, in Lesson 38, students work on a discrimination exercise that mixes all types:

$$\begin{array}{rrr} 24 & 73 & 6 \\ \times\,5 & \times\,40 & \times\,50 \end{array}$$

The next problem type that is introduced does not have zeros:

$$\begin{array}{r} 32 \\ \times\,24 \end{array}$$

The steps they follow are: 1) Cover the first digit of 24 and work the problem for the ones. 2) Write it below the problem. 3) Cover the second digit of 24. 4) Work the problem for the tens. That problem has a zero in the ones column. 5) Add the two answers.

The workbook problems prompt students to work two multiplication problems and then add.

In Lesson 41, students first go over the general rules in their textbook. Then they work problems in their workbook. Here's the first part of that introduction:

- Some problems multiply by 2-digits values that do not end in zero.
- This problem multiplies by 24:

$$\begin{array}{r} 3\,2 \\ \times\,2\,4 \end{array}$$

- To get the answer, you have to work two problems. If you cover the first digit of 24, you can see the first problem you work.
- You multiply 32 x 4. The answer is 128. You write the answer right below the problem.

$$\begin{array}{r} 3\,2 \\ \times\,\blacksquare\,4 \\ \hline 1\,2\,8 \end{array}$$

- If you cover the second digit of 24, you can see the second problem you work: 32 x 20. There's a zero in the ones column of the answer.
- You write the answer below the answer for 32 x 4. The answer is 640. You write the answer here: ⟶

$$\begin{array}{r} 3\,2 \\ \times\,2\,\blacksquare \\ \hline 1\,2\,8 \\ 6\,4\,0 \end{array}$$

- To find the answer to the whole problem, you add 128 and 640. The answer to the whole problem is 768.

$$\begin{array}{r} 3\,2 \\ \times\,2\,4 \\ \hline 1\,2\,8 \\ +\,6\,4\,0 \\ \hline 7\,6\,8 \end{array}$$

a. Find part 5.
You're going to learn to work very difficult multiplication problems.

b. I'll read what it says in the box. Follow along: Some problems multiply by 2-digit values that do not end in zero.
- This problem multiplies by 24.
- You can see the problem: 32 times 24.
- To get the answer, you have to work two problems. If you cover the first digit of 24, you can see the first problem you work. The first digit of 24 is blocked out.
- You multiply 32 times 4. The answer is 128.
- You write the answer right below the problem. That's the first thing you do.

- If you cover the second digit of 24, you can see the **second problem** you work: 32 times 20.
- Remember, that's not just 2 you're multiplying by. That's 20. So you have to have a zero in the ones column of the answer.
- You write the answer below the answer for 32 times 4. The answer is 640. Remember, that answer goes right below the answer for the first problem.
- Then to find the answer to the whole problem, you **add** 128 and 640.
- You can see the answer to the whole problem is 768.
- Remember the steps: Cover the first digit. Work the problem and write the answer right below the problem.
- Cover the second digit. Work the problem and write the answer right below the first answer.
- Then add both answers to find the answer to the whole problem.

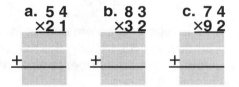

a. 5 4
  ×2 1

b. 8 3
  ×3 2

c. 7 4
  ×9 2

WORKBOOK PRACTICE

a. Open your workbook to lesson 41 and find part 1. √
b. Problem A: 54 times 21.
- Cover the first digit of 21.
- You can see the problem you'll work first. That's 54 times 1.
c. Your turn: Write the answer to that problem in the top answer box. Raise your hand when you've done that much. √
- (Write on the board:)

a.   5 4
      × 2 1
        5 4

- Here's what you should have so far.
d. Now cover the second digit of 21. You'll work the problem 54 times 20. Remember, that's 20, not 2. So the first thing you do is write a zero in the ones column. Then multiply the way you always do.
- Write the answer for 54 times 20. Raise your hand when you've done that much. √
- (Write to show:)

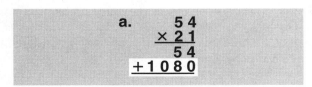

a.   5 4
      × 2 1
        5 4
    + 1 0 8 0

- Here's what you should have: 54 times 21 equals 54 plus 1080.
e. Now you just add the numbers and write the answer to the whole problem. Do it. Raise your hand when you're finished. √
- (Write to show:)

a.   5 4
      × 2 1
      ¹ 5 4
    + 1 0 8 0
    ――――――――
      1 1 3 4

- Here's what you should have: 54 times 21 equals 1134.

Teaching Notes

Again, the biggest problem that students will have is not maintaining column alignment. Remind them: All digits for the ones column must be lined up. All digits for the tens column must be lined up. DO NOT ACCEPT SLOPPY WORK. IT WILL REINFORCE CONFUSION THAT WILL REQUIRE LATER REMEDIES. Repeat the set of problems if student work is sloppy.

In the following lessons, students work these problems with diminished structure. When the problems are presented in the textbook, students work the problem on the back of the lined paper they use during the lesson.

They orient the paper so the lines are vertical, and they copy the problems so that there's only one digit in a column.

Be picky about how students work these problems. If they copy and align the digits properly, they will learn the operation faster and understand it better.

Problems of the type $54 \times 21 =$ do not involve carrying. Following the introduction, students work problems that involve only one digit that is carried.

In Lesson 45, students are introduced to double carrying. They learn the rule that they multiply by the ones digit. Then they cross out (or erase) any carried digits before working the problem for the tens digit.

Here's the first part of the introduction from Lesson 45:

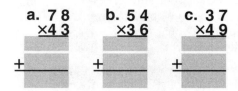

a. Find part 3. To work these multiplication problems, you'll have to do carrying when you work your first problem. Write the number you carry very lightly. And then erase it or cross it out before you work the problem for the tens digit.

b. Problem A: 78 times 43.

• Start with the top number and say the first problem you'll work. (Signal.) *78 times 3.*

• Say the other problem you'll work. (Signal.) *78 times 40.*

• Remember, when you work the first problem—78 times 3—write the number you carry very lightly. Then erase it or cross it out before you work the problem that multiplies by 40.

• Work both problems. Remember the zero in the ones column when you work 78 times **40.** Then add the answers. Raise your hand when you're finished. (Observe students and give feedback.)

• (Write on the board:)

$$
\begin{array}{r}
\overset{3}{\overset{2}{}} \\
78 \\
\times\ 43 \\
\hline
234 \\
+3120 \\
\hline
3354
\end{array}
$$

• Check your work. Here's what you should have. 78 times 3 equals 234. 78 times 40 equals 3120. 78 times 43 equals 3354. Raise your hand if you got everything right.

In Lessons 49 through 51, students work problems that have 3-digit values times 2-digit values.

Division

The simplest type of division problems with answers of more than one digit is introduced in Lesson 33. For these problems, students write one digit in the answer above each digit of the dividend. There are no remainders from one digit to the next, and there are no remainders after the last digit.

For example:

$$
\begin{array}{r} 24 \\ 2\overline{)48} \end{array}
\qquad
\begin{array}{r} 203 \\ 3\overline{)609} \end{array}
$$

Students practice problems of this type following Lesson 33.

The next type of problem introduced involves a 2-digit problem in the dividend:

$$6\overline{)240}$$

To work the problem, students first underline the problem they work to get the first digit of the answer. They can't work the problem 2 divided by 6. So they work the problem 24 divided by 6. They underline **24** and write the answer above the last underlined digit:

$$
\begin{array}{r} 4 \\ 6\overline{)\underline{24}0} \end{array}
$$

Work on this type of problem occurs in Lessons 36 through 53. Initially, the necessary digits are underlined and students write answers in the appropriate places.

The first time students underline is in Lesson 38. Here's the introduction:

a. Open your workbook to lesson 38 and find part 1. √

• For some problems, you write the first digit of the answer right above the first digit under the division sign. For other problems, you write the first digit of the answer right above the **second** digit under the division sign.

b. Here's how you figure out where to write the first digit of the answer: If the first digit under the division sign is less than the number you divide by, you work a 2-digit problem.

c. Problem A. Say the division problem for the first digit. (Signal.) *1 divided by 3.*

• Is the digit under the division sign less than 3? (Signal.) *Yes.*

• So you work a 2-digit problem.

• Problem B. Say the division problem for the first digit. (Signal.) *2 divided by 3.*

• Is the digit under the division sign less than 3? (Signal.) *Yes.*

• So you work a 2-digit problem.

• Problem C. Say the division problem for the first digit. (Signal.) *6 divided by 3.*

• Is the digit under the division sign less than 3? (Signal.) *No.*

• So you don't have to work a 2-digit problem.

d. Go back to problem A.
Say the division problem for the first digit. (Signal.) *1 divided by 3.*

- Is the digit under the division sign less than 3? (Signal.) *Yes.*
- Underline the first two digits. Then stop. √
- Problem B. Say the division problem for the first digit. (Signal.) *2 divided by 3.*
- Is the digit under the division sign less than 3? (Signal.) *Yes.*
- Underline the first two digits. Then stop. √

e. Your turn to do the underlining for the rest of the problems. Remember; say the division problem for the first digit to yourself. If the first digit under the division sign is less than 3, underline the first two digits. Raise your hand when you're finished. **(Observe students and give feedback.)**

f. (Write on the board:)

$$\text{a. } 3\overline{|\underline{18}6}\qquad \text{d. } 3\overline{|\underline{9}30}$$

$$\text{b. } 3\overline{|\underline{24}3}\qquad \text{e. } 3\overline{|\underline{12}9}$$

$$\text{c. } 3\overline{|\underline{6}06}$$

- Here's what you should have. Raise your hand if you did the right underlining.

g. Now you can write answers to the problems. The first digit of the answer goes above the last underlined digit. Work the problems in part 1. Raise your hand when you're finished. **(Observe students and give feedback.)**

h. (Write to show:)

$$\text{a. } 3\overline{|\underline{18}6}^{\,62}\qquad \text{d. } 3\overline{|\underline{9}30}^{\,310}$$

$$\text{b. } 3\overline{|\underline{24}3}^{\,81}\qquad \text{e. } 3\overline{|\underline{12}9}^{\,43}$$

$$\text{c. } 3\overline{|\underline{6}06}^{\,202}$$

i. Here's what you should have.
- Problem A: 186 divided by 3 equals 62.
- Problem B: 243 divided by 3 equals 81.
- Problem C: 606 divided by 3 equals 202.
- Problem D: 930 divided by 3 equals 310.
- Problem E: 129 divided by 3 equals 43.

j. Raise your hand if you got everything right.

Teaching Notes

Students apply the rule: If the digit under the division sign is less than the number you divide by, you have to work a 2-digit problem. If students make mistakes, remind them of the rule. Apply the rule to their error: "You can't work the problem 1 divided by 3, because 1 is less than 3. You have to underline a 2-digit number."

In later lessons, different variations of 2-digit underlining are introduced. Starting in Lesson 50, students work 2-digit "interior" problems. The digits involved are not the first two digits of the problem. For all interior problems that involve two digits, a zero is needed in the answer.

For example:

$$2\overline{|\underline{6}142}^{\;\;3}$$

The same basic analysis holds for the first digits and for the interior digits. Students can't work the problem 1 divided by 2. So they write a zero in the answer, then work the problem 14 divided by 2. The answer to 14 divided by 7 is written above the last digit of 14:

$$2\overline{|\underline{6}1\underline{4}2}^{\;307}$$

The first work with remainders begins in Lesson 68. The first problem presented has "interior" remainders. The digits under the division sign, in other words, are not correct fact numbers.

For example:

$$4\overline{|260}$$

26 is not a fact number for 4. The steps required to figure out the first digit of the answer involve some form of multiplication/division and addition/subtraction. The student must recognize that 26 is not a fact number for multiplying by 4s, that 24 is the appropriate fact number, and that the difference between 26 and 24 is 2.

$$4\overline{|2\,6_2\,0}^{\;\;6} \atop \overline{|2\,4}$$

By the time students reach Lesson 68, they have practiced this combination of steps in an equation context:

$$26 = 4 \times \underline{\hphantom{6}} + \underline{\hphantom{2}}$$
$$\square$$

The steps are the same as those in the division problem. The number that goes in the box is the correct fact number: 24. To complete the equation, students must work the problem: 24 plus what number equals 26?

$$26 = 4 \times \underline{6} + \underline{2}$$
$$\boxed{24}$$

The first exercise that combines operations appears in Lesson 45:

3	6	9
12	15	18
21	24	27
30		

a. $17 = 3 \times \underline{\hphantom{x}} + \underline{\hphantom{x}}$

b. $23 = 3 \times \underline{\hphantom{x}} + \underline{\hphantom{x}}$

c. $25 = 3 \times \underline{\hphantom{x}} + \underline{\hphantom{x}}$

d. $13 = 3 \times \underline{\hphantom{x}} + \underline{\hphantom{x}}$

e. $\ 5 = 3 \times \underline{\hphantom{x}} + \underline{\hphantom{x}}$

f. $10 = 3 \times \underline{\hphantom{x}} + \underline{\hphantom{x}}$

a. Find part 2.
- This is a number map for counting by 3.
- I'm going to say numbers that are not numbers for counting by 3. For each number, you'll write the number of **times** for the number that comes just before the number I say.

b. Listen: **17.** That's not a number for counting by 3.
- Touch the number on the number map that comes just before 17.
- Everybody, what number are you touching? (Signal.) *15*
- New number: **22.**
- Touch the number for 3 that comes just before 22.
- Everybody, what number are you touching? (Signal.) *21.*
- New number: **14.**
- Touch the number for 3 that comes just before 14.
- Everybody, what number? (Signal.) *12.*
- New number: **25.**
- Touch the number for 3 that comes just before 25.
- Everybody, what number? (Signal.) *24.*

c. Find the problems next to the number map. You're going to complete each equation to tell how to get to the numbers that are not numbers for 3.

d. Touch A. It says that 17 equals 3 times some number. 17 is not a number for 3.
- What is the number on the map that comes just before 17? (Signal.) *15.*
- How many **times** do you count to get to 15? (Signal.) *5.*
- (Write on the board:)

> **a. 17 = 3 × 5**

- We're at 15. We have to add to get to 17.
- How many do we add? (Signal.) *2.* (Write to show:)

> **a. 17 = 3 × 5 + 2**

- Complete equation A. √
e. Problem B. What's the number? (Signal.) *23.*
- That's not a number for counting by 3. What's the number for 3 that comes just before 23? (Signal.) *21.*
- How many times do you count to get to 21? (Signal.) *7.*
- Complete the first part of the equation. Raise your hand when you're finished. √
- (Write on the board:)

> **b. 23 = 3 × 7**

- Here it is: 3 times 7 is 21. You want to get to 23. How many do you have to add? (Signal.) *2.*
- Complete equation B. Raise your hand when you're finished. √
- (Write to show:)

> **b. 23 = 3 × 7 + 2**

- Here's what you should have. 23 equals 3 times 7 plus 2.
f. Problem C. What's the number? (Signal.) *25.*
- That's not a number for counting by 3. What's the correct number? (Signal.) *24.*
- How many times do you count to get to 24? (Signal.) *8.*
- How many more do you have to add to get to 25? (Signal.) *1.*
- Complete equation C. Raise your hand when you're finished. √
- (Write on the board:)

> **c. 25 = 3 × 8 + 1**

- Here it is: 25 equals 3 times 8 plus 1.

g. Problem D. What's the number? (Signal.) *13.*
• What's the correct number for 3? (Signal.) *12.*
• How many times do you count to get to 12? (Signal.) *4.*
• How many more do you have to count to get to 13? (Signal.) *1.*
• Complete equation D. Raise your hand when you're finished. √
• (Write on the board:)

> **d. 13 = 3 × 4 + 1**

• Here's what you should have. 13 equals 3 times 4 plus 1.
h. Your turn: Work the rest of the problems in part 2. Raise your hand when you're finished.
(Observe students and give feedback.)
i. (Write on the board:)

> **e. 5 = 3 × 1 + 2**
> **f. 10 = 3 × 3 + 1**

j. Here's what you should have for E and F.
• Problem E. Read the equation. (Signal.) *5 equals 3 times 1 plus 2.*
• Problem F. Read the equation. (Signal.) *10 equals 3 times 3 plus 1.*
k. Raise your hand if you got both of them right.

Students use a number map for 3s. All the problems presented specify 3 as the number multiplied by.

Using the number map makes it easy for students to identify the number that comes just before the number in the problem. For 17 = 3 × □ + ___, students identify the number for 3s that comes just before 17. Then they identify the number of times. Finally, they work the problem: 15 + ___ = 17 to figure out the amount that is added.

In Lesson 52, students work problems of the same type, but without using a number map. Students write the appropriate fact number in a box below the equation. Here's the chalkboard demonstration that acquaints students with the box:
a. (Write on the board:)

> **39 = 4 × ___ + ___**
> □

• You're going to complete equations without using a number map.

b. Here's how you work the problems. First, you write the correct number for fours in the shaded box below the times sign. 39 equals 4 times some number plus some number. 39 is not a number for fours.
• What's the number for fours that comes just before 39? (Signal.) *36.*
• So I write 36 in the shaded box.
• (Write to show:)

> **39 = 4 × ___ + ___**
> **36**

• Now I complete the equation. 4 times what number equals 36? (Signal.) *9.*
• I write 9.
• (Write to show:)

> **39 = 4 × 9 + ___**
> **36**

• We're at 36. How many do we add to get to 39? (Signal.) *3.*
• (Write to show:)

> **39 = 4 × 9 + 3**
> **36**

• All done. The equation is 39 equals 4 times 9 plus 3.
Following this work, students work a variety of problems involving both multiplication and addition.

By Lesson 68, the final variation is introduced. Students treat the part that is added as the remainder: 39 = 9 × □ + R ___.

The steps are the same as the earlier problems.

Division with remainders involves these steps: First, underline the part of the dividend that is to be worked for the first digits of the answer:

$$6 \overline{\smash{)}3\,9\,0}$$

Write the answer for that part above the last digit of the underlined part:

$$6 \overline{\smash{)}\underline{3\,9}\,0}$$ with 6 above

Write the fact number below (the number that would appear on the number map):

$$6\overline{)390} \\ \underline{36}$$

with quotient 6 above.

Subtract and write the remainder before the next digit of the dividend:

$$6\overline{)39\,_30} \\ \underline{36}$$

with quotient 6 above.

Finally, underline the part of the dividend that is to be worked for the last digit of the answer, and work the problem.

$$6\overline{)39\,_30} \\ \underline{36}$$

with quotient 65 above.

The part of the operation that is new involves writing the fact number below the underlined part.

Here's the part of the introduction that follows a textbook explanation of the procedure:

a. Find part 2 in your workbook.
b. Problem A: 344 divided by 4. Underline the part for the first digit of the answer. Raise your hand when you're finished. √

- (Write on the board:)

a. $4\overline{)\underline{34}\,4}$

- Here's what you should have. 34 is not a number for fours.
- So I change the underlining into a division sign.
- (Write to show:)

a. $4\overline{)34\,4}$

- Your turn: Make the division sign. Write the correct number for fours under the sign. Raise your hand when you're finished. √
- (Write to show:)

a. $4\overline{)34\,4} \\ \underline{32}$

- Here's what you should have. The correct number is 32. Now you can work the problem 32 divided by 4. Do it and write the answer. √
- (Write to show:)

a. $4\overline{)34\,4} \\ \underline{32}$

with quotient 8 above.

- Here's what you should have. You show a division sign below, so you must have a remainder. That's the difference between 34 and 32. Everybody, what's the remainder? (Signal.) 2.
- Write that remainder in front of the next digit. Then underline both digits. √
- (Write to show:)

a. $4\overline{)34\,_24} \\ \underline{32}$

with quotient 8 above.

- Here's what you should have. Everybody, read the division problem for the underlined part. (Signal.) *24 divided by 4.*
- Is 24 a number for fours? (Signal.) *Yes.*
- What's the answer? (Signal.) *6.*
- (Write to show:)

a. $4\overline{)34\,_24} \\ \underline{32}$

with quotient 86 above.

- So 344 divided by 4 is 86. Copy the rest of the problem that is on the board.
c. Problem B. 924 divided by 4. Underline the part for the first digit of the answer. If that part is not a number for fours, make a division sign and write the correct number below. Raise your hand when you've done that much.
- (Write on the board:)

b. $4\overline{)92\,4} \\ \underline{8}$

- Here it is. You should have underlined one digit, not two. 9 is not a number for fours. 8 is.
- Write the answer for 8 divided by 4. Then write the remainder in front of the next digit. Raise your hand when you've done that much.

- (Write to show:)

b. $4\overline{\smash{)}9_12\ 4}$ 2
    $\overline{8}$

- Here's what you should have. Underline the part for the next digit in the answer. Raise your hand when you're finished.
- (Write to show:)

b. $4\overline{\smash{)}9_12\ 4}$ 2
    $\overline{8}$

- Whenever you carry a digit, you'll work a 2-digit problem. You should have underlined 12.
- Say the problem for that underlining. (Signal.)
  12 divided by 4.
- Write the answers for the rest of the problem.
- Raise your hand when you're finished.
- (Write to show:)

b. $4\overline{\smash{)}9_12\ 4}$ 2 3 1
    $\overline{8}$

- Here's the completed problem. 924 divided by 4 equals 231.
d. Problem C. Underline the part for the first digit of the answer. If that part is not a number for fives, make a division sign and write the correct number below. Raise your hand when you've done that much.
- (Write on the board:)

c. $5\overline{\smash{)}8\ 0\ 5}$
    $\overline{5}$

- Here's what you should have. Now write the answer for 5 divided by 5. Then write the remainder in front of the zero. Underline the digit you carry and the next digit in the problem. Work the rest of problem C. Raise your hand when you're finished.
  (Observe students and give feedback.)
- (Write to show:)

c. $5\overline{\smash{)}8_30\ 5}$ 1 6 1
    $\overline{5}$

- Here's what you should have. You carried 3. You worked the problem 30 divided by 5. The answer is 6. The answer for the last digit is 1.
  805 divided by 5 equals 161.
e. Remember, if you make a division sign, there's a remainder. You carry that remainder and work a 2-digit problem for the next digit of the answer.

Teaching Notes

The underlining is very important. For this problem type, changing the underlining to a division sign shows a problem that does not have a remainder. The only places in which students show a division sign below are places that do not already have fact numbers.

Remind students: "If the underlined part is not a fact number, make a division sign. Write the correct fact number below."

Also remind students that, if there is a division sign below, there must be a carried digit and the next problem they must work is a 2-digit problem. Finally, remind students that, after the first digit of the answer, there must be a digit for every digit below.

The system works well; however, students must be perfectly firm on the mechanics. They underline each problem they work. If the problem involves more than one digit, the answer goes above the last digit. If the 2-digit problem is an interior problem, there must be a zero above the first digit of that dividend. If the underlined value (whether one digit or two) is not a fact number, the correct fact number must be shown below.

Take the time needed to firm work on these problems when they are first introduced in Lessons 68 and 69. If students have followed the conventions for working division problems that appear before Lesson 68, students should not bog down; however, expect some of them to need reminders about the mechanical details of working the problems with remainders.

Terminal remainders are introduced in Lesson 106 after students have practiced interior remainders extensively.

The convention that students follow is to express the remainder with both a plus sign and a capital R:

$$\begin{array}{r} 9 + R1 \\ 3\,\overline{\smash)2\,8} \\ \overline{2\,7} \end{array}$$

The convention of showing the R as a value that is added preserves the relationship the students have learned about combined operations (multiplication and addition). The problem above translates into the familiar problem: $28 = 3 \times \square + R\underline{}$.

For this problem, the R is added. The division problem provides the same relationship and the same implied test. If you multiply 3×9, then add 1, you'll end up with the value under the division sign: 28.

Calculator Skills

Starting on Lesson 4, students do a considerable amount of work with calculators. They use calculators to work problems involving addition, subtraction, and multiplication. They use calculators to check answers to ratio problems, to problems that involve tables, and problems involving fraction operations. They also use calculators to check their independent work.

Here's part of the exercise from Lesson 4.

a.	474	b.	319	c.	903	d.	784
	− 98		× 8		− 865		+ 265
	376		3040		38		1059

- Listen: You'll use your calculator and see if the student's answer is correct.
- Take out your calculator and turn it on.
b. Everybody, hold up your calculator and show me that it's operating. √
- Enter the digits for 474. If you make a mistake, clear the number by pressing **C** and then start over. √
- Next press **plus.**
- Next press the digits of the second number in the problem. √
- Then press the sign that will give you the answer.
- Everybody, hold your calculator up and show me the answer when you have one. √
- The student's answer is wrong. He made a mistake when adding in one of the columns.

- Everybody, in which column did he make a mistake? (Signal.) *The tens column.*
- Yes, the tens. 474 plus 98 equals 572, not 582.
c. Find the problems under the box. You're going to check the answer to each problem. Write A through D on your lined paper.
d. Touch problem A. You'll enter the digits for 474, then a minus sign, then the digits for 98, then an equal sign. Do it. Hold up your calculator when it has an answer.
  (Observe students and give feedback.)
- Everybody, what answer does your calculator show? (Signal.) *376.*
- So the answer to A is correct. Write a **C** after the letter A on your paper to show it's correct.

Throughout the program, students use an icon

as a guide of whether they are to use their calculator. The calculator icon appears on every workbook or textbook activity that calls for the calculator. If the icon does not appear, students are not to use their calculator to work the problems. (They could use their calculator, however, to check their work.)

Equations and Relationships

Level D places strong emphasis on equations and how they are related. Equations involving fractions relate to division problems:

$$\frac{8}{4} = \square \text{ can be expressed as } 4\,\overline{\smash)8}$$

Multiplication problems with either the first or second factor missing can be written as division problems:

$$2 \times h = 12 \text{ is the same problem as } 2\,\overline{\smash)12}$$

Some equations can also be written different ways without changing the information that is conveyed: $8 \times 2 = 16$ gives the same information as $16 = 8 \times 2$ and as $2 \times 8 = 16$.

Level D provides students with a lot of practice in converting equations into equivalent forms. The goal is to make students facile with these conversions and thereby strengthen students' understanding of the relationship between multiplication, division, and fractions. Another goal is to increase the flexibility that students have in constructing legitimate equations.

The first work with equations requires students to identify the missing number or the missing sign. The purpose of this work is to make sure that students approach equations as statements that must be consistent and "make sense."

Here's the set of problems students work in Lesson 10:

> a. 3 ■ 2 = 6   c. 8 ■ 4 = 12
> b. 4 + ■ = 7   f. ■ + 2 = 10
> c. ■ − 1 = 8   g. 3 × ■ = 15
> d. 5 ■ 3 = 2   h. 6 ■ 3 = 3

a. Find part 2. For all these problems, a number is missing or a sign is missing.
b. Problem A: 3 blank 2 equals 6. Raise your hand when you know the missing sign. √
- Everybody, what's the missing sign? (Signal.) *A times sign.*
c. Problem B: 4 plus blank equals 7. A number is missing. Everybody, what's the missing number? (Signal.) *3.*
d. Listen: Use lined paper. Write the **complete** equation for each problem. Copy the problem and put in the missing sign or number. Raise your hand when you're finished.
(Observe students and give feedback.)
e. Check your work. Read each equation.
- Equation A. (Signal.) *3 times 2 equals 6.*
- Equation B. (Signal.) *4 plus 3 equals 7.*
- Equation C. (Signal.) *9 minus 1 equals 8.*
- Equation D. (Signal.) *5 minus 3 equals 2.*
- Equation E. (Signal.) *8 plus 4 equals 12.*
- Equation F. (Signal.) *8 plus 2 equals 10.*
- Equation G. (Signal.) *3 times 5 equals 15.*
- Equation H. (Signal.) *6 minus 3 equals 3.*

Students work with similar sets in following lessons.

Starting in Lesson 27, students work problems in which they are given three numbers and must write either the multiplication equation or the addition equation that uses those numbers. For example, the numbers for one problem are 14, 2, and 7. Students write the equation 2 × 7 = 14 or 7 × 2 = 14.

Here are the items from Lesson 27:

> a. 7, 9, 2   b. 10, 5, 2   c. 4, 12, 3   d. 10, 6, 4
> e. 7, 7, 1   f. 3, 15, 5   g. 3, 6, 3

Teaching Notes

Following the structured work with writing equations from three numbers (Lessons 27–32), you may practice variations of this exercise in a game format. Have teams challenge each other by presenting sets of three compatible numbers that "stump" their opponents. One variation is to permit students to use their calculators to experiment. Another variation is for students to use logical analysis to work the problem. For example, if one of the numbers is greatly larger than either of the others, it's a multiplication equation. A final variation of the game is to direct students to write either the division or subtraction problem. All games, however, require students to write the equation that incorporates the three numbers.

Another important equation skill involves rewriting equations such as 3 + 5 = 8 so they begin with the number that is alone on one side of the equation: 8 = 3 + 5. This skill is important because many equations students encounter are of this form. Typical formulas are expressed in this "backward" order: Area equals length times width.

Also, much of the work that students do with "place-value addition" (expanded notation) begins with the number that is alone: 37 = 30 + 7. Some of the complex equations that are associated with remainders are most reasonably expressed in this form: 39 = 9 × □ + ___. This order is preferred because students see the 39 and 9. The equation juxtaposes these values.

Beginning in Lesson 37, students rewrite equations of the unfamiliar form □ = □ [sign] □ as familiar facts. Here's the introductory exercise from Lesson 37:

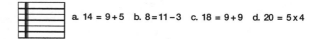

> a. 14 = 9 + 5   b. 8 = 11 − 3   c. 18 = 9 + 9   d. 20 = 5 × 4

a. Find part 1 in your textbook. √
- All these equations are correct, but they may be new to you.
b. Equation A: 14 equals 9 plus 5. That's true. It says that you'll end up with 14 if you add 9 plus 5. It says the same thing as 9 plus 5 equals 14.
c. Equation A. Start with 9 and say the familiar fact. (Signal.) *9 plus 5 equals 14.*
(Repeat step c until firm.)
d. Equation B: 8 equals 11 minus 3. Everybody, say that equation. (Signal.) *8 equals 11 minus 3.*
- Start with 11 and say the familiar fact. (Signal.) *11 minus 3 equals 8.*

- Equation C: 18 equals 9 plus 9. Everybody, say that equation. (Signal.) *18 equals 9 plus 9.*
- Start with 9 and say the familiar fact. (Signal.) *9 plus 9 equals 18.*
- Equation D. Read it. (Signal.) *20 equals 5 times 4.* (Repeat step d until firm.)
e. Your turn: You're going to start with the numeral after the equal sign and rewrite each equation as a familiar fact. Raise your hand when you're finished. (Observe students and give feedback.)
f. Check your work. Read each familiar fact.
- Fact A. (Signal.) *9 plus 5 equals 14.*
- Fact B. (Signal.) *11 minus 3 equals 8.*
- Fact C. (Signal.) *9 plus 9 equals 18.*
- Fact D. (Signal.) *5 times 4 equals 20.*

Teaching Notes

In step d, students are to repeat the statement and say the familiar fact. Expect some students to have problems saying the equations. They will tend to have trouble saying "equals" after the first number. Give them enough practice to make them facile. If they are not firm after repeating step d three times, you can assume that they do not understand the information the statement conveys. They will probably have serious problems later. Go on to the next exercise in the lesson and return to step d later.

Students are to write the equations exactly as you indicate in step e.

In Lesson 46, students complete equations that start with $\square =$. The sign is missing in each problem.

Here's the set of problems presented in Lesson 46:

a. $30 = 5 \,\blacksquare\, 6$

b. $40 = 42 \,\blacksquare\, 2$

c. $19 = 4 \,\blacksquare\, 15$

d. $45 = 40 \,\blacksquare\, 5$

e. $45 = 9 \,\blacksquare\, 5$

f. $45 = 50 \,\blacksquare\, 5$

By writing the missing sign, students must think about the information provided by the equation. For example:

$$12 = 3 \,\square\, 4$$

The left side shows 12. Therefore, the other side must show 12. The only sign that could make 12 on that side is $\times$: $12 = 3 \boxtimes 4$.

Problems of this type also help strengthen the idea that the second side begins with the number after the equal sign.

For example:

$$8 = 12 \,\square\, 4$$

The only combination that makes the second side equal to 8 is $12 - 4$.

Level D provides many exercises that express the relationship between multiplication, division, and fractions. The basic formats are:

$$\frac{36}{9} = \square$$

which can be expressed as a multiplication problem:

$$9 \times \square = 36$$

which can be expressed as a division problem:

$$9\overline{)36}$$

Therefore:

$$9 \times \square = 36; \; 9\overline{)36}; \; \frac{36}{9} = \square$$

all express the same "problem" and relationship.

A lot of work that forges these relationships in Level D involves tables. The ultimate table has columns for multiplication, division, and fraction equations. Given rows that show one form, students show the equivalent forms.

The work with these relationships begins in Lesson 14, with students working multiplication problems of two types:

$$2 \times 8 \,\square\, \text{ and } 2 \times \square = 8$$

This work sets the stage for students to express $2 \times \square = 8$ as a division problem.

Here's the exercise from Lesson 14:

a. (Write on the board:)

a. $5 \times \square = 10$
b. $5 \times 10 = \square$
c. $2 \times 6 = \square$
d. $2 \times \square = 6$
e. $6 \times \square = 12$
f. $3 \times 9 = \square$

- Some students confuse these problems. For problem A, they multiply 5 times 10. That's silly. When you say these problems as multiplication problems, you start with the first number and say the values in order.

b. My turn to say the first problems.
- Problem B. 5 times 10 equals what number?
- Problem C. 2 times 6 equals what number?
- Problem D. 2 times what number equals 6?

c. Your turn to say each problem.
- Say problem A. (Signal.) *5 times what number equals 10?*
- What's the answer? (Signal.) *2.*
  (Repeat step c until firm.)

d. Say problem B. (Signal.) *5 times 10 equals what number?*
- What's the answer? (Signal.) *50.*
- Say problem C. (Signal.) *2 times 6 equals what number?*
- What's the answer? (Signal.) *12.*
- Say problem D. (Signal.) *2 times what number equals 6?*
- What's the answer? (Signal.) *3.*
- Say problem E. (Signal.) *6 times what number equals 12?*
- What's the answer? (Signal.) *2.*
- Say problem F. (Signal.) *3 times 9 equals what number?*
- What's the answer? (Signal.) *27.*

e. Your turn: Use lined paper. Copy each problem with the box. Then write the answer. Raise your hand when you're finished.
  (Observe students and give feedback.)

f. Check your work. Read the multiplication fact for each problem.
- Problem A. (Signal.) *5 times 2 equals 10.*
- Problem B. (Signal.) *5 times 10 equals 50.*
- Problem C. (Signal.) *2 times 6 equals 12.*
- Problem D. (Signal.) *2 times 3 equals 6.*
- Problem E. (Signal.) *6 times 2 equals 12.*
- Problem F. (Signal.) *3 times 9 equals 27.*

Teaching Notes

Verbal performance is very important. If students do not say the problems correctly, they'll have problems later. The most obvious problem is in relating division to multiplication. A secondary problem, however, will be in working word problems that give information about "what number," i.e., 5 times what number equals 30?

Make sure that students are firm in steps c and d of the exercise. Don't be shy about telling students that they need this skill for the work they'll do later.

In Lesson 21, after students are familiar with problems of the form $4 \times \square = 12$, they express these problems as division problems.

Here's the exercise from Lesson 21 after a textbook introduction:

b. Open your workbook to lesson 21 and find part 1. √ These are multiplication problems with the middle number missing.

c. Problem A. Say the problem. (Signal.) *5 times what number equals 40?*
- Problem B. Say the problem. (Signal.) *3 times what number equals 21?*
- Problem C. Say the problem. (Signal.) *9 times what number equals 18?*

d. (Write on the board:)

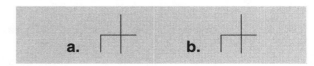

- You're going to tell me how to write those problems as division problems.

e. Problem A is 5 times what number equals 40? What do I write in front of the division sign? (Signal.) *5.*
- (Write **5**:)

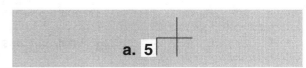

- What do I write on top? (Signal.) *A box.*
- (Write to show:)

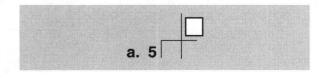

- What do I write under the division sign? (Signal.) *40.*
- (Write **40**:)

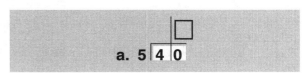

- There's the problem: 5 times what number equals 40 written with a division sign.

f. Problem B: 3 times what number equals 21? What do I write in front of the division sign? (Signal.) *3.*
- What do I write on top of the division sign? (Signal.) *A box.*
- What do I write under the division sign? (Signal.) *21.*
- (Write to show:)

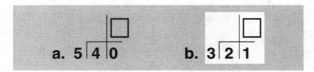

a. 5 4 0   b. 3 2 1

g. Your turn: Write division problems for all the items in part 1. Make sure your box is in the column for the ones. Raise your hand when you're finished. (Observe students and give feedback.)
h. (Write on the board:)

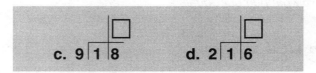

c. 9 1 8   d. 2 1 6

- Check your work. Here's what you should have for problems C and D.
i. To figure out the answers to the division problems, you can say the multiplication problems. You must start with the first number, and then go to the box.
j. Here's how to say problem A: 5 times what number equals 40? Say that problem. (Signal.) *5 times what number equals 40?*
- Say the problem for B. Get ready. (Signal.) *3 times what number equals 21?*
- Say the problem for C. Get ready. (Signal.) *9 times what number equals 18?*
- Say the problem for D. Get ready. (Signal.) *2 times what number equals 16?*
k. Your turn: Say the problems to yourself and write the answers to the division problems—just to the division problems. Raise your hand when you're finished. (Observe students and give feedback.)
l. Check your work. I'll say the problems as multiplication. You tell me the answer you wrote.
- Problem A: 5 times what number equals 40? (Signal.) *8.*
- Problem B: 3 times what number equals 21? (Signal.) *7.*
- Problem C: 9 times what number equals 18? (Signal.) *2.*
- Problem D: 2 times what number equals 16? (Signal.) *8.*
m. Raise your hand if you wrote all the answers correctly.

Teaching Notes

The exercise addresses three major skills. The first is positioning the numbers. The numbers shown in the problem are in the same relative position for both multiplication and division.

The first number in the multiplication problem is written first in the division problem. The other number is written under the division sign.

The next major skill is writing the answer to the division problem in the appropriate place. This skill is prompted by the shaded column in the student material. The last digit of the number under the division sign is written in the shaded column. The answer to the problem is written above this digit.

The third skill is figuring out the answer to the division problem by saying the related multiplication problem. In step j, students say the "multiplication wording" by referring to the division problem. You can prompt the correct responses by touching the parts in order:

Students say: *5 times what number equals 20?*

Make sure that students are firm on saying the problems for step j before they work the problems in step k.

In Lesson 25, students write division problems from multiplication problems that are dictated. All these problems are of the type: 4 times what number equals 20? Students write:

They write a box for "what number." Then they write the answer. Note that this task is similar to the earlier exercises in which students wrote multiplication problems of the form:

$$4 \times \square = 20$$

In Lesson 66, students complete tables that have columns for multiplication and corresponding division problems.

	□ × __ = □	⌐
a.	4 × 7 = 28	7 4⟌2 8
b.	3 × 8 = 24	8 3⟌2 4
c.	2 × 8 = 16	8 2⟌1 6
d.	4 × 2 = 8	2 4⟌8

Students complete all the rows. Most of the rows require students to go from division problems to corresponding multiplication problems. The extension is not very difficult, but the exercise is important.

As the relationship between multiplication and division is developed in Level D, other exercises develop the relationship between fractions and division problems. Starting in Lesson 56, students learn to say and write fractions as division problems.

Here's the introductory exercise from Lesson 56:

a. $\dfrac{14}{7}$ b. $\dfrac{54}{9}$ c. $\dfrac{45}{5}$ d. $\dfrac{30}{5}$

a. Open your textbook to lesson 56 and find part 1. √
• You can write fractions as division problems. The top number is the number under the division sign. The bottom number is the number you divide by.
b. Touch 14-sevenths. I'll say the division problem: 14 divided by 7.
• Your turn: Say the division problem. (Signal.) *14 divided by 7.*
• What's the answer? (Signal.) 2.
c. Say the division problem for 54-ninths. (Signal.) *54 divided by 9.*
• What's the answer? (Signal.) *6.*
• Say the division problem for 45-fifths. (Signal.) *45 divided by 5.*
• What's the answer? (Signal.) *9.*
• Say the division problem for 30-fifths. (Signal.) *30 divided by 5.*
• What's the answer? (Signal.) *6.*
(Repeat step c until firm.)
d. Your turn: For each fraction, write the division problem and the answer. Raise your hand when you're finished.
(Observe students and give feedback.)
e. Check your work. Say the division fact and the answer for each fraction.

• Fraction A. (Signal.) *14 divided by 7 equals 2.*
• Fraction B. (Signal.) *54 divided by 9 equals 6.*
• Fraction C. (Signal.) *45 divided by 5 equals 9.*
• Fraction D. (Signal.) *30 divided by 5 equals 6.*

Teaching Notes

This exercise sets the stage for students to integrate a lot of information about the nature of fractions and the nature of division. All the fractions in Lesson 56 equal whole numbers, but the general rule implied by the procedure presented in the exercise is that it is possible to read **any fraction** as a division problem. Students who have this knowledge learn decimal relationships much easier than students who don't clearly understand the relationship between fractions and division. Decimal relationships are most dramatically observed when fractions like 4/5 are read as a division problem and worked on a calculator. The answer (.8) is $\dfrac{8}{10}$, which is a fraction that equals $\dfrac{4}{5}$.

When presenting the exercise in Lesson 56 (step c especially) and in the following lessons, make sure that students are very firm at reading fractions as division problems.

Starting in Lesson 64, students write fraction equations from division problems.

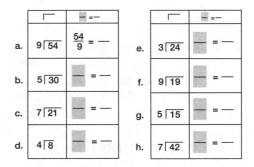

The exercise is quite easy for students. When they read the division problem, they say the fraction.

The last type of table is introduced in Lesson 78. This table has columns for multiplication equations, division problems, and corresponding fraction equations.

Here's the table that appears in Lesson 78:

□x _ =□	⌐	□ =□
a.	4 x ____ = 36	⌐	▨ = ▨
b.		7⌐56	
c.		6⌐54	
d.		⌐	$\frac{15}{3}$ = ▨

Tables of this form also appear in following lessons. A variation is introduced in Lesson 98. For that table, there are four columns. One is for division equations written with this sign: ÷. To write the equation, an equation or problem is read as a division problem. Then the numbers and signs are written in the same order they are said in the problem: 20 divided by 4 equals 5: 20 ÷ 4 = 5.

□ x _ = □	⌐	□ =□	□÷□=
a. 7 x _ = 49			
b.			36 ÷ 4 =
c.			87 ÷ 3 =
d.		$\frac{92}{2}$ =	

Place Value

THOUSANDS NUMERALS

Level D expands what students have learned about reading and writing numerals. The work that students do at the beginning of Level D assumes knowledge of hundreds numerals. In Lesson 1, students read thousands numerals that have four digits. They say "thousand" after the first digit. Thousands numerals with more than four digits are reviewed in Lesson 7. These numerals are written with a comma, and students say "thousand" for the comma.

Beginning in Lesson 13, students write thousands numerals in their workbook which provides shaded columns and a comma to prompt proper alignment of each numeral. Students write one digit in each column. Here's the first part of the exercise and the student

material from Lesson 13. It presents the rule about the comma:

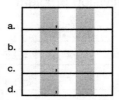

a. Find part 2. You're going to write thousands numerals. The comma shows where the thousands digits end. Remember, the digits for the thousands come before the comma.
b. Touch A. The numeral for A is 21 thousand 4 hundred. Write the digits for 21 thousand before the comma. Then write 4 hundred. I'll say numeral A again: 21 thousand 4 hundred. Raise your hand when you're finished. √
• (Write on the board:)

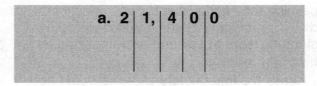

• Here's what you should have for 21 thousand 4 hundred.
c. Numeral B: 84 thousand 9 hundred 60. Write the numeral for 84 thousand 9 hundred 60. Raise your hand when you're finished. √
• (Write on the board:)

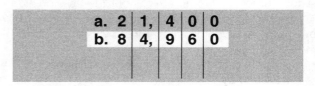

• Here's what you should have for 84 thousand 9 hundred 60.

The work involving thousands numerals continues through Lesson 21.

DECIMALS

In Lesson 87, students are introduced to decimals. By this lesson, students have worked with dollars-and-cents values. They have written dollars-and-cents values from descriptions and in column problems that require lining up the decimal points. The work on decimals simply expands what they already know.

In Lessons 87 and 88, students write decimal numbers from descriptions such as "4 and 12-hundredths." Students write the decimal point for the word **and**.

In Lesson 89, students write equations that show decimal values and the fractions they equal. Here's part of the introduction from Lesson 89:

b. Find the decimal numbers for part 5. For each item, you'll copy the decimal number that is shown and then complete the equation to show the fraction that equals that decimal number.

c. Decimal number A is 6-hundredths. Copy that item and write the fraction for 6-hundredths. Raise your hand when you're finished.
(Observe students and give feedback.)

• (Write on the board:)

$$a.\ .06 = \frac{6}{100}$$

• Here's what you should have for equation A.

Teaching Notes

If students have trouble with the fractions for decimals that are more than 1, tell them that the top of the fraction has the same digits as the decimal number. The bottom is 100.

Beginning in Lesson 91, students write **mixed numbers** for decimal values. By reading the decimal number, students say the words for the mixed number. The word **and** tells where to write the plus sign. 4 and 36-hundredths is

$$4 + \frac{36}{100}$$

In Lesson 92, students rank values according to size. They learn that zeros after the decimal point do not change the value of a whole number.

Students order a list of numerals, most of which have three digits.

Here's the list from Lesson 92:

3.00   400   9   100   5   2.00

This type of exercise is very important in correcting possible misconceptions that the number of digits indicates the size of the number. 5 is more than 3.00 and more than 2.00.

Starting in Lesson 93, students work with a variety of tables that show the relationship between fractions, mixed numbers, and decimal values. In Lesson 96, students work with the first table that has all three types of notation.

Here's the table from Lesson 96 and the first part of the exercise:

	Decimal Number ▨.▨▨	Mixed Number ▨ + ▨▨/100	Fraction ▨▨/100
a.			$\frac{307}{100}$
b.			$\frac{1105}{100}$
c.		$1 + \frac{67}{100}$	
d.	10.50		
e.	71.09		

a. Find part 3. Each row of this table will show the decimal number, the mixed number and the fraction.

b. Row A shows the fraction 307-hundredths. The decimal number has the same digits as the numerator.

• Write the decimal number in the first column. Then write the mixed number. Raise your hand when you're finished.
(Observe students and give feedback.)

• (Write on the board:)

$$a.\ 3.07 \qquad 3 + \frac{7}{100} \qquad \frac{307}{100}$$

• Here's what you should have for row A: 3 and 7-hundredths. The decimal number has two digits after the decimal point. 3 and 7-hundredths equals 3 plus 7-hundredths equals 307-hundredths.

c. Complete row B. Raise your hand when you're finished. √

• (Write on the board:)

$$b.\ 11.05 \qquad 11 + \frac{5}{100} \qquad \frac{1105}{100}$$

• Here's what you should have for row B: 11 and 5-hundredths. The decimal number has two digits after the decimal point.

d. Your turn: Complete the table. Raise your hand when you're finished.
(Observe students and give feedback.)
e. Find part J on page 312 in your textbook. That shows what you should have for rows C, D, and E.
f. Raise your hand if you got everything right.

The work with these conversions assures that students learn how to relate decimal values to what they know about mixed numbers and what they know about the relationship between mixed numbers and fractions.

During this lesson range (starting in Lesson 89), students learn to multiply a dollars-and-cents value by a whole number.

The problems only have one decimal part, so the answers are always hundredths.

$$\begin{array}{r} 1 \\ \$\,4.12 \\ \times\ 8 \\ \hline \$32.96 \end{array}$$

Fractions

Level D teaches students many important relationships involving fractions. Fractions are related to equivalent fractions, to whole numbers, and to decimal notation. Students learn more about the basic operations of adding, subtracting, and multiplying fractions. They also use fractions to solve problems involving ratios and proportions.

The work with fractions begins in Lesson 1 with a review of the basic analysis: The bottom number tells the number of parts in each whole unit. The top number tells the number of parts that are used or shaded. Note that the description does not refer to "numerator" or "denominator." These terms are introduced later in Level D; however, the early work uses very simple language that will not confuse students and create possible "reversals."

Here is the first exercise from Lesson 1.

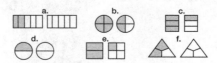

a. (Draw on the board:)

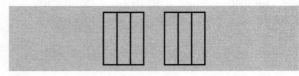

- You're going to make fractions from pictures. To write a fraction, you have to know how many parts are in each unit.
b. Look at the units on the board. There are the same number of parts in each unit. Everybody, how many parts are in each unit? (Signal.) *3.*
- That's the bottom number of the fraction.
- (Write to show:)

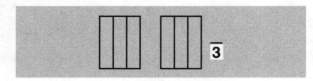

- Now I'll shade parts.
- (Shade 4 parts:)

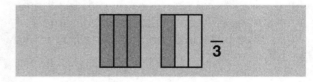

- Everybody, how many parts are shaded? (Signal.) *4.*
- That's the top number of the fraction.
- (Write **4** to show:)

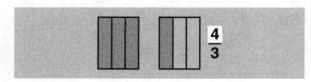

- The picture shows 4-thirds.
- Remember, the bottom number of the fraction tells about the number of parts in each unit. The top number tells about the number of parts that are used or shaded.
c. Find part 2. For each item, there's a picture. You'll write the fraction for the picture.
d. Picture A. Raise your hand when you know the number of parts in each unit. √
- Everybody, how many parts are in each unit? (Signal.) *5.*
- That's the bottom number of the fraction you'll write. The top number is the number of parts that are shaded. Everybody, how many parts are shaded? (Signal.) *2.*

- Your turn: The diagram in front of the pictures of fractions shows that your paper should have the lines going from side to side. That diagram tells you to follow these rules: Turn to the front of your paper. Turn your paper so that your name is at the top. Do it. Write the letter A and write the fraction for picture A. Don't crowd your fraction. Write it on two lines of your paper. Raise your hand when you're finished.
  (Observe students and give feedback.)
- **(Write on the board:)**

> a. $\dfrac{2}{5}$

- Here's the fraction you should have for picture A.
- e. Picture B. Raise your hand when you know the bottom number of the fraction you'll write. √
- Everybody, what's the number? **(Signal.)** *4.*
- Yes, there are 4 parts in each unit.
- Raise your hand when you know the top number of the fraction you'll write. √
- Everybody, what's the number? **(Signal.)** *6.*
- Yes, there are 6 parts shaded.
- Your turn: Write fraction B. Write the letter and the fraction. Raise your hand when you're finished.
  (Observe students and give feedback.)
- **(Write on the board:)**

> b. $\dfrac{6}{4}$

- Here's what you should have for B.
- f. Write the fraction for C. Raise your hand when you're finished.
  (Observe students and give feedback.)
- **(Write on the board:)**

> c. $\dfrac{4}{3}$

- Here's what you should have. There are 3 parts in each unit. So the bottom number is 3. 4 parts are shaded. So the top number is 4.
- g. Write the fractions for D, E, and F. Raise your hand when you're finished.
  (Observe students and give feedback.)
- **(Write on the board:)**

> d. $\dfrac{1}{2}$ e. $\dfrac{5}{4}$ f. $\dfrac{2}{3}$

- Check your work. Here's what you should have.
- For D, there are 2 parts in each unit. So the bottom number is 2. There is 1 part shaded. So the top number is 1. Picture D shows 1-half.
- For E, there are 4 parts in each unit. So the bottom number is 4. 5 parts are shaded. So the top number is 5. Picture E shows 5-fourths.
- For F, there are 3 parts in each unit. So the bottom number is 3. There are 2 parts shaded. So the top number is 2. Picture F shows 2-thirds.

Teaching Notes

This set of problems involves fractions that are more than 1, as well as those that are less than 1. When you correct student mistakes, make sure that they apply the fraction analysis. Ask these questions:
How many parts are in **each** unit?
So what's the bottom number of the fraction?
How many parts are shaded?
So what's the top number of the fraction?

Starting in Lesson 3, students work with pictures of fractions and circle fractions that are more than 1. Starting in Lesson 4, students indicate whether fractions are more than 1 without referring to pictures. They simply identify whether the top number is more than the bottom number.

Lesson 6 introduces fractions on a number line. Although these fractions are basically the same as fractions shown with "separate units," the number line display often confuses students because the end of one unit is the beginning of the next. To compensate for this problem, Level D provides students with a lot of practice in working with fractions pictured as separate units and fractions shown on number lines.

Here's the introduction of the number line from Lesson 6:
a. (Draw on the board:)

- Here's a number line. You can show fractions on a number line. You just divide each unit into the same number of parts. Each unit on a number line is the space from one number to the next number. From zero to 1 is **one** unit. From 1 to 2 is **one** unit. From 2 to 3 is **one** unit.

- (Draw lines to show:)

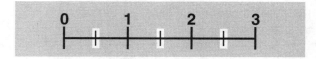

- Now there are 2 parts in **each unit.** I'll shade 5 parts.
- (Shade 5 parts:)

- (Write to show:)

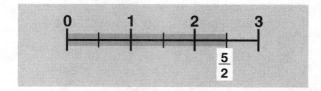

- Here's the fraction. 2 parts are in each unit. So the bottom number is 2. 5 parts are shaded. So the top number is 5. The fraction is 5-halves.
b. I'm going to change the number line.
- (Change to show 2 more lines in each unit:)

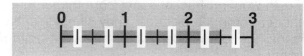

- There aren't 2 parts in each unit now. Raise your hand when you know how many parts are in each unit.
- Everybody, how many parts are in each unit? (Signal.) *4.*
c. Your turn: Use lined paper. Write the fraction for the shaded part of this number line. Raise your hand when you're finished.
   (Observe students and give feedback.)
- (Write to show:)

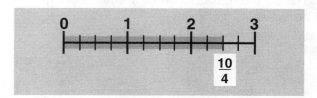

- Here's what you should have: 10-fourths.
- Remember, the number line works just like other units except that the units are stuck together on the number line. Where one unit stops, the next unit starts. There's no space between them.

Following the introduction, students write fractions for different displays, some showing fractions on a number line and others showing separate units.

Beginning with Lesson 7, students write fractions from verbal descriptions. The type of description introduced in Lesson 7 indicates the two numbers that make up the fraction and indicates whether the fraction is more or less than 1.

Here's the exercise from Lesson 7:

a. I'm going to describe fractions by telling the numbers and telling whether the fraction is more than 1 or less than 1. Remember, if the fraction is more than 1, the top number is bigger than the bottom number.
- I'll give you two clues about each fraction. The first clue will tell the numbers in the fraction. The second clue will tell whether the fraction is more than 1 unit or less than 1 unit.
b. Here's the first clue about a fraction: The numbers are 4 and 5. What are the numbers for this fraction? (Signal.) *4 and 5.*
- (Write on the board:)

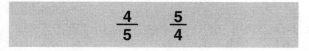

- Both these fractions have the numbers 4 and 5. So if you just know the numbers, you don't know which fraction I'm thinking about.
- Here's the second clue: The fraction I'm thinking of is more than 1 unit. Now you know which fraction I'm thinking of.
- Which fraction? (Signal.) *5-fourths.*
- (Circle 5-fourths:)

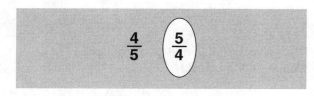

5-fourths has the numbers 4 and 5. 5-fourths is more than 1.
c. Your turn: Use lined paper. Write A through E on the front of your paper. √
   Write the correct fraction for each description.
d. Here are the clues for fraction A. The numbers for this fraction are 10 and 3. The fraction is more than 1. Write the fraction. Raise your hand when you're finished.
   (Observe the students and give feedback.)
- (Write on the board:)

a. $\dfrac{10}{3}$

- Here's fraction A. The numbers are 10 and 3. The fraction is more than 1.
e. Fraction B. The numbers are 3 and 1. The fraction is less than 1. Write the fraction. Raise your hand when you're finished.
   (Observe students and give feedback.)
- (Write on the board:)

b. $\dfrac{1}{3}$

- Here's fraction B. The numbers are 3 and 1. 1-third is less than 1.
f. Fraction C: The numbers are 11 and 7. The fraction is less than 1. Write the fraction. Raise your hand when you're finished.
   (Observe students and give feedback.)
- (Write on the board:)

c. $\dfrac{7}{11}$

- Here's fraction C. The numbers are 7 and 11. 7-elevenths is less than 1.
g. Fraction D: The numbers are 9 and 8. The fraction is more than 1. Write the fraction. Raise your hand when you're finished.
   (Observe students and give feedback.)
- (Write on the board:)

d. $\dfrac{4}{8}$

- Here's fraction D. The numbers are 9 and 8. 9-eighths is more than 1.
h. Fraction E: The numbers are 100 and 37. The fraction is less than 1. Write the fraction. Raise your hand when you're finished.
(Observe students and give feedback.)
- (Write on the board:)

e. $\dfrac{37}{100}$

- Here's fraction E. The numbers are 100 and 37. 37-hundredths is less than 1.

Teaching Notes

Hold students to a very high criterion of performance. In other words, they should not make any mistakes. If they do make mistakes, repeat the fractions that gave them trouble. Also, observe students very closely as they work. If they are scratching their head or taking a long time before writing the fraction, they don't understand what they are supposed to be doing.

Don't let them stew. Tell students how to figure out the fraction. Keep your explanations very simple: "The fraction is less than 1 so the smaller number goes on top. Which number is that?" Or: "The fraction is more than 1 so the bigger number goes on top. Which number is that?"

Repeat the examples until the students can perform without prompting. If they get it right the first time you present it, they will have a very easy time with much of the fraction work that follows.

In Lesson 9, a second type of description is introduced. This description tells the number of parts in each unit and the number of parts shaded. The information is not always presented in the same order. The description takes this form: The picture for this fraction has 3 parts in each unit and 1 part is shaded. 3 parts in each unit and 1 part shaded. Write the fraction.

The information about the parts in each unit tells the bottom number of the fraction. The information about the parts shaded tells about the top number. Again, make sure that students are very accurate in their writing of fractions.

In Lesson 10 and continuing through Lesson 16, students work with a mixed set of descriptions. Some tell about the parts; some tell the numbers and whether the fraction is more or less than 1. After students write fractions for the set, they circle all the fractions that are more than 1. Note that the discrimination of whether a fraction is more or less than 1 is very important for work with multiplying fractions, ratio and proportion problems, and figuring out whether fractions are equivalent.

In Lesson 74, students are introduced to the term **denominator**. In Lesson 81, **numerator** is introduced. Following the introduction of these terms, students write fractions from descriptions that use the words numerator and denominator.

Level D provides a lot of work with fraction equivalence. The various exercises reinforce the relationship between whole numbers on a number line and fractions for whole numbers.

In Lesson 16, students learn how to analyze fractions that equal whole numbers. To analyze $\frac{40}{5}$, students start with the bottom number and say: "5 times what whole number equals 40?"

The answer is the whole number that equals $\frac{40}{5}$

Here's the introduction from Lesson 16:

a. (Write on the board:)

$$\frac{40}{5} = \qquad \frac{45}{9} =$$

- Each fraction equals a whole number. You can figure out the whole number by starting with the bottom number.
- (Touch 5.) Listen: 5 times **what whole number** equals 40?

b. Everybody, say the question. (Signal.) *5 times what whole number equals 40?*
   (Repeat step b until firm.)

c. What's the answer? (Signal.) *8.*
- So 40-fifths equals 8.
- (Write to show:)

$$\frac{40}{5} = 8 \quad \frac{45}{9} =$$

d. (Touch **9**.)

e. Start with 9 and say the question for the fraction. Get ready. Go. (Signal.) *9 times what whole number equals 45?*
   (Repeat step e until firm.)

f. What's the answer? (Signal.) *5.*
- So 45-ninths equals 5.

a. $\frac{12}{4} =$ b. $\frac{63}{9} =$ c. $\frac{15}{5} =$ d. $\frac{18}{3} =$ e. $\frac{30}{5} =$

WORKBOOK PRACTICE

a. Open your workbook to lesson 16 and find part 1. √
b. Problem A. Touch the bottom number and say the question. Get ready. Go. (Signal.) *4 times what whole number equals 12?*
   (Repeat step b until firm.)
c. What's the answer? (Signal.) *3.*
   So 12-fourths equals 3. Write the answer. √
d. Problem B. Touch the bottom number and say the question. (Signal.) *9 times what whole number equals 63?*

- What's the answer? (Signal.) *7.*
- So 63-ninths equals 7.
- Write the answer.
e. Problem C. Say the question to yourself and write the answer. Raise your hand when you're finished. (Observe students and give feedback.)
- Get ready to tell me the answer. 5 times what whole number equals 15? (Signal.) *3.*
- So 15-fifths equals 3. Raise your hand if you got it right.
f. Your turn: Write the whole numbers that equal the fractions in problems D and E. Raise your hand when you're finished. (Observe students and give feedback.)
g. Check your work.
- Problem D: 3 times what number equals 18? (Signal.) *6.*
- So 18-thirds equals 6. Raise your hand if you got it right.
- Problem E: 5 times what number equals 30? (Signal.) *6.*
- So 30-fifths equals 6. Raise your hand if you got it right.

Teaching Notes

Make sure that students are very firm in saying the question (steps b and e in the board demonstration; step b in workbook practice). When correcting mistakes, start by having students say the question: "Touch the bottom number and say the question....What's the answer?"

Students will use variations of this question throughout the program. If they are firm on it early, they will have far fewer problems learning about the relationships between fractions, whole numbers, and mixed numbers.

In Lesson 21, students do a similar task in which they aren't prompted to say the multiplication question. They just copy the fraction and write the whole number it equals. Make sure that students include the equals sign. Do not permit them to write only part of the equation.

In Lesson 22, students write fractions for whole numbers on a number line. This exercise is important because it acquaints students with the conventions that are involved in adding or subtracting fractions. Students learn that, when you add fractions, they must be on the same number line, indicating that the denominators are the same.

Here's the workbook practice from Lesson 22. This exercise follows a textbook introduction that explains why fractions on the same number line have the same bottom number.

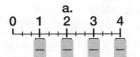 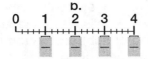

a. Open your workbook to lesson 22 and find part 1. √
• You're going to write fractions for all the whole numbers on these number lines. All the fractions on a number line will have the same bottom number, because each unit on the number line has the same number of parts.
b. Number line A. Look at each unit. How many parts are in each unit? (Signal.) *3.*
• So each fraction has the bottom number of 3.
c. Your turn: Write the bottom number for each fraction. Raise your hand when you're finished. √
d. Now you'll write the top numbers.
• Touch **1** on the number line. The number 1 always tells you that the top of the fraction is **1** times the bottom. What's 1 times 3? (Signal.) *3.*
• 3 is the top number at 1.
• Touch **2** on the number line. The number 2 tells you that the top of the fraction is **2** times the bottom. What's 2 times 3? (Signal.) *6.*
• That's the top number at 2.
• Touch **3** on the number line. The number 3 tells you that the top of the fraction is how many times the bottom number? (Signal.) *3.*
• What's 3 times 3? (Signal.) *9.*
• That's the top number at 3.
e. Your turn: Complete all the fractions for the number line. Raise your hand when you're finished.
(Observe students and give feedback.)
f. (Write on the board:)

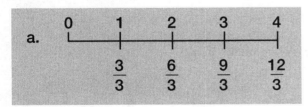

g. Here are the fractions for the whole numbers on the number line.
• What fraction equals 1? (Signal.) *3-thirds.*
• What fraction equals 2? (Signal.) *6-thirds.*
• What fraction equals 3? (Signal.) *9-thirds.*
• What fraction equals 4? (Signal.) *12-thirds.*
h. Number line B. Remember, all the fractions have the same bottom number. The number of parts in each unit tells the bottom number for the fractions.
• Write the bottom number for each fraction. Raise your hand when you're finished.
(Observe students and give feedback.)

• Everybody, what's the bottom number of each fraction? (Signal.) *5.*
• (Write on the board:)

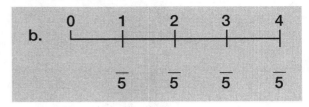

• Here's what you should have so far.
i. Now complete each fraction. Start at 1 on the number line. Remember, the 1 tells that the top is 1 times the bottom. The 2 tells that the top is 2 times the bottom, and so forth. Raise your hand when you've completed all your fractions.
(Observe students and give feedback.)
j. (Write to show:)

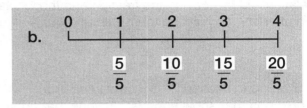

k. Here are the fractions you should have for the whole numbers.
• What fraction equals 1? (Signal.) *5-fifths.*
• What fraction equals 2? (Signal.) *10-fifths.*
• What fraction equals 3? (Signal.) *15-fifths.*
• What fraction equals 4? (Signal.) *20-fifths.*
l. Raise your hand if you got everything right.

Teaching Notes

This work is different from what students have done with pictures of fractions because there are no shaded parts. There is simply a correspondence between the whole numbers and the fractions. If students have trouble understanding the links between the numbers and the fractions, point to the 1 on the number line and the fraction below it: "These values tell about the same place on the number line. On this number line, the whole number 1 is 5-fifths.... The whole number 2 is 10-fifths. Remember how that works, because you'll be doing a lot of work with fractions on number lines."

Beginning in Lesson 24, students work with vertical number lines. These number lines make it easy for students to write equations that relate fractions to whole numbers they equal.

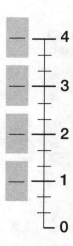

When students complete the fraction for 4, ($\frac{12}{3}$), they can write an equation showing the relationship by copying the fraction and the whole number and connecting them with an equals sign:

$$\frac{12}{3} = 4$$

Starting in Lesson 29, students construct equations that show various fractions that equal the same whole number.

The basic rule that students use to complete these equivalent fractions is that all fractions that equal a particular whole number, like 4, have a top number that is 4 times the bottom number. To make fractions that equal 4, start with the bottom number and multiply by 4 to figure out the top number.

Here's the student material from Lesson 29, where students apply the rule about the top number to complete the fractions:

a. $3 = \dfrac{}{1} = \dfrac{}{2} = \dfrac{}{4} = \dfrac{}{6}$

b. $4 = \dfrac{}{1} = \dfrac{}{3} = \dfrac{}{5} = \dfrac{}{9}$

Teaching Notes

The fractions with 1 as a denominator are particularly important. They show that a simple fraction that equals 3 is $\frac{3}{1}$, and a simple fraction that equals 4 is $\frac{4}{1}$. Students later use this analysis to work problems that multiply a whole number by a fraction. Students change the whole number into a simple fraction and multiply.

FRACTION ADDITION AND SUBTRACTION

In Lesson 27, students are introduced to the rule that fractions can be added or subtracted if the bottom numbers are the same. To work a problem, students copy the bottom number (which tells about the number line), and then add or subtract the top numbers. Following a textbook introduction, students copy problems that can be worked and work them.

Here's part of the introduction from Lesson 27:

a. $\dfrac{3}{7} + \dfrac{2}{3} =$ b. $\dfrac{3}{9} + \dfrac{1}{9} =$ c. $\dfrac{5}{4} - \dfrac{4}{5} =$ d. $\dfrac{11}{3} - \dfrac{11}{9} =$

b. $\dfrac{7}{3} - \dfrac{3}{3} =$ f. $\dfrac{8}{7} + \dfrac{2}{7} =$ g. $\dfrac{8}{8} + \dfrac{8}{3} =$ h. $\dfrac{5}{6} - \dfrac{5}{6} =$

b. Find the problems for part 3. You can work some of these problems, but you can't work other problems because the bottom numbers are not the same.

c. Problem A: 3-sevenths plus 2-thirds. Can you work it? (Signal.) *No.*

• Right, the bottom numbers are not the same. So the problem tells about two different number lines.

• Problem B: 3-ninths plus 1-ninth. Can you work it? (Signal.) *Yes.*

• What's the bottom number in the answer? (Signal.) *9.*

• Problem C: 5-fourths minus 4-fifths. Can you work it? (Signal.) *No.*

• Problem D: 11-thirds minus 11-ninths. Can you work it? (Signal.) *No.*

• Problem E: 7-thirds minus 3-thirds. Can you work it? (Signal.) *Yes.*

d. Your turn: Copy all the problems in part 3 that you **can** work. Don't work them. Just copy all the problems you can work. Don't copy any problems you can't work. Remember, you can't work them unless the bottom numbers are the same. Raise your hand when you're finished.

(Observe students and give feedback.)

e. (Write on the board:)

b. $\dfrac{3}{9} + \dfrac{1}{9} =$

e. $\dfrac{7}{3} - \dfrac{3}{3} =$

f. $\dfrac{8}{7} + \dfrac{2}{7} =$

h. $\dfrac{5}{6} - \dfrac{5}{6} =$

- You should have copied problems B, E, F, and H. You should not have copied any of the other problems.
- f. Problem B: 3-ninths plus 1-ninth. The problem tells about ninths. So your answer will be ninths because it has to be on the same number line.
- Write 9 for the bottom number in your answer. √
- (Write to show:)

$$b. \ \frac{3}{9} + \frac{1}{9} = \frac{\ }{9}$$

- Now add on top and write the answer. Raise your hand when you're finished.
- (Write to show:)

$$b. \ \frac{3}{9} + \frac{1}{9} = \frac{4}{9}$$

- Here's what you should have: 3-ninths plus 1-ninth equals 4-ninths.
- g. Your turn: Work problem E. Remember, both fractions are thirds. So the answer is thirds. Just copy **3** in the answer. Then work 7 minus 3 on top. Raise your hand when you're finished.
  (Observe students and give feedback.)
- (Write to show:)

$$e. \ \frac{7}{3} - \frac{3}{3} = \frac{4}{3}$$

- Check your work. Here's what you should have for problem E: 7-thirds minus 3-thirds equals 4-thirds. Raise your hand if you got it right.

Teaching Notes

If students make mistakes by adding the denominators, remind them: "The bottom numbers just tell about the number line. All fractions must have the same bottom number. That means the answer must have the same bottom number as the other fractions."

MIXED NUMBERS

Mixed numbers are introduced in Lesson 34. In Level D, mixed numbers are shown as a whole number, a plus sign, and a fraction. They are not shown without the plus sign.

The mixed number provides clues for locating it on a number line. The fractional part of the mixed number tells about the number line. For $4 + \frac{1}{5}$, you go to a number line that is divided into fifths. You go to the whole number marker for 4; then you count 1-fifth from that point.

Here's the part of the exercise from Lesson 34 that follows a textbook introduction:

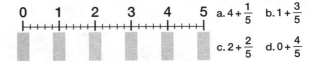

- a. Open your workbook to lesson 34 and find part 1. √
- b. Raise your hand when you know the bottom number for the fractions on the number line.
- Everybody, what's the bottom number? (Signal.) *5.*
- c. Write the fractions for the whole numbers. Raise your hand when you're finished.
  (Observe students and give feedback.)
- d. What fraction equals zero? (Signal.) *Zero-fifths.*
- What fraction equals 1? (Signal.) *5-fifths.*
- What fraction equals 2? (Signal.) *10-fifths.*
- What fraction equals 3? (Signal.) *15-fifths.*
- What fraction equals 4? (Signal.) *20-fifths.*
- What fraction equals 5? (Signal.) *25-fifths.*
- e. You're going to show where mixed numbers go on the number line.
- f. Touch mixed number A: 4 plus 1-fifth. That's 1-fifth past the whole number 4.
- (Write on the board:)

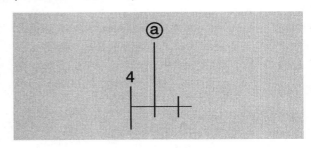

- Everybody, touch the mark on the number line for 4 plus 1-fifth.
- You'll write the letter A at the mark. Write your letter in a circle above the line for 4 plus 1-fifth. Then make a line to the right mark on the number line. Do it like I've shown on the board. Raise your hand when you're finished.
  (Observe students and give feedback.)
- g. Your turn: Write the letters and make the lines to show where the rest of the mixed numbers go. Raise your hand when you're finished.
  (Observe students and give feedback.)
- h. Check your work. Go back to your textbook and find part J on page 112.

- That shows where you should have put letters for the mixed numbers.
  i. Raise your hand if you got everything right.

In later lessons, students work exercises that show more than one number line.

In Lesson 38, students figure out the fraction that equals a mixed number. They change a whole number into a fraction and then add the fractional part.

Here's the exercise:

a. (Write on the board:)

$$6 + \frac{1}{5}$$

- Here's a mixed number. We're going to write the fraction that equals 6 plus 1-fifth. That fraction will equal 6 wholes plus 1-fifth.
- We have to change 6 into a fraction that has the **same bottom number as 1-fifth**. What bottom number is that? (Signal.) *5.*

b. I'll write the new equation below.
- (Write to show:)

$$6 + \frac{1}{5}$$
$$\frac{}{5} + \frac{1}{5} =$$

- I've shown the bottom number of the fraction for 6 wholes below the 6.
- The fraction equals **6.** So the top number is how many times the bottom? (Signal.) *6.*
- What's 5 times 6? (Signal.) *30.*
- That's the top number.
- (Write to show:)

$$\frac{30}{5} + \frac{1}{5} =$$

c. Now we add 30-fifths plus 1-fifth. What's the answer? (Signal.) *31-fifths.*
- (Write to show:)

$$\frac{30}{5} + \frac{1}{5} = \frac{31}{5}$$

a. 3⟌186   b. 3⟌243   c. 3⟌606   d. 3⟌930   e. 3⟌129

WORKBOOK PRACTICE

a. Find part 2.
b. Mixed number A: 4 plus 3-fifths. You're going to change 4 into a fraction with the same bottom number as 3-fifths. What's the bottom number? (Signal.) *5.*
- (Write on the board:)

$$\text{a. } 4 + \frac{3}{5}$$
$$\frac{}{5} + \frac{3}{5} =$$

- The first fraction will equal 4. So the top number will be how many times the bottom? (Signal.) *4.*
- Write the fraction that equals 4 below the 4. Then complete the equation. Raise your hand when you're finished.
  (Observe students and give feedback.)
- (Write to show:)

$$\frac{20}{5} + \frac{3}{5} = \frac{23}{5}$$

- Here's what you should have for the mixed number 4 plus 3-fifths. 4 plus 3-fifths equals 23-fifths. Raise your hand if you got it right.
c. Mixed number B. What's the bottom number of the fraction you're going to change 7 into? (Signal.) *2.*
- Change the whole number into a fraction with the right bottom number. Write the equation below and figure out the answer. Raise your hand when you're finished.
  (Observe students and give feedback.)
- (Write on the board:)

$$\text{b. } 7 + \frac{1}{2}$$
$$\frac{14}{2} + \frac{1}{2} = \frac{15}{2}$$

- Here's what you should have. 7 is 14-halves. 14-halves plus 1-half equals 15-halves.
d. Problem C. Change the whole number into a fraction with the right bottom number. Write the equation below and figure out the answer. Raise your hand when you're finished.
  (Observe students and give feedback.)

- (Write on the board:)

$$\text{c. } 4 + \frac{6}{9}$$

$$\frac{36}{9} + \frac{6}{9} = \frac{42}{9}$$

- Here's what you should have. 4 is 36-ninths. 36-ninths plus 6-ninths equals 42-ninths.
- e. Problem D. Change the whole number into a fraction with the right bottom number. Then write the complete equation. Raise your hand when you're finished.
  (Observe students and give feedback.)
- (Write on the board:)

$$\text{d. } 5 + \frac{4}{7}$$

$$\frac{35}{7} + \frac{4}{7} = \frac{39}{7}$$

- Here's what you should have. 5 is 35-sevenths. 35-sevenths plus 4-sevenths equals 39-sevenths.
- f. Raise your hand if you wrote correct equations for all the mixed numbers in part 2.

Teaching Notes

If students are firm on skills taught earlier in the program, they should have very few problems with this concept. The mechanics of writing the equation are fairly easy. Below the whole number, they write the fraction for the whole number. They copy the sign between the whole number and the fraction. Then they work the problem and write the answer. The fraction after the equal sign is computed by copying the bottom number and adding the top numbers.

Starting in Lesson 42, students work mixed sets of problems. Some involve adding fractions with the same denominator. Some involve working mixed-number problems.

In Lesson 43, students expand what they have learned about mixed numbers to include combinations that start with the fraction:

$$\frac{2}{3} + 8$$

And combinations that involve subtraction:

$$8 - \frac{2}{3} \; ; \; \frac{11}{2} - 3$$

Students work these problems the same way they worked earlier problems. Below the whole number, they write the fraction for the whole number. They copy the sign between the whole number and the fraction. Then they work the problem and write the answer. Note that although the work is quite easy for the students, they are working a type of "common denominator" problem, starting with Lesson 43.

In Lesson 49, students figure out the mixed number that equals an improper fraction and write equations of the form:

$$\frac{14}{3} = 4 + \frac{2}{3}$$

Students first indicate the fractions for the whole numbers on a vertical number line. They then draw a line to show where the fraction $\frac{14}{3}$ goes on the number line. Finally, they write the equation.

Here's the exercise from Lesson 49:

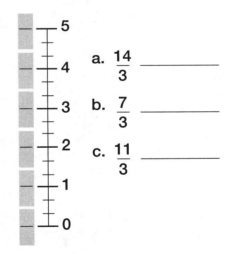

a. Find part 3. Write all the fractions for whole numbers. Raise your hand when you're finished. (Observe students and give feedback.)
b. Tell me the fractions.
- What's the fraction that equals zero? (Signal.) *Zero-thirds.*
- What's the fraction that equals 1? (Signal.) *3-thirds.*
- What's the fraction that equals 2? (Signal.) *6-thirds.*

- What's the fraction that equals 3? (Signal.)
  9-thirds.
- What's the fraction that equals 4? (Signal.)
  12-thirds.
- What's the fraction that equals 5? (Signal.)
  15-thirds.

c. You're going to show where fractions that are **not** for whole numbers go. Then you're going to write equations that tell about the mixed numbers that equal those fractions.

d. Write the fraction 14-thirds in a circle next to the number line with a line to show exactly where it goes. Draw it on the **left** side of the line. Raise your hand when you're finished.

- (Write on the board:)

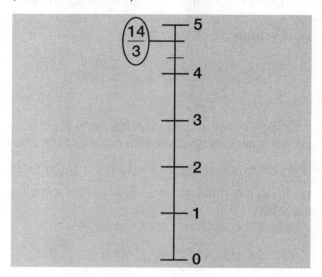

- Here's what you should have.

e. Now you're going to write the mixed number that equals 14-thirds. You go to the whole number just before 14-thirds. Everybody, what whole number is that? (Signal.) *4.*

- So 14-thirds equals 4 plus some thirds.
- First you go to 4 and then see how many thirds you have to add to get 14-thirds. Everybody, how many thirds do you add? (Signal.) *2.*

f. (Write on the board:)

$$\text{a.} \quad \frac{14}{3} = 4 + \frac{2}{3}$$

- Here's the equation for 14-thirds. 14-thirds equals 4 plus 2-thirds.

g. 14-thirds is already written in item A of your workbook. Complete the equation for 14-thirds. Then put 7-thirds where it goes on the number line. Raise your hand when you're finished with A and B. (Observe students and give feedback.)

h. Check your work. On the number line, you should have 7-thirds at the mark just after the whole number 2.

- (Write on the board:)

$$\text{b.} \quad \frac{7}{3} =$$

- Now complete the equation to show the mixed number 7-thirds equals. Remember, go to the whole number just before 7-thirds. Write that whole number. Then write the number of thirds you add to get to 7-thirds. Raise your hand when you're finished.
  (Observe students and give feedback.)
- (Write to show:)

$$\text{b.} \quad \frac{7}{3} = \boxed{2 + \frac{1}{3}}$$

- Here's what you should have. 7-thirds equals 2 plus 1-third. Raise your hand if you got it right.

i. Item C. Put 11-thirds on the number line. Then complete the equation to show the mixed number 11-thirds equals. Raise your hand when you're finished. (Observe students and give feedback.)

- Check your work. On your number line, you should have 11-thirds at the second mark after the whole number 3.
- Everybody, read the equation. (Signal.) *11-thirds equals 3 plus 2-thirds.*

j. Raise your hand if you got it right.

Teaching Notes

If students have trouble with placement of the equals sign, show them that they're just replacing the mark for $\frac{14}{3}$ on the number line with an equals sign. $\frac{14}{3}$ comes first. Next, there's the mark (the equals sign). Then, there's a mixed number.

Starting in Lesson 57, students complete equations for improper fractions without referring to a number line. The first set of problem types the students work shows the improper fraction and the whole number. Students complete the fraction.

Here's the introduction from Lesson 57:

a. (Write on the board:)

$$\text{a.} \quad \frac{14}{4} = 3 + \qquad \text{b.} \quad \frac{13}{5} = 2 +$$

- The answers to these problems are mixed numbers. Remember, a mixed number is a whole number plus a fraction. The whole number part of the answer is shown. You're going to write the fraction part of the answer.
b. Fraction A is 14-fourths. 14 is not a number for multiplying by 4. Here's the question you ask: 4 times what **whole number gets near** 14? The answer is 3.
- What's 4 times 3? (Signal.) *12.*
- So 12-fourths is 3 wholes. How many fourths do you add to 12-fourths to get to 14-fourths? (Signal.) *2.*
- So 14-fourths equals 3 wholes plus 2-fourths.
c. (Point to 13-fifths.)
- Fraction B is 13-fifths. 13 is not a number for fives. So 13-fifths is 2 wholes plus a fraction.
- First you say the multiplication problem for the fraction that equals 2 wholes. That's 5 times 2 equals 10.
- So 2 wholes equal 10-fifths.
- You have to get to 13-fifths. How much do you add to 10-fifths? (Signal.) *3-fifths.*
- (Write to show:)

$$\text{b. } \frac{13}{5} = 2 + \frac{3}{5}$$

- 13-fifths equals 2 wholes plus 3-fifths. The mixed number is 2 and 3-fifths.

Teaching Notes

This work is important because it requires students to identify the number of parts that have been used up by the whole number, then subtract that number from the number of parts shown in the improper fraction. For instance:

$$\frac{14}{4} = 3 + \underline{}$$

To figure out the number of parts used by 3 wholes, students multiply 3 times 4. That's 12. The difference between 14 and 12 is 2. So the top number of the fraction is 2. The bottom is the same as the bottom number of $\frac{14}{4}$:

$$\frac{14}{4} = 3 + \frac{2}{4}$$

In Lesson 61, students write the complete equation. For this exercise, all the fractions have a denominator of 3. Students use the number map for 3 as a basis for identifying the closest number that is less than the number shown.

3	6	9
12	15	18
21	24	27
30		

a. $\frac{29}{3} = \underline{} + \blacksquare$ b. $\frac{22}{3} = \underline{} + \blacksquare$

c. $\frac{26}{3} = \underline{} + \blacksquare$ d. $\frac{16}{3} = \underline{} + \blacksquare$

a. Find part 3. Each fraction equals a whole number.
b. Fraction A is 18-thirds. Say the question for the number of wholes. Get ready. (Signal.) *3 times what number equals 18?*
- What's the answer? (Signal.) *6.*
- Fraction B is 27-thirds. Say the question for the number of wholes. Get ready. (Signal.) *3 times what number equals 27?*
- Fraction C is 6-thirds. Say the question for the number of wholes. Get ready. (Signal.) *3 times what number equals 6?*
- Fraction D is 12-thirds. Say the question for the number of wholes. Get ready. (Signal.) *3 times what number equals 12?*
c. Your turn: Write the complete equation for each fraction. Write an equal sign and the whole number each fraction equals. Raise your hand when you're finished.
   (Observe students and give feedback.)
d. Check your work. Read each equation.
- Equation A. (Signal.) *18-thirds equals 6.*
- Equation B. (Signal.) *27-thirds equals 9.*
- Equation C. (Signal.) *6-thirds equals 2.*
- Equation D. (Signal.) *12-thirds equals 4.*
e. Find part 4.
- (Write on the board:)

$$\frac{14}{3} =$$

- Here's a fraction that does not equal a whole number. It equals a mixed number. That's a whole number plus a fraction.
- First you figure out the whole number. You find the number for threes that comes just before the top number of the fraction.
- What's the top number of the fraction? (Signal.) *14.*
f. Touch the number on the map for threes that comes just before 14. √
- You should be touching 12.
g. My turn to say the question for 12: 3 times what number equals 12? The answer is 4.

- (Write to show:)

$$\frac{14}{3} = \boxed{4}$$

- I've figured out the whole number. Now I need the fraction. Raise your hand when you know the fraction we have to add to get from 12-thirds to 14-thirds.
- Everybody, what fraction? (Signal.) *2-thirds.*
- (Write to show:)

$$\frac{14}{3} = 4 + \boxed{\frac{2}{3}}$$

- We figured out the mixed number for 14-thirds. 14-thirds equals 4 plus 2-thirds. Remember, say the question for the number that comes just before the top number of the fraction. The answer is the whole number that gets you as close as you can get to the fraction.
h. Touch fraction A. It's 29-thirds. Is 29 a number for multiplying by 3? (Signal.) *No.*
- Touch the number for 3 on the map that comes just before 29. √
- Everybody, what number are you touching? (Signal.) *27.*
- Start with 3 and say the question for 27. Get ready. (Signal.) *3 times what number equals 27?*
- What's the answer? (Signal.) *9.*
- That's the whole number. Write the whole number. Then figure out the missing fraction for A. Write it. Raise your hand when you've completed the equation with the mixed number for fraction A.
- (Write on the board:)

$$\text{a. } \frac{29}{3} = 9 + \frac{2}{3}$$

- Here's what you should have: 29-thirds equals 9 wholes plus 2-thirds. Raise your hand if you got it right.
i. Fraction B: 22-thirds. Is 22 a number for multiplying by 3? (Signal.) *No.*
- Touch the number for 3 that comes just before 22. √
- Everybody, what number are you touching? (Signal.) *21.*
- Start with 3 and say the question for 21. Get ready. (Signal.) *3 times what number equals 21?*
- What's the answer? (Signal.) *7.*
- That's the whole number. Write it. Then figure out the missing fraction for B. Raise your hand when you have the equation for B. (Observe students and give feedback.)

- (Write on the board:)

$$\text{b. } \frac{22}{3} = 7 + \frac{1}{3}$$

- Here's what you should have: 22-thirds equals 7 plus 1-third. Raise your hand if you got it right.
j. Fraction C: 26-thirds. Touch the number that comes just before 26. √
- Everybody, what number are you touching? (Signal.) *24.*
- Say the question for 24. (Signal.) *3 times what number equals 24?*
- Write the answer. Then write the fraction. Raise your hand when you've completed the equation. (Observe students and give feedback.)
- (Write on the board:)

$$\text{c. } \frac{26}{3} = 8 + \frac{2}{3}$$

- Here's what you should have: 26-thirds equals 8 plus 2-thirds.
k. Fraction D: 16-thirds. Touch the number that comes just before 16. Say the question for that number and write the number of wholes. Then write the fraction you add. Raise your hand when you've completed the equation. (Observe students and give feedback.)
- (Write on the board:)

$$\text{d. } \frac{16}{3} = 5 + \frac{1}{3}$$

- Here's what you should have: 16-thirds equals 5 plus 1-third. Raise your hand if you got it right.
l. You're working some difficult mixed-number problems.

Teaching Notes

Prompt students in the steps. For example: "What's the number that comes just before 14 on the number map?" *12.*

"What **number of times** for that number?" *4.*

"Subtract to find the number of parts left over...."

"What's 14 minus 12?" *2.*

$$\frac{14}{3} = 4 + \frac{2}{}$$

"Write the appropriate denominator for the fraction:"

$$\frac{14}{3} = 4 + \frac{2}{3}$$

Starting in Lesson 66, students work with mixed sets of fractions. Some are written as mixed numbers; some are written as whole numbers. Students apply what they have learned. They identify whether the numerator is a number for multiplying by the denominator. If not, they write the closest fact number, then they subtract to figure out the fractional part of the mixed number. This series of steps is what students do when they work division problems with remainders (which begins in Lesson 68).

FRACTION MULTIPLICATION

In Level D, students work on multiplying a fraction by a fraction, multiplying a fraction by a whole number, and relating fractions that are involved in multiplication equations. Students apply the rule that if you multiply the first value by less than 1, the value you end up with is less than the value you started with. If the first value is multiplied by 1, the values are equal. This understanding of multiplying by 1 is extremely important for the understanding of equivalent fractions, simplifying fractions, and ratios.

The work with multiplication begins in Lesson 46. Students learn the basic steps of multiplying on the top and writing the answer on top; multiplying on the bottom and writing the answer on the bottom.

- When you multiply fractions, you multiply the top numbers and write the answer on top. Then you multiply the bottom numbers and write the answer on the bottom.

Here's: $\frac{3}{4} \times \frac{2}{5}$

- The multiplication problem for the top is 3 × 2. That's 6. You write 6 on top. $\frac{3}{4} \times \frac{2}{5} = \boxed{\frac{6}{20}}$

- The multiplication problem for the bottom is 4 × 5. That's 20. You write 20 on the bottom. $\frac{3}{4} \times \frac{2}{5} = \boxed{\frac{6}{20}}$

a. $\frac{2}{9} \times \frac{4}{2} = \square$ b. $\frac{2}{3} \times \frac{4}{1} = \square$ c. $\frac{7}{2} \times \frac{2}{10} = \square$

d. $\frac{1}{3} \times \frac{5}{2} = \square$ e. $\frac{2}{8} \times \frac{4}{1} = \square$

a. Find part 2. You've learned to add and subtract fractions. The rules in the box show how to **multiply** fractions. I'll read what it says. Follow along: When you multiply fractions, you multiply the top numbers and write the answer on top. Then you multiply the bottom numbers and write the answer on the bottom.

b. You can see the problem 3-fourths times 2-fifths.

- The multiplication problem for the top is 3 times 2. That's 6. You write 6 on top.

- The multiplication problem for the bottom is 4 times 5. That's 20. You write 20 on the bottom. I'll read the whole equation: 3-fourths times 2-fifths equals 6-twentieths.

c. Your turn: Use lined paper. Copy problem A and write the answer. Remember, multiply the top numbers and write that answer on top. Then multiply the bottom numbers and write that answer on the bottom. Raise your hand when you've worked problem A.

- (Write on the board:)

a. $\frac{2}{9} \times \frac{4}{2} = \frac{8}{18}$

- Check your work. You multiplied the top numbers, 2 times 4, and got 8 on the top. Then you multiplied 9 times 2 and got 18 on the bottom. 2-ninths times 4-halves equals 8-eighteenths. Raise your hand if you got everything right.

d. Your turn: Copy problem B and work it. Raise your hand when you're finished.
(Observe students and give feedback.)

- Everybody, what does 2-thirds times 4 over 1 equal? (Signal.) *8-thirds.*

- Raise your hand if you got it right.

e. Your turn: Copy problem C and work it. Raise your hand when you're finished.
(Observe students and give feedback.)

- Everybody, what does 7-halves times 2-tenths equal? (Signal.) *14-twentieths.*

- Raise your hand if you got it right.

f. Your turn: Copy and work the rest of the problems in part 2. Raise your hand when you're finished.
(Observe students and give feedback.)

g. Check your work.

- Problem D. What does 1-third times 5-halves equal? (Signal.) *5-sixths.*

- Problem E. What does 2-eighths times 4 over 1 equal? (Signal.) *8-eighths.*

- That's 1.

h. Raise your hand if you got everything right.

After students have practiced working multiplication problems in Lessons 47 through 49, they work with mixed sets of fraction problems. Some call for addition or subtraction; some require multiplication.

Here's an activity from Lesson 51:

a. $\frac{3}{4} \times \frac{8}{4} = \square$ b. $\frac{3}{4} + \frac{8}{4} = \square$ c. $\frac{7}{2} - \frac{3}{2} = \square$

d. $\frac{8}{2} \times \frac{3}{5} = \square$ e. $\frac{1}{6} + \frac{4}{6} = \square$ f. $\frac{4}{3} \times \frac{5}{2} = \square$

a. Find part 4. Some of these problems add or subtract fractions. Some multiply. Remember, when you add or subtract, you just copy the bottom number and work on top. When you multiply, you multiply on top **and** on the bottom.

b. Copy and work the problems in part 4. Raise your hand when you're finished.
(Observe students and give feedback.)

c. Check your work. Read each problem and the answer.
- Problem A. (Signal.) *3-fourths times 8-fourths equals 24-sixteenths.*
- Problem B. (Signal.) *3-fourths plus 8-fourths equals 11-fourths.*
- Problem C. (Signal.) *7-halves minus 3-halves equals 4-halves.*
- Problem D. (Signal.) *8-halves times 3-fifths equals 24-tenths.*
- Problem E. (Signal.) *1-sixth plus 4-sixths equals 5-sixths.*
- Problem F. (Signal.) *4-thirds times 5-halves equals 20-sixths.*

d. Raise your hand if you got all the problems right.

Teaching Notes

At this point, students should be very firm in working both types of problems. The problem sets are designed so that students must read the problems and attend to the sign. Students receive no spurious clues (whether the denominators are the same). The problem set, therefore, reveals any misconceptions students may have. Hold students to a high criterion of performance. Those who make operational mistakes (adding on the top and on the bottom, for instance) should repeat all the problems in the set. If students are not perfectly firm on problems of these types, they will experience difficulties when they work with whole numbers and fractions.

In Lesson 53, students are taught a procedure for multiplying a whole number by a fraction. They write a "simple" fraction for the whole number, which is the whole number over 1.

The key discrimination for fraction operations comes after students have worked for several lessons on fraction-multiplication problems that have a whole number. In Lesson 61, students work a mixed set of problems that require multiplication, addition or subtraction. Each problem has a whole number and a fraction. Students apply the rule for changing the whole number into an appropriate fraction. If the problem multiplies, they write the whole number over 1. If the problem adds or subtracts, they write the whole number as an equivalent fraction with the same denominator as the other fraction in the problem.

a. $3 \times \frac{4}{3} =$ b. $3 - \frac{4}{3} =$ c. $6 + \frac{3}{7} =$

d. $8 \times \frac{5}{9} =$ e. $\frac{4}{5} \times 9 =$ f. $\frac{4}{5} + 9 =$

a. Open your workbook to lesson 61 and find part 1. √
- All these problems have a whole number and a fraction. For some problems, you'll add or subtract. For other problems, you'll multiply. Remember, when you add or subtract, you must change the whole number into a fraction that has the same bottom number as the other fraction. When you multiply, you can make a simple fraction with 1 as the bottom number.

b. Problem A: 3 times 4-thirds. You're multiplying. Does 3 have to have the same bottom number as 4-thirds? (Signal.) *No.*
- Problem B. 3 minus 4-thirds. Does 3 have to have the same bottom number as 4-thirds? (Signal.) *Yes.*
- Problem C. 6 plus 3-sevenths. Does 6 have to have the same bottom number as 3-sevenths? (Signal.) *Yes.*
- Problem D. 8 times 5-ninths. Does 8 have to have the same bottom number as 5-ninths? (Signal.) *No.*
- You can write 8 as 8 over 1.

c. Your turn: In the space below each problem, write the problem with the correct fraction for the whole number and write the answer. Raise your hand when you're finished.
(Observe students and give feedback.)

d. Check your work. Read the whole equation you wrote for each problem.
- Problem A. (Signal.) *3 over 1 times 4-thirds equals 12-thirds.*
- Problem B. (Signal.) *9-thirds minus 4-thirds equals 5-thirds.*
- Problem C. (Signal.) *42-sevenths plus 3-sevenths equals 45-sevenths.*
- Problem D. (Signal.) *8 over 1 times 5-ninths equals 40-ninths.*
- Problem E. (Signal.) *4-fifths times 9 over 1 equals 36-fifths.*
- Problem F. (Signal.) *4-fifths equals 49-fifths.*

Teaching Notes

Students who make more than one operational mistake should repeat the set of problems. Dictate each problem. Direct students to write it on lined paper. Below, write the equation with the whole number shown as a fraction and the answer. Remind them that if the problem adds or subtracts, they are working on a number line. The answer will have the same bottom number as the fraction in the problem.

Equivalent Fractions

Students learn the following rules about multiplying: If you multiply a value by more than 1, you end up with more than the starting value. If you multiply by 1, you end up with a value that's equivalent to the starting value. If you multiply by less than 1, you end up with less than the starting value.

The rule for multiplying by 1 generates procedures for working with ratios, proportions, and equivalent fractions. That rule is presented in Lesson 54. Here's the first part of the exercise:

- If you multiply any value by a fraction that equals 1, the answer equals the value you started with.

- Here's 2 times 1 equals 2:
  So 2 times **any fraction that equals 1** equals 2.
- Here's 2 times a fraction that equals 1:

$$2 \times 1 = 2$$
$$2 \times \frac{5}{5} = 2$$

- First, we change 2 into a fraction that equals 2: $\frac{2}{1} \times \frac{5}{5} = \boxed{}$

- Then we multiply. When we multiply on top, we get 10. $\frac{2}{1} \times \frac{5}{5} = \boxed{10}$
- When we multiply on the bottom, we get 5. $\frac{2}{1} \times \frac{5}{5} = \boxed{\frac{10}{5}}$

- Here's a picture of $\frac{10}{5}$. The picture shows that $\frac{10}{5}$ equals 2 whole units.

a. $5 \times \frac{2}{2} =$ b. $\frac{3}{3} \times 9 =$ c. $\frac{7}{7} \times 3 =$ d. $8 \times \frac{4}{4} =$

a. Find part 3. I'll read what it says in the box. Follow along: If you multiply any value by a fraction that equals 1, the answer equals the value you started with.
- You can see the equation: 2 times 1. That equals 2.
- So 2 times **any fraction that equals 1** equals 2. You can see the equation: 2 times 5-fifths equals 2.
- Here's how to show that 2 times 5-fifths equals 2.
- First, we change 2 into a fraction that equals 2. That's 2 over 1.

- Then we multiply. When we multiply on top, we get **10.** 2 times 5 equals 10.
- When we multiply on the bottom, we get **5.** 1 times 5 equals 5.
- You can see a picture below the last equation. The picture shows the fraction for 2 over 1 and for 10-fifths. Both of these fractions equal 2 whole units.
- So 2 time 5-fifths **does** equal 2 wholes.
- Remember, any value times 1 equals that value. That's true for whole numbers and for all fractions.

b. Find the problems for part 3. All these problems have whole numbers multiplied by fractions. All the fractions equal 1. So the answer to all the problems will be the same as the whole number in the problem.

c. Problem A: 5 times 2-halves. When you multiply, you'll end up with a fraction that equals the whole number 5.

d. Your turn: Copy the problem and work it. Remember to change 5 into a simple fraction. Raise your hand when you're finished. (Observe students and give feedback.)

- (Write on the board:)

a. $\dfrac{5}{1} \times \dfrac{2}{2} = \dfrac{10}{2}$

- Here's what you should have. 5 over 1 times 2-halves equals 10-halves.

e. Problem B: 3-thirds times 9. You're multiplying a whole number and a fraction that equals 1. So you'll end up with a fraction that equals the whole number.

- Copy the problem and work it. Remember to change the whole number into a simple fraction. Raise your hand when you're finished. (Observe students and give feedback.)

- (Write on the board:)

b. $\dfrac{3}{3} \times \dfrac{9}{1} = \dfrac{27}{3}$

- Here's what you should have. 3-thirds times 9 over 1 equals 27-thirds.

Teaching Notes

If students are firm on the exercises that are being concurrently presented with whole numbers and fractions, they will be able to follow your explanations. If not, students may become seriously confused. The notion of multiplying by 1 is not easy for students to grasp. Level D provides lots of work to firm this understanding; however, students must perform at a relatively high criterion of performance.

> If students have trouble, ask them questions:
> "Does this problem multiply by a fraction that equals 1? Show me that fraction."
> "If it multiplies by 1, what do you know about the size of the fraction you end up with? Remember the rule. If you multiply by 1, the fraction you end up with is exactly the same size as the fraction you start out with."

Beginning in Lesson 56, students work a problem set that requires them to discriminate whether the first value in the problem and the ending fraction are equivalent. The test is whether the first value is multiplied by 1. Students first work a set of problems, some of which multiply by a fraction that equals 1. Students then identify the problems that have equivalent fractions. Next to these problems, students write a simple equation showing only the two equivalent fractions:

$$\frac{5}{4} \times \frac{10}{10} = \boxed{\frac{50}{40}} \qquad \frac{5}{4} = \frac{50}{40}$$

Starting in Lesson 59, students work problem sets that show the starting and ending fractions. Students figure out the missing middle fraction. If the fraction equals 1, students write out the simple equation.

Here's part of the exercise from Lesson 59:

a. $\frac{2}{5} \times \boxed{} = \frac{10}{15}$ b. $\frac{4}{9} \times \boxed{} = \frac{12}{27}$ c. $\frac{5}{3} \times \boxed{} = \frac{15}{21}$

d. $6 \times \boxed{} = \frac{30}{5}$ e. $\frac{1}{4} \times \boxed{} = \frac{4}{36}$

a. Find part 2 in your workbook.
b. Problem A: 2-fifths times some fraction equals 10-fifteenths. You're going to figure out the missing fraction. Say the problem for the bottom numbers. Get ready. (Signal.) *5 times what number equals 15?*
• What's the answer? (Signal.) *3.*
• Say the problem for the top numbers. Get ready. (Signal.) *2 times what number equals 10?*
• What's the answer? (Signal.) *5.*
• Write the missing fraction. Raise your hand when you're finished.
  (Observe students and give feedback.)
• You figured out what to multiply 2-fifths by to get 10-fifteenths. What did you multiply by? (Signal.) *5-thirds.*
c. Problem B: 4-ninths times some fraction equals 12-twenty-sevenths.

• Say the problem for the bottom numbers. (Signal.) *9 times what number equals 27?*
• What's the answer? (Signal.) *3.*
• Say the problem for the top numbers. (Signal.) *4 time what number equals 12?*
• What's the answer? (Signal.) *3.*
• Write the missing fraction. Raise your hand when you're finished.
  (Observe students and give feedback.)
• Everybody, 4-ninths times some fraction equals 12-twenty-sevenths. What's the missing fraction? (Signal.) *3-thirds.*
• That's 1.
d. Your turn: Write the missing fraction for problem C. Raise your hand when you're finished.
  (Observe students and give feedback.)
• (Write on the board:)

c. $\frac{5}{3} \times \boxed{\frac{3}{7}} = \frac{15}{21}$

• The missing fraction is 3-sevenths. 5-thirds times 3-sevenths equals 15-twenty-firsts.
e. Write the missing fractions for the rest of the problems in part 2. Raise your hand when you're finished. (Observe students and give feedback.)
• (Write on the board:)

d. $\frac{6}{1} \times \boxed{\frac{5}{5}} = \frac{30}{5}$

e. $\frac{1}{4} \times \boxed{\frac{4}{9}} = \frac{4}{36}$

f. Here's what you should have for problems D and E.
  Problem D. Read the equation. (Signal.) *6 over 1 times 5-fifths equals 30-fifths.*
  Problem E. Read the equation. (Signal.) *1-fourth times 4-ninths equals 4-thirty-sixths.*
g. Raise your hand if you got everything right.
h. For some of these problems you multiplied by 1. So you ended up with the same value you started with. If you multiplied by 1, write the number you started with and the fraction it equals in the shaded box after the problem. Write the equations only for the problems you multiplied by 1.
i. (Write on the board:)

b. $\frac{4}{9} = \frac{12}{27}$

d. $6 = \frac{30}{5}$

j. Here's what you should have.
- For problem B, you multiplied by 3-thirds. The equation you wrote is 4-ninths equals 12-twenty-sevenths.
- For problem D, you multiplied by 5-fifths. The equation you wrote is 6 equals 30-fifths.

Teaching Notes

Generally, when the work is structured in this manner, students don't have a lot of trouble with the discrimination. Later, however, when they work with equivalent fractions in other contexts, students may have some comprehension problems. Remind them of what they know. If the fractions are equivalent, the first fraction is multiplied by 1.

The final set of problems that require the discrimination of multiplying by 1 or not 1 begins in Lesson 62. Students are presented with problems of the form:

$$\frac{6}{2} \times \frac{}{7} = \frac{24}{}$$

$$\frac{3}{5} \times \frac{4}{} = \frac{}{20}$$

These problems provide a super review of everything students have learned about equivalent fractions as they relate to multiplication. The problems also set the stage for the work that students will do with ratio and proportion problems.

To work the first problem, students work a division problem on top: 24 ÷ 6. Students then work a multiplication problem on the bottom: 2 x 7.

They determine whether the fractions are equivalent by attending to whether the middle fraction equals 1. That fraction ($\frac{4}{7}$) does not

equal 1 so $\frac{6}{2}$ and $\frac{24}{14}$ are not equal.

In Lesson 66, students are introduced to the basic "ratio equation":

$$\frac{3}{5} \times \frac{}{} = \frac{}{20}$$

The fractions are equivalent. Therefore, the first fraction must be multiplied by 1.

To figure out that fraction and to complete the fraction after the equals sign, students first figure out whether they can work on the top or on the bottom. They can work on the bottom because there are two numbers on the bottom. (There's only one number on top.)

When students work the problem on the bottom (20 ÷ 5), they have the bottom number of the missing fraction:

$$\frac{3}{5} \times \frac{}{4} = \frac{}{20}$$

Students know that the two fractions in the original equation are equivalent; therefore, 4 is the denominator of a fraction that equals 1. Students complete the fraction, then multiply on top to complete the fraction after the equals sign:

$$\frac{3}{5} \times \frac{4}{4} = \frac{[12]}{20}$$

After students receive an explanation and a board demonstration with the problem shown above, students apply the problem-solving steps to other problems.

Here's the first part of the workbook practice:

In each problem, the fraction you start with and the fraction you end up with are equal.

a. $\frac{3}{5} \times \frac{}{} = \frac{}{20}$

b. $\frac{7}{2} \times \frac{}{} = \frac{}{18}$

c. $\frac{3}{4} \times \frac{}{} = \frac{21}{}$

d. $\frac{6}{5} \times \frac{}{} = \frac{60}{}$

a. Find part 3. You're going to work some of these hard problems.
b. Problem A is the problem on the board. The first thing you do is figure out the fraction that equals 1. You can't start on top because there's only one number on top. You can start on the bottom.
- Say the question for the bottom numbers. (Signal.) *5 times what number equals 20?*
- What's the answer? (Signal.) *4.*
- So what's the fraction that equals 1? (Signal.) *4-fourths.*

- Write the fraction that equals 1. Then multiply on top and complete the last fraction. Raise your hand when you're finished.
  (Observe students and give feedback.)
c. Problem B: 7-halves times a fraction equal to 1 equals some fraction with 18 on the bottom. The first thing you do is figure out the fraction that equals 1.
- Can you say the question for the top numbers of the fraction? (Signal.) *No.*
- There's only one top number so you can't say the question.
- Can you say the question for the numbers on the bottom? (Signal.) *Yes.*
- Say the question. (Signal.) *2 times what number equals 18?*
- What's the answer? (Signal.) *9.*
- Write the fraction that equals 1. Raise your hand when you're finished.
  (Observe students and give feedback.)
- (Write on the board:)

$$\text{b. } \frac{7}{2} \times \frac{9}{9} = \frac{\square}{18}$$

- Here's what you should have so far. Say the problem for the top numbers. (Signal.) *7 times 9 equals what number?*
- Write the answer. Raise your hand when you're finished. √
- (Write to show:)

$$\text{b. } \frac{7}{2} \times \frac{9}{9} = \frac{\boxed{63}}{18}$$

- Here's what you should have. You figured out a fraction that equals 7-halves. That fraction is 63-eighteenths. You had to multiply 7-halves by 9-ninths.

Teaching Notes

Make sure students understand the following about each problem: "The fractions shown are equivalent. So the first fraction must be multiplied by 1. You work a problem to figure out either the top or the bottom number of that fraction. The fraction equals 1, so the top and bottom numbers are the same. After writing the fraction that equals 1, complete the fraction after the equals sign."

Students practice working problems of this type through Lesson 70. The work provides students with all the prerequisite skills needed to work ratio problems.

RATIOS AND PROPORTIONS

Starting in Lesson 64, students practice writing names and the fraction for sentences that express proportional relationships. The sentences are of the type: There are 4 fleas for every 3 dogs. Students write the names in the same order they occur in the sentence: **fleas** and **dogs.**

They write the fraction showing the number for fleas and the number for dogs:

$$\frac{\text{fleas}}{\text{dogs}} \quad \frac{4}{3}$$

This is the first step that students will later take when they work ratio word problems.
Here's the first part of the exercise from Lesson 64:
a. Open your textbook to lesson 64 and find part 1. √
- You're going to write fractions and names for sentences. Learning to do this is very important because you'll need it later when you solve hard word problems. Each sentence tells you about a fraction.
b. Touch sentence A. The sentence says: There were 3 girls for every 4 boys. The words **girls** and **boys** are underlined. So here's what you write.
- (Write on the board:)

$$\text{a. } \frac{\text{girls}}{\text{boys}}$$

- Now you write the number for girls and the number for boys. What's the number for girls? (Signal.) *3.*
- So I write **3** on top.
- What's the number for boys? (Signal.) *4.*
- So I write **4** on the bottom.
- (Write to show:)

$$\text{a. } \frac{\text{girls}}{\text{boys}} \quad \frac{3}{4}$$

- The names and the fraction show that there are 3 girls for every 4 boys.
- Your turn: Copy the names and the fraction for sentence A. Raise your hand when you're finished.
  (Observe students and give feedback.)

In Lesson 68, students learn that **each** box or **each** house refers to **1** box or **1** house. For this sentence: There were 8 shoes in each box, students write:

$$\frac{\text{shoes}}{\text{boxes}} \quad \frac{8}{1}$$

In Lesson 71, students work word problems. Students combine what they have learned about equivalent fractions with the skill of writing names and fractions for sentences that tell about proportions.

Here's the first part of the exercise from Lesson 71:

a. Find part 2. You're going to work ratio problems. They are difficult, and many high school students have trouble with ratios. But you already know how to work them. They are just equivalent-fraction problems with names. You have to figure out a missing number in the equivalent-fraction equation.

b. Touch problem A. Here's the first sentence: There are 4 boys for every 7 girls. I'll write the names and the fraction for that sentence.
• What are the names? (Signal.) *Boys and girls.*
• What's the fraction? (Signal.) *4-sevenths.*
• (Write on the board:)

a. $\dfrac{\text{boys}}{\text{girls}}$ $\dfrac{4}{7}$

c. We've done the first sentence. Before we do the second sentence, I'll write an equal sign.
• (Write =, leaving space between fraction and =:)

a. $\dfrac{\text{boys}}{\text{girls}}$ $\dfrac{4}{7}$ $=$

• The next sentence will tell about one of the names. If the sentence tells about boys, I write the number on top. That's where any number for **boys** belongs.
• Where would I write a number for girls? (Signal.) *On the bottom.*

d. Listen to the next sentence: There are 21 girls.
• Does that sentence give a number for boys or a number for girls? (Signal.) *A number for girls.*
• So do I write **21** on top or on the bottom? (Signal.) *On the bottom.*
• (Write to show:)

a. $\dfrac{\text{boys}}{\text{girls}}$ $\dfrac{4}{7}$ $= \dfrac{}{21}$

e. The last sentence asks: How many boys are there? So I make a box for **boys.**
• Does that box go on top or on the bottom? (Signal.) *On top.*

• (Write to show:)

a. $\dfrac{\text{boys}}{\text{girls}}$ $\dfrac{4}{7}$ $= \dfrac{\square}{21}$

• Now we just work the equivalent-fraction problem and find the missing number. 4-sevenths equals the fraction after the equal sign, so 4-sevenths is multiplied by a fraction that equals 1.
• (Write to show:)

a. $\dfrac{\text{boys}}{\text{girls}}$ $\dfrac{4}{7}$ $\times \dfrac{}{} = \dfrac{\square}{21}$

f. Now we have a problem that you can work. Can you work the problem on top or on the bottom? (Signal.) *On the bottom.*
• Say the problem for the bottom numbers. (Signal.) *7 times what number equals 21?*
• What number? (Signal.) *3.*
• So what's the fraction that equals 1? (Signal.) *3-thirds.*
• (Write to show:)

a. $\dfrac{\text{boys}}{\text{girls}}$ $\dfrac{4}{7}$ $\times \dfrac{3}{3} = \dfrac{\square}{21}$

g. Now you multiply on top to find the number of boys. 4 times 3. What's the answer? (Signal.) *12.*
• (Write to show:)

a. $\dfrac{\text{boys}}{\text{girls}}$ $\dfrac{4}{7}$ $\times \dfrac{3}{3} = \dfrac{12}{21}$

• The number 12 is on top. Are the top numbers for boys or for girls? (Signal.) *Boys.*
• So we answered the question: How many boys are there?
• If there are 21 girls, there are **12 boys.**
• Your turn: Copy the work for problem A.
• Then write the answer on the line. Raise your hand when you're finished. √

Teaching Notes

The first steps of the analysis (through step e in the exercise) set up the problem. The conventions that are new involve the fraction after the equals sign.

If the question in the problem asks about boys, you make a box for boys. If the fraction gives a number for boys, you show the number for boys.

When you work the problem, you answer the question that is signaled by the box in the equation.

Students tend to have problems with the equals sign and the fraction after the equals sign. Remind them to, after they've made the first fraction, leave a space and make an equals sign before they write a number for the next fraction.

If students take a lot of time working the problems presented in Lesson 71, repeat the problem set. Make sure that students can write the equations quickly and accurately from your directions.

Once students have set up the problem, the rest of the work is familiar. They write the fraction that equals 1; then they multiply to complete the fraction after the equals sign. Remind students that the number in the box is the answer to the question: How many boys are there?

Work with ratios continues in every lesson through 78. In Lesson 75, students work problems that involve large numbers.

For example: There were 7 perch for every 9 bass. There were 963 bass. How many perch were there?

Students set up the problem:

$$\frac{\textbf{perch}}{\textbf{bass}} \quad \frac{7}{9} \times \frac{}{} = \frac{\boxed{}}{963}$$

To work the problem on the bottom, students divide:

$$\begin{array}{r} 107 \\ 9\overline{)963} \end{array}$$

Then they complete the fraction that equals 1 and figure out the number that goes in the box:

$$\frac{\textbf{perch}}{\textbf{bass}} \quad \frac{7}{9} \times \frac{107}{107} = \frac{\boxed{749}}{963}$$

There were 749 perch.

In Lesson 81, students are introduced to sentences that refer to the **ratio**: The ratio of dogs to cats is 6 to 11.

Students write:

$$\frac{\textbf{dogs}}{\textbf{cats}} \quad \frac{6}{11}$$

Students use a variation of the ratio analysis to work problems that involve measurement equivalences (starting in Lesson 83).

Students also work ratio problems that refer to time and to dollar amounts. (3 pounds of nuts cost $4.56. How much do 12 pounds cost?) Students are taught the meaning of **per.** (The car got 23 miles per gallon of gas.) Finally, students work "price-list" problems. (The list shows prices for 2 pounds of nuts. Students figure out how much 8 pounds would cost, or how many pounds of nuts they could buy for $10.00.)

The final type of ratio-related problem involves probability, and begins in Lesson 91. (See Probability on page 109.)

FRACTION COMPARISONS

For students to understand the relationship of one fraction to another, they must have some basis for comparison. If the fractions have the same denominator, the fraction with the larger numerator is the larger fraction. If the numerators are the same, the fraction with the smaller denominator is the larger fraction. Students also use information about whether fractions are more than 1 or less than 1 to compare their size. This analysis is taught in Lessons 72 through 102.

Another important basis for comparing fractions involves **multiplication**. The idea is that it is possible to go from one fraction to the other fraction using multiplication:

If $\frac{10}{16}$ equals $\frac{5}{8}$, you can multiply $\frac{5}{8}$ by 1 to get $\frac{10}{16}$.

If $\frac{9}{16}$ is less than $\frac{5}{8}$, you multiply $\frac{5}{8}$ by less than 1 to get $\frac{9}{16}$.

If $\frac{11}{16}$ is more than $\frac{5}{8}$, you multiply $\frac{5}{8}$ by more than 1 to get $\frac{11}{16}$.

The hardest part of this concept for students to understand is that, if you multiply by less than 1, you end up with less than you start with.

Work with this idea begins in Lesson 71. After the introduction, students indicate whether a concealed value is more than 1 or less than 1.

Here's the workbook practice exercise from Lesson 71:

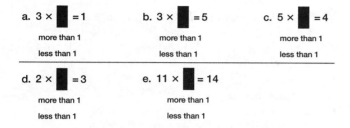

a. Open your workbook to lesson 71 and find part 1. √
- For each problem, you'll indicate whether you multiply by more than 1 or less than 1.
b. Problem A: 3 times some fraction equals 1. Do you end up with more than you start with or less than you start with? (Signal.) *Less than you start with.*
- So what do you know about the number you multiply by? (Signal.) *It's less than 1.*
c. Circle **less than 1**. Then work problem B. Remember, if you end up with **less** than you start with, you're multiplying by **less than 1**. If you end up with **more** than you start with, you're multiplying by **more than 1**. Raise your hand when you've finished problem B.
   (Observe students and give feedback.)
- Check your work.
- Problem B: 3 times some fraction equals 5. What do you start with in that problem? (Signal.) *3.*
- What do you end up with? (Signal.) *5.*
- Do you end up with more than you start with or less than you start with? (Signal.) *More than you start with.*
- So what do you know about the number you multiply by? (Signal.) *It's more than 1.*
d. Work the rest of the problems in part 1. Raise your hand when you're finished.
   (Observe students and give feedback.)
e. Check your work.
- Problem C: 5 times some fraction equals 4. Do you end up with more than you start with or less than you start with? (Signal.) *Less than you start with.*
- So what do you know about the number you multiply by? (Signal.) *It's less than 1.*
- Problem D: 2 times some fraction equals 3. Do you end up with more than you start with or less than you start with? (Signal.) *More than you start with.*
- So what do you know about the number you multiply by? (Signal.) *It's more than 1.*

- Problem E: 11 times some fraction equals 14. Do you end up with more than you start with or less than you start with? (Signal.) *More than you start with.*
- So what do you know about the number you multiply by? (Signal.) *It's more than 1.*
f. Remember the rule about multiplying by more than 1 or less than 1.

Teaching Notes

Students sometimes use words without thinking about what they are saying. Here's a mistake pattern you should watch for:

"5 times some fraction equals 4. Do you end up with more than you start with or less than you start with?" *Less than you start with.*

"So what do you know about the number you're multiplying by?" *It's less than you start with.*

Correction: **"It's less than 1."**
Repeat the series of questions.
Bring students to a very firm criterion of performance on step e of the exercise.

In Lesson 74, students work problems that show the larger fraction in a multiplication equation circled. Students infer whether the first fraction in the problem is multiplied by more than 1 or less than 1.

Here's the set of problems from Lesson 74:

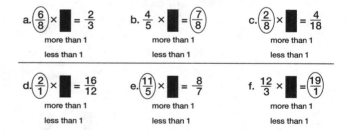

For problem A, the first fraction is circled. That means the fraction $\frac{2}{3}$ is less. To end up with a value that is less, you multiply by less than 1.

For problem B, the last fraction is circled. To end up with a fraction that is larger, you multiply by more than 1.

Teaching Notes

Some students may become confused about whether the value is less than 1 versus less than you start with. Here's the simplest procedure for focusing students on the relationship between starting number, ending number, and amount the starting number is multiplied by. Ask this set of questions about each item that had been worked:

"What's the starting value?"

"Is the ending value more than that or less than that?"

"So did you multiply the starting value by more than 1 or less than 1?"

In Lesson 81, students work a variation of the problem that gives information about the value after the times sign. For instance:

$$\frac{11}{17} \times \blacksquare = \blacksquare$$

more
than
1   than

Given that $\frac{11}{17}$ is multiplied by more than 1, the answer must be more than $\frac{11}{17}$.

Here's the exercise from Lesson 81:

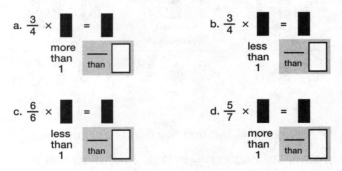

a. Open your workbook to lesson 81 and find part 1. √
*   This is a new kind of problem. The problem shows the value you start with. It doesn't show what you multiply by, but it tells whether that value is more than 1 or less than 1. You have to tell about the value you **end up with**. If you multiply by less than 1, that value is less than you start with. If you multiply by more than 1, that value is more than you start with.
b. Problem A. What are you starting with? **(Signal.)** *3-fourths.*

*   What do you know about the number you multiply by? **(Signal.)** *It's more than 1.*
*   So the number you end up with is more than 3-fourths. What do you know about the number you end up with? **(Signal.)** *It's more than 3-fourths.*
*   Problem B. What are you starting with? **(Signal.)** *3-fourths.*
*   What do you know about the number you multiply by? **(Signal.)** *It's less than 1.*
*   So what do you know about the number you end up with? **(Signal.)** *It's less than 3-fourths.*
*   Yes, it's less than 3-fourths.
*   Problem C. What are you starting with? **(Signal.)** *6-sixths.*
*   What do you know about the number you multiply by? **(Signal.)** *It's less than 1.*
*   So what do you know about the number you end up with? **(Signal.)** *It's less than 6-sixths.*
*   Yes, it's less than 6-sixths.
c. Go back to problem A.
*   Do you end up with more than 3-fourths or less than 3-fourths? **(Signal.)** *More than 3-fourths.*
*   Complete the statement under the box you end up with to say **more than 3-fourths.** Then complete the words for the rest of the problems in part 1. Raise your hand when you're finished. **(Observe students and give feedback.)**
d. Check your work.
*   Problem A. Tell me about the number you end up with. **(Signal.)** *It's more than 3-fourths.*
*   You should have written **more than 3-fourths**.
*   Problem B. Tell me about the number you end up with. **(Signal.)** *It's less than 3-fourths.*
*   Problem C. Tell me about the number you end up with. **(Signal.)** *It's less than 6-sixths.*
*   Problem D. Tell me about the number you end up with. **(Signal.)** *It's more than 5-sevenths.*

Teaching Notes

In step b, hold students to a very high criterion of performance. If they are mushy in their responses to the questions, they are not thinking about the relationship. Remind them, "This relationship is very important. Think about what you're saying."

If students are firm on the earlier material, they will not have serious problems with this exercise; however, if they are weak on earlier verbal tasks, they may become confused here. Give them the practice they need to respond perfectly.

In Lesson 83, students work a problem set that requires them to apply several of the discriminations they have learned.

Each problem shows the starting value and the ending value:

$$\frac{2}{9} \times \blacksquare = \frac{5}{9}$$

more than 1
= 1
less than 1

Students first compare the values that are shown to determine which is larger. They circle the larger fraction.

Now they can figure out whether the missing value is more than 1, equal to 1, or less than 1. $\frac{5}{9}$ is more than $\frac{2}{9}$. Therefore, $\frac{2}{9}$ is multiplied by more than 1.

In Lesson 101, students learn how to compare fractions like $\frac{5}{4}$ and $\frac{15}{11}$. The procedure is to start with the fraction that has smaller numbers: $\frac{5}{4}$.

Then use one of the numbers from the other fraction. Select the number that can be reached by multiplying:

$$\frac{5}{4} \times \frac{}{} = \frac{15}{\boxed{}}$$

Work the problem to find out what the second fraction would be if it equaled the first fraction:

$$\frac{5}{4} \times \frac{3}{3} = \frac{15}{\boxed{12}}$$

Compare the fraction you end up with ($\frac{15}{12}$) with the original fraction ($\frac{15}{11}$) and tell whether it's more or less. Since $\frac{15}{12}$ is less than $\frac{15}{11}$, $\frac{5}{4}$ is less than $\frac{15}{11}$.

This procedure permits students to compare a wide range of fractions.

Here's part of the textbook practice from the introductory exercise in Lesson 101:

a. $\frac{12}{5}$? $\frac{3}{2}$ b. $\frac{2}{3}$? $\frac{7}{9}$ c. $\frac{5}{3}$? $\frac{9}{6}$

b. Find the problems for part 1. Each item shows two fractions you'll compare.

c. Item A: You'll compare 12-fifths and 3-halves. To compare these fractions, you start with the fraction that has smaller numbers. Which fraction? (Signal.) *3-halves.*
- Write that fraction with an equal sign after it. Leave a space for the fraction that equals 1. Raise your hand when you're finished.
- (Write on the board:)

a. $\frac{3}{2}$ =

- Now we'll write a fraction that equals 3-halves. That fraction will have one of the numbers from 12-fifths.
- (Write to show:)

a. $\frac{3}{2} = \frac{12}{\boxed{}}$

$\frac{3}{2} = \frac{\boxed{}}{5}$

- Here are the two choices. 3-halves equals 12 over some number or 3-halves equals some number over 5. You can't work one of those problems.
- Copy the problem you can work. Raise your hand when you've done that much.
- You should have the equation: 3-halves equals 12 over some number. You can work that problem. Do it and figure out what 3-halves equals. Then write whether that fraction is more or less than 12-fifths. Write **more** or **less** after the equation. √
- Everybody, what does 3-halves equal? (Signal.) *12-eighths.*
- Is that fraction more or less than 12-fifths? (Signal.) *Less.*
- So **3-halves** is less than **12-fifths.**

d. Problem B. You'll compare 2-thirds and 7-ninths. Start with the fraction that has the smaller numbers. Write the equation that has one of the numbers in the other fraction. Pick the number you can get to by multiplying. Raise your hand when you have that much.
- (Write on the board:)

b. $\frac{2}{3} = \frac{\boxed{}}{9}$

- Here's the problem you should have written. Figure out the fraction. Then write whether that fraction is more or less than 7-ninths. Raise your hand when you're finished.

- (Write to show:)

b. $\dfrac{2}{3}$ = $\dfrac{\boxed{6}}{9}$ **less**

- Here's what you should have. The fraction that equals 2-thirds is 6-ninths. That fraction is less than 7-ninths, so 2-thirds is less than 7-ninths.

Another comparison type begins in Lesson 104. Problems give information about ratios. For instance: At Joe's, 4 pounds of rice cost $3. At Fran's, 18 pounds of rice cost $15.

Students write the information for each store:

$$\dfrac{\text{Joe's pounds}}{\text{Joe's \$}} \qquad \dfrac{4}{3}$$

$$\dfrac{\text{Fran's pounds}}{\text{Fran's \$}} \qquad \dfrac{18}{15}$$

Students pick the ratio with the smaller numbers and complete the equation, using the number from the other fraction. (They select the number they can reach through multiplication.)

$$\dfrac{\text{Joe's pounds}}{\text{Joe's \$}} \qquad \dfrac{4}{3} = \dfrac{}{15}$$

When they complete the equation, they'll know how many pounds of rice you could buy for $15 at Joe's.

The answer is 20. Students then compare the fraction $\dfrac{18}{15}$ and $\dfrac{20}{15}$. The best deal is at Joe's.

The last type of comparison problem students work involves fractions and decimal values.

For example: Which is more, $\dfrac{2}{3}$ or .66?

Students write the decimal value as a fraction with a denominator of 100 ($\dfrac{66}{100}$).

Then they write this problem:

$$\dfrac{2}{3} \qquad = \dfrac{66}{}$$

The completed equation is:

$$\dfrac{2}{3} \times \dfrac{33}{33} = \dfrac{66}{99}$$

$\dfrac{66}{99}$ is larger than $\dfrac{66}{100}$. So $\dfrac{2}{3}$ is more than .66.

Number Families

FAMILIES WITH WHOLE NUMBERS

Level D uses number families to connect a wide range of word problems, table configurations, and applications. Number families rest on the logic that, if you know two of three values that are added or subtracted, you can figure out the missing value.

The number family provides for arranging the three related values. Two are "small numbers." One is the "big number." The big number goes at the end of the number-family arrow. The small numbers go on top:

$$\xrightarrow{\quad 30 \qquad 12 \quad} 42$$

If a small number is missing, it can be identified through subtraction:

$$\xrightarrow{\quad 30 \qquad 12 \quad} 42 \qquad \begin{array}{r} 42 \\ -\ 30 \\ \hline 12 \end{array}$$

Note: Subtraction always starts with the big number and involves the small number that is shown.

If the big number is missing, it can be identified through addition:

$$\xrightarrow{\quad 30 \qquad 12 \quad} 42 \qquad \begin{array}{r} 30 \\ +\ 12 \\ \hline 42 \end{array}$$

The small numbers are added to obtain the big number.

In Level D, the logic of number families is extended to problems that involve fractions and tables that are designed so each row and column have the properties of a number family.

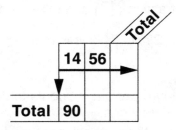

The missing number in the top row and the first column can be computed. The top row is a number family with the big number missing. By adding 14 and 56, we find that the big number is 70.

The first column is a vertical number family with a missing small number. The problem for this column is 90 minus 14 equals 76.

A variety of word problems that are often not taught uniformly to students can be presented through logical, workable analyses that involve number families. For example:

The weight of the bus is 1304 pounds more than the weight of the trailer. If the trailer weighs 9999 pounds, how much does the bus weigh?

The first sentence tells that the bus weighs more. Therefore, it's the big number. The difference between the bus and the trailer is 1304 pounds:

difference	trailer	bus
1304		

The next sentence gives the weight of the trailer:

difference	trailer	bus
1304	9999	

To find the big number, we add the small numbers. The bus weighs 11,303 pounds.

The work with number families begins in Lesson 1. After students receive an explanation of how to find the missing big number or a missing small number, they work a set of problems.

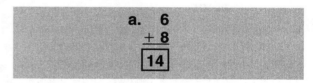

e. Each number family has a missing number. In some problems, the big number is missing. Remember, that's the number at the end of the arrow.

• In some problems, one of the small numbers is missing. That's one of the numbers on top of the arrow. Remember the rules: To find the big number, you **add** the small numbers. To find the small number, you **start with the big number** and **subtract**.

f. Touch problem A. Is the big number or a small number missing? (Signal.) *The big number.*

• What do you do to find the missing big number? (Signal.) *Add.*

• Say the adding problem. (Signal.) *6 plus 8.*

g. Touch problem B. Is the big number or a small number missing? (Signal.) *A small number.*

• What do you do to find a missing small number? (Signal.) *Subtract.*

• Say the subtraction problem. (Signal.) *17 minus 6.*

h. Touch problem C. Is the big number or a small number missing in that problem? (Signal.) *A small number.*

• What do you do to find a missing small number? (Signal.) *Subtract.*

• Say the subtraction problem. (Signal.) *321 minus 150.*

i. Touch problem D. Is the big number or a small number missing? (Signal.) *The big number.*

• What do you do to find the missing big number? (Signal.) *Add.*

• Say the addition problem. (Signal.) *67 plus 135.*

j. Touch problem E. Is the big number or a small number missing in that problem? (Signal.) *A small number.*

• Say the subtraction problem. (Signal.) *89 minus 76.*

k. Your turn: Use lined paper. Turn to the back and turn it sideways. Write the number problem and the answer for family A. Write the problem in a column. Make a box around the answer. Raise your hand when you're finished.

(Observe students and give feedback.)

• (Write on the board:)

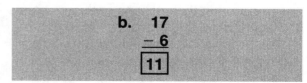

• Here's what you should have for family A. You added: 6 plus 8. The answer is 14. That's the big number.

l. Your turn again: Write the number problem and the answer for family B. Raise your hand when you're finished.

(Observe students and give feedback.)

• (Write on the board:)

b. 17
− 6
[11]

• Here's what you should have for family B. You subtracted: 17 minus 6. The missing small number is 11.

m. Write the number problem and the answer for family C. Raise your hand when you're finished.

(Observe students and give feedback.)

- (Write on the board:)

$$
\begin{array}{r}
\overset{2}{\cancel{3}}21 \\
-150 \\
\hline
\boxed{171}
\end{array}
$$

- Here's what you should have for family C. You subtracted: 321 minus 150. The missing small number is 171.
n. Your turn: Write the problems and the answers for the rest of the families in part 6. Remember, if the big number in a family is missing, you add to find it. If a small number is missing, you start with the big number and subtract to find the missing small number. Raise your hand when you're finished. (Observe students and give feedback.)
o. Check your work.
- Family D. The big number is missing. Read the addition problem and the answer. (Signal.) *67 plus 135 equals 202.*
- Family E. A small number is missing. Read the subtraction problem and the answer. (Signal.) *89 minus 76 equals 13.*
- Family F. The big number is missing. Read the addition problem and the answer. (Signal.) *23 plus 71 equals 94.*

Teaching Notes

Make sure that students are firm on steps f through i. If students make mistakes, repeat these steps (starting with f). Tell students: "You'll use this procedure a lot. So make sure you really understand how to find the missing numbers."

In step k, students are to turn their paper sideways. This practice permits students to write problems neatly and to keep the digits lined up. Students are to write only one digit in each "column."

When you check the students' work, make sure that their column problems have the appropriate addition or subtraction signs. Consider all problems **wrong** if the sign is not shown. Let students know your criterion. "You must show the sign or your problem is wrong." If students are firm on the convention of showing signs, they will tend not to make as many silly mistakes later in the program.

Students practice working with horizontal number families through Lesson 5. In Lesson 6, they work with number families that are oriented vertically, with the big number at the bottom.

The procedure for teaching students to work with vertical families is basically the same as that used for horizontal families. Students work with a variety of problems that show either the big number or a small number missing.

Here's the set of problems from Lesson 6:

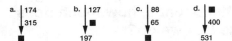

Students first identify what's missing in the family, then what operation they would use to find the missing number. For the first family, the big number is missing; you add to find it. For the second family, a small number is missing; you start with 197 and subtract to find it.

The work with vertical number families prepares students for computing missing values in the columns of tables.

NUMBER-FAMILY TABLES

Work with 3-by-3 tables begins in Lesson 6. Here's the table from that lesson:

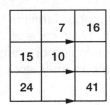

The arrows show that the first two spaces in each row are for small numbers. The last space is for the big number.

Students identify whether the missing value in each row is a small number or the big number. Then they say the addition or subtraction problem. For the top row, a small number is missing. The problem is 16 minus 7. For the middle row, a big number is missing. The problem is 15 plus 10.

Starting in Lesson 11 and continuing through 16, students work with tables that show number families for rows and tables that show families for columns. In a typical lesson, students work one table of each type.

Here's the pair of tables from Lesson 14:

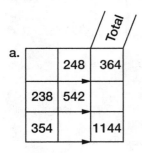

a.
		Total
	248	364
238	542	
354		1144

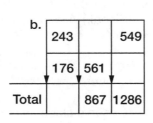

b.
243		549
	176	561
Total		867	1286

Teaching Notes

To find the missing numbers, students write column problems. Make sure they are writing the appropriate problem for each missing number. The tables are designed so the rows and columns are connected which means that a student could identify a missing number by working the "wrong" problem. Therefore, it is very important to check their work, not just the number they obtain.

In Lesson 17, the same table appears twice, first with arrows for the columns, and then with arrows for the rows. Students work the columns they can work (columns with two numbers) and write the missing values. Then students work the rows they can work. Finally, students identify the number that is in the first table that is not in the second table. They write this number where it goes in the second table and then figure out the last missing number in that table.

Here's the workbook practice from Lesson 17:

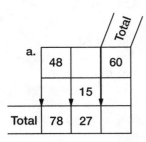

a.
		Total
48		60
	15	
Total	78	27	

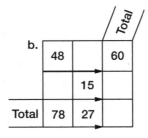

b.
		Total
48		60
	15	
Total	78	27	

a. Open your workbook to lesson 17 and find part 1. √
- Here's a table shown twice with the same numbers. For table A, you'll work the columns. For table B, you'll work the rows.

b. Touch table A. The arrows show that the number families are in columns. You can't work one of these columns because it doesn't have two numbers.

- Touch the column you can't work. The column you can't work has only one number. What's the number? (Signal.) *60.*
- Yes, you can't work the last column because it has only one number.
- Touch the first column. You can work that column. Is the big number or a small number missing in that column? (Signal.) *A small number.*
- Say the problem for the first column. (Signal.) *78 minus 48.*
- Touch the second column. You can work that column. Is the big number or a small number missing in that column? (Signal.) *A small number.*
- Say the problem. (Signal.) *27 minus 15.*
- Touch the third column. You can't work that column.

c. Your turn: Use lined paper. Turn it to the back and turn it sideways. Write the column problems for the first two columns. Copy the answers in table A. Raise your hand when you're finished.
(Observe students and give feedback.)
- Check your work. The problem for the first column is 78 minus 48. What's the answer? (Signal.) *30.*
- The problem for the second column is 27 minus 15. What's the answer? (Signal.) *12.*

d. Now work table B. The arrows show that you'll do the rows.

e. Touch the top row. How many numbers are in that row? (Signal.) *2.*
- Can you work that row? (Signal.) *Yes.*
- Say the problem. (Signal.) *60 minus 48.*
- Touch the next row. How many numbers are in that row? (Signal.) *1.*
- Can you work that row? (Signal.) *No.*
- Touch the bottom row. How many numbers are in that row? (Signal.) *2.*
- Can you work that row? (Signal.) *Yes.*
- Say the problem for the bottom row. (Signal.) *78 plus 27.*
(Repeat step e until firm.)

f. Your turn: Use your lined paper. Write the problem for the top row and the bottom row. Copy the answers in table B. Raise your hand when you're finished.
(Observe students and give feedback.)
- Check your work.
- The problem for the top row is 60 minus 48. What's the answer? (Signal.) *12.*
- The problem for the bottom row is 78 plus 27. What's the answer? (Signal.) *105.*

g. Look at the numbers in table A and table B.
- You have **one number** in table A that you **don't** have in table B. All the other numbers should be the same.
- Circle the number in table A that's not in table B.
- Everybody, what number is in table A but not in table B? (Signal.) *30.*

h. Listen: copy 30 where it belongs in table B. √
- (Write on the board:)

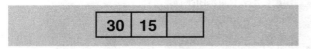

- Here's what you should have for the middle row in table B. You can work the middle row now, because you have two numbers in that row.
- Say the problem. (Signal.) *30 plus 15.*
i. Write the problem and the answer for that row. Copy the answer in table B. Raise your hand when you're finished.
- Read the problem and the answer for the middle row. (Signal.) *30 plus 15 equals 45.*
j. You've figured out every number in the table. Raise your hand if you got everything right.

Teaching Notes

By now, some students have figured out more flexible strategies for finding out the missing numbers in the table. Require them to follow the procedures you've established. Don't permit them to work ahead or to use mnemonics or methods that deviate from the procedures you specify in your directions.

On the other hand, move quickly. Students should be able to do most of the work for these tables very quickly. Pace your presentation accordingly.

In Lesson 22, students work a single table, first by working all the rows with two numbers, then by working all the columns with two numbers.

Here's the exercise from Lesson 22:

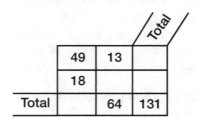

a. Find part 3. There are no number-family arrows in the table. Here's how we're going to work the table. First we'll work all the rows we can work. Then we'll work all the columns we can work. When we're done, we'll have all the missing numbers filled in.
b. We'll start with the rows. You can't work one of the rows. What's the number in that row? (Signal.) *18.*
- Touch the top row.
- What's missing in that row? (Signal.) *The big number.*

- Say the problem. (Signal.) *49 plus 13.*
- Touch the next row. Can you work that row? (Signal.) *No.*
- Touch the bottom row. What's missing in that row? (Signal.) *A small number.*
- Say the problem. (Signal.) *131 minus 64.*
c. Your turn: Use your lined paper. Turn it to the back and turn it sideways. Figure out the missing row numbers and write them in the table. Raise your hand when you're finished with the rows.
(Observe students and give feedback.)
- (Write on the board:)

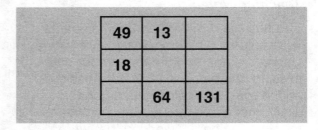

d. Check your work.
- Read the problem and the answer for the top row. (Signal.) *49 plus 13 equals 62.*
- Read the problem and the answer for the bottom row. (Signal.) *131 minus 64 equals 67.*
- (Write to show:)

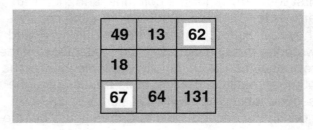

- Here's how your table should look so far.
e. Now we'll do the columns. The first column has all its numbers.
- A small number is missing in the second column. Say the problem. (Signal.) *64 minus 13.*
- A small number is missing in the last column. Say the problem. (Signal.) *131 minus 62.*
f. Figure out the missing column numbers and write them in the table. When you're done, you should have all the numbers in the table. Raise your hand when you're finished.
(Observe students and give feedback.)
g. Check your work.
- You figured out the missing number in the second column. Say the problem and the answer. (Signal.) *64 minus 13 equals 51.*
- You figured out the missing number in the last column. Say the problem and the answer. (Signal.) *131 minus 62 equals 69.*

- (Write to show:)

49	13	62
18	**51**	**69**
67	64	131

h. You figured out every number in the table. Remember how you did that. First you worked all the rows you could work. Then you worked all the columns that had two numbers.

Teaching Notes

The work with the tables provides students with lots of computation work that requires thinking and reinforces the skills taught in other tracks of the program. To work the problems for the bottom row, students must align the values that are shown horizontally in a column problem:

$$131$$
$$-\ 64$$

Students must then rename the top number and work the problem.

The 3-by-3 tables reinforce computation work. The tables also serve as a source of information for answering questions.

The work with table questions begins in Lesson 18.

	Monday	Tuesday	Total for both days
Dick	4	6	10
Mary	2	8	10
Total for both people	6	14	20

a. How many hours did Mary work on Tuesday?
b. How many hours did both people work on Monday?
c. How many hours did Dick work on both days?
d. How many hours did Mary work on both days?
e. How many hours did both people work on Tuesday?

a. Open your textbook to lesson 18 and find part 1. √
- I'll read what it says in the box. Follow along: Here's a table that has totals at the end of each row and totals at the bottom of each column. This table shows the number of hours two people worked on Monday and Tuesday.

- The heading for the first column is **Monday**. That column shows how many **hours** Dick worked on Monday and how many **hours** Mary worked on Monday.
- Touch the number for Dick on Monday. Everybody, what's Dick's number on Monday? (Signal.) *4.*
- How many hours did Mary work on Monday? (Signal.) *2.*
- The number at the bottom of the column shows the total hours worked on Monday.
- Touch the total for Monday. How many total hours were worked on Monday? (Signal.) *6.*
- The second column shows the number of hours worked on **Tuesday**. Dick worked 6 hours. Mary worked 8 hours. The total for Tuesday was 14 hours.
- The rows show the hours for each person. The top row is for Dick.
b. Touch the number for Dick on Monday. How many hours did Dick work on Monday? (Signal.) *4.* Touch the number for Dick on Tuesday. How many hours did Dick work on Tuesday? (Signal.) *6.*
- The numbers at the ends of the rows show the total hours worked on both days.
- Touch the total for Dick for both days. How many hours did Dick work on both days? (Signal.) *10.*
- The next row is for Mary.
- Touch the number for Mary on Monday. She worked 2 hours on Monday.
- Touch the number for Mary on Tuesday. How many hours did she work on Tuesday? (Signal.) *8.*
- Touch the total for both days. How many hours did Mary work on both days? (Signal.) *10.*

Teaching Notes

Make sure that students are firm in responding to steps a and b in the exercise. If students understand the information provided by the rows and columns, they will have very little trouble in understanding the table or in answering the questions. Note that all questions in Lesson 18 are answered by referring to a single cell and all answers are numbers. Consider answers correct even if they are not written with a unit name.

After students work with table questions for seven lessons, they work with information tables that have missing numbers. Students first figure out the missing numbers, then answer the questions. By now, students have worked with questions that ask about individual cells in the table and questions that require comparing two cells. For the table above, a comparison question would be: Which person worked more hours on Tuesday?

Here's the exercise and table from Lesson 27:

	East Coast	West Coast	Total for both coasts
March		19	
April		22	35
Total for both months	31	41	

a. Find part 3. This is a table with missing numbers. When the numbers are filled in, the table will show the number of meetings on the east coast and the west coast during March and April.
b. Your turn: Use lined paper. Work the number problems. Write all the missing numbers in the table. Raise your hand when you're finished. (Observe students and give feedback.)

	East	West	Total for both coasts
March	18	19	37
April	13	22	35
Total for both months	31	41	72

c. Check your work.
• Open your textbook to lesson 27 and find part 1. √
• That shows the number problems and the completed table. Make sure your table has the correct numbers.
d. Below the table in the textbook are questions. Use your lined paper and answer all the questions. Raise your hand when you're finished. (Observe students and give feedback.)
e. Check your work. Tell me the answer to each question.
• Question A: How many meetings were there on the east coast in April? (Signal.) *13.*
• Question B: In which month were there more meetings on both coasts? (Signal.) *March.*
• Question C: On which coast were there more meetings in March? (Signal.) *West.*

• Question D: How many total meetings were there on both coasts during both months? (Signal.) *72.*
• Question E: On which coast were there fewer meetings in March and April? (Signal.) *East.*

Teaching Notes

If earlier teaching is in place, students should work quickly and accurately. They should make occasional mistakes, but there should not be a pattern. Some items are difficult. For instance, item e may be difficult for some students. The answer can be determined, however, by examining the totals for both months.

In Lesson 53, students use facts to put some numbers in a table. Students then figure out the missing numbers and answer questions.

Here's the table, the facts, and the questions for Lesson 53:

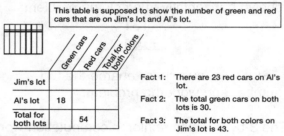

This table is supposed to show the number of green and red cars that are on Jim's lot and Al's lot.

	Green cars	Red cars	Total for both colors
Jim's lot			
Al's lot	18		
Total for both lots		54	

Fact 1: There are 23 red cars on Al's lot.
Fact 2: The total green cars on both lots is 30.
Fact 3: The total for both colors on Jim's lot is 43.

Questions
a. Are there fewer green cars or red cars on both lots?
b. How many green and red cars are on Al's lot?
c. There are 31 cars of some color on Jim's lot. What color cars?
d. Are there more green cars on Jim's lot or Al's lot?

In Lesson 61, students work with a table that has all but three numbers missing. A comparative fact gives information about one more number. This fact refers to one number already shown in the table.

Here's the part of the exercise from Lesson 61 for the first table:

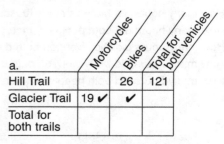

a.	Motorcycles	Bikes	Total for both vehicles
Hill Trail		26	121
Glacier Trail	19 ✔	✔	
Total for both trails			

Fact: On Glacier Trail, there were 28 more bikes than motorcycles.

a. Find part 2. Each table has two check marks. One check mark is in a cell that does not have a number.

The fact below each table tells about the cells with check marks. That fact gives you information for figuring out the number that goes in the cell that does not have a number.

b. Table A shows the number of motorcycles and bikes that are on Hill Trail and Glacier Trail.

- Look at the check marks in table A. One check mark is for bikes on Glacier Trail. What's the other check mark for? (Signal.) *Motorcycles on Glacier Trail.*
- The fact below the table compares the number of bikes and motorcycles on Glacier Trail.
- The fact says: On Glacier Trail, there were 28 more bikes than motorcycles.
- That fact gives you information for making a number family. Use lined paper. Make the number family for bikes and motorcycles. Show three names and the difference number. Raise your hand when you've done that much. √
- (Write on the board:)

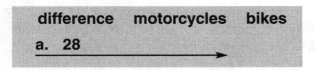

difference   motorcycles   bikes

a. 28

- Here's the number family you should have. You can't write a number problem for this family because it has only one number. But if you look at the cells that are compared in the table, you'll see that you can write another number for one of the names.

c. Touch the cell that has a check mark and a number.

- Does that cell tell about the bikes or the motorcycles on Glacier Trail? (Signal.) *The motorcycles.*
- Copy the number for motorcycles in your number family. Then work the number problem. Figure out the number of **bikes** that were on Glacier Trail. Raise your hand when you're finished. (Observe students and give feedback.)
- (Write to show:)

difference   motorcycles   bikes

a.   28   19

- Here's the number family with one missing number.
- Say the number problem and the answer. (Signal.) *28 plus 19 equals 47.*
- Write **47** where it goes in the table. Raise your hand when you're finished.

- You should have **47** in the cell with a check mark. Now you have enough numbers to figure out the rest of the missing numbers in the table.
- You'll do that later.

Teaching Notes

The checks in the table show the two cells that are being compared. The fact tells that **bikes** is the big number for the number family. The steps that students are to follow are: Start with the fact and make the number family. Then refer to the cell in the table that has a check mark and a number. That cell tells about one of the names for the number family. Write the number in the family. Figure out the missing number. Write it in the table where the other check mark is.

Make sure that students are firm in these steps.

In Lesson 64, students make check marks in the table. The information for where to put the check marks is provided by the fact.

The first part of the fact tells about the row or column.

For the table from Lesson 61, a fact that begins "On Hill Trail" would tell about the top row. A fact that begins "The number of bikes" would tell about the second column. A fact that begins "On Glacier Trail" would tell about the second row.

The rest of the fact names the two cells that are being compared in the row or column. For instance: On Hill Trail, there are 69 more motorcycles than bikes. In the top row, the cells for motorcycles and bikes are being compared. Students put a check in each of those cells.

Here's another example: The number of motorcycles on Hill Trail is 76 more than on Glacier Trail.

The first part of the statement names the first column. The cells compared are for Hill Trail and for Glacier Trail. For the remainder of the level, students work on variations of table types that have been presented in the program.

FRACTION NUMBER FAMILIES

Beginning in Lesson 66, students learn about number families that have fractions. The rules for these number families are: All denominators must be the same; the numerators are like whole numbers, in that the three numerators generate addition and subtraction facts.

In Lesson 66, students figure out the missing number in each fraction number family. Here are the problems they work:

a. $\dfrac{3}{5} \longrightarrow \dfrac{9}{5}$ b. $\dfrac{2}{12} \quad \dfrac{5}{12} \longrightarrow$ c. $\dfrac{9}{3} \longrightarrow \dfrac{14}{3}$

d. $\dfrac{6}{30} \quad \dfrac{10}{30} \longrightarrow$ e. $\dfrac{14}{1} \longrightarrow \dfrac{19}{1}$

In the following lesson, students work with a set that has 1 as a number in each family. Here are the problems from Lesson 67:

a. $\rule{1cm}{0.5cm} \quad \dfrac{4}{7} \longrightarrow 1$ b. $\dfrac{4}{9} \quad 1 \longrightarrow \rule{1cm}{0.5cm}$

c. $1 \quad \rule{1cm}{0.5cm} \longrightarrow \dfrac{16}{10}$ d. $\dfrac{6}{7} \quad \rule{1cm}{0.5cm} \longrightarrow 1$

To complete each family, students rewrite 1 as a fraction with the appropriate denominator. Then they either add or subtract to figure out the fraction for the shaded box.

Later problem sets present whole numbers other than 1 (starting in Lesson 69) and fractions with 2- and 3-digit denominators (starting in Lesson 76).

The work with fraction number families sets the stage for students to solve word problems involving fractions and to express the probability of events occurring.

Coordinate System and Functions

In Level D, students learn to plot points on a coordinate system, learn to figure out the "function" of X, learn to use information about "sequence" to determine a function, learn to plot lines, and learn how these lines relate to equivalent fractions.

The work with functions begins in Lesson 72 and continues through the end of the level.

In Lesson 72, students learn to find points on a coordinate system. They follow the rule that the X value tells about movement from the origin in this direction: $\longrightarrow$.

The Y value tells about movement from the

origin in this direction: $\uparrow$.

For the description: ($x = 7$, $y = 5$), students start at zero, go 7 places along the X arrow, then 5 places up. They write the letter of the dot they reach.

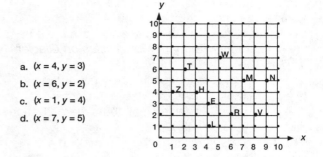

a. ($x = 4$, $y = 3$)
b. ($x = 6$, $y = 2$)
c. ($x = 1$, $y = 4$)
d. ($x = 7$, $y = 5$)

In Lesson 75, students write the X and Y values for specified points. For V on the display above, students would complete the description: letter V ($x = 8$, $y = 2$).

Work with function tables begins in Lesson 77. Students complete rows of a table by first writing the function, then indicating the answer.

Here's the completed function table from Lesson 77. The function is $X + 5$ and the values for X are 4, 1, 6, and 8:

	Function	Answer
x	$x + 5$	■
4	$4 + 5$	9
1	$1 + 5$	6
6	$6 + 5$	11
8	$8 + 5$	13

Starting in Lesson 83, students work with tables that show rows with X values and Y values. Students plot the point for each row. Then they draw a line that connects the points.

In Lesson 85, students first complete a table that shows the function and the X values. Then they plot the point for each row and draw a line for the function.

Here's the exercise from Lesson 85:

> **Note: Each student will need a ruler for this exercise.**

a. Find part 4. This part tells about making lines on a coordinate system. I'll read what it says in the box. Follow along: You've made points on the coordinate systems by using a table that shows X values and Y values. When you connect the points, you get a straight line. The reason you get a straight line is that all the points follow the same **function rule.**

• That's important. If you're following the same rule about adding, subtracting, multiplying, or dividing, you get a straight line on the coordinate system.

• You can see a table you've worked with and the line on the coordinate system. The point for A is X equals 5 and Y equals 7. The point for B is X equals 1 and Y equals 3. The point for C is X equals 7 and Y equals 9.

• Below the first table, you can see the same table with the function shown for each row. The function is X plus 2.

b. What does X equal for row A? (Signal.) *5.*
• The function is 5 plus 2. That's 7. 7 is the Y value.
• Row B. What's X? (Signal.) *1.*
• What's the function? (Signal.) *1 plus 2.*
• What's Y? (Signal.) *3.*
• Row C. What's X? (Signal.) *7.*
• What's the function? (Signal.) *7 plus 2.*
• What's Y? (Signal.) *9.*

c. The points and the lines are the same for both tables. Remember, you work the function for X. The answer is Y. And when you plot the points and connect them, you get a straight line.

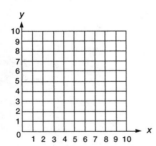

WORKBOOK PRACTICE

a. Open your workbook to lesson 85 and find part 1. √
• The table shows the function and X values.
• You're going to figure out the Y value for each row. Then you're going to plot the points for A, B, and C.
• Everybody, what's the function for the table? (Signal.) *X minus 2.*

b. Your turn: Write the function and the Y value for each row. Raise your hand when you're finished.

c. (Write on the board:)

	x	x − 2	y
A	5	5 − 2	3
B	3	3 − 2	1
C	9	9 − 2	7

d. Check your work. Here's what you should have for rows A, B and C.
• Row A. What's X? (Signal.) *5.*
• What's Y? (Signal.) *3*
• Row B. What's X? (Signal.) *3.*
• What's Y? (Signal.) *1.*
• Row C. What's X? (Signal.) *9.*
• What's Y? (Signal.) *7.*

e. Now you're going to make points. For each point, you need an X value and a Y value. That's what you have in each row.
• Row A. What's the X value? (Signal.) *5.*
• What's the Y value? (Signal.) *3.*

f. Those values tell you where to make the point. Do it. Then make points for rows B and C. Label each point with the correct letter. Raise your hand when you're finished.
(Observe students and give feedback.)

g. Now use your ruler and make a straight line. If you do it right, your line should go right through a point on the X axis. Raise your hand when you've found the point.
(Observe students and give feedback.)

h. Listen: Your line should go right through a point on the X axis. What is the X value for that point? (Signal.) *2.*
• Your line should go through the point for 2 on the X axis.

i. Remember, when you work a function problem for X, the answer is Y on the coordinate system.

In Lesson 88, students figure out the simple addition function and the simple multiplication function for an X value and a Y value. For example: If X is 5 and Y is 10, the function could be 5 × 2 or 5 + 5.

In Lessons 89–92, students do a similar exercise, except the functions begin with X. For these examples above, students would write the "simple" functions: **x × 5** or **x × 2**.

In Lesson 93, students work with a table that shows two pairs of X and Y values. From this information, students test the two "simple" rules that could account for the outcomes. Students select the function that applies to both pairs. Then students apply that function to the rest of the X values shown in the table.

Here are the tables students work with in Lesson 93:

a.

x	Function	y
4	x × 2 / x × 4	8
6		10
1		
2		
0		

b.

x	Function	y
3	x − 2 / $\frac{x}{3}$	1
9		3
5		
27		
12		

For the first table, students test both rules (X × 2 and X + 4) on the second pair of X and Y values. The function X + 4 works for this row. Students cross out X × 2 and write the missing functions and Y values.

For table B, the function is $\frac{x}{3}$. Students apply this function to each row of table B. Note that some of the Y values are fractions.

Starting in Lesson 95, students work with tables that do not prompt the possible rules. Students write the two possible functions for the first pair of values. They test the functions on the second pair to determine which is the right function. Then they complete the table by writing the Y values for the various X values that are shown.

In Lesson 97, students complete function tables from lines graphed on a coordinate system. Here's the student material from Lesson 97:

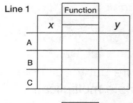

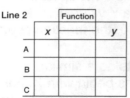

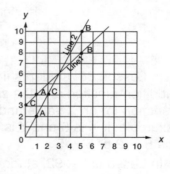

Students do all the steps in relating the lines to the tables. First, they write the X value and the Y value for each point on the line. For line 1, they would show point A as having an X value of 1 and a Y value of 4. Point B has an X value of 5 and a Y value of 8.

Next, students indicate the possible functions for the first row of the table. For line 1, the possible functions are X × 4 and X + 3.

Students test these functions for point B and determine that the correct function is X + 3. Here's the completed table for line 1:

Line 1		Function	
	x	x + 3 / ̶x̶ ̶×̶ ̶4̶	y
A	1		4
B	5		8
C	0		3

SEQUENCES

The work with functions leads naturally to sequences. The rule for generating the numbers in a sequence can be expressed as a function that tells how to go from one number to the next number.

Work on sequences begins in Lesson 100. Here's the initial exercise that follows a textbook introduction:

a. 1 2 4 ____ ____ ____

Rule

b. 12 10 8 ____ ____ ____

Rule

c. 3 6 9 ____ ____ ____

Rule

a. Open your workbook to lesson 100 and find part 1. √
b. Sequence A. The first two numbers in this sequence are 1 and 2.
c. (Write on the board:)

> **x × 2**
> **x + 1**

- Here are the two rules for going from 1 to 2: X times 2 and X plus 1. The number after the 2 in the sequence is 4.
- One of the rules works when you go from 2 to 4. Which rule? (Signal.) *X times 2.* (Cross out the rule X plus 1.)
d. Everybody, copy the rule for sequence A and complete the sequence. Raise your hand when you're finished. (Observe students and give feedback.)
- Everybody, read the sequence. Get ready. (Signal.) *1, 2, 4, 8, 16, 32.*

e. Series B. The first two numbers are 12 and 10. Write the rule for going from 12 to 10. Then complete the sequence. Raise your hand when you're finished.
(Observe students and give feedback.)
Check your work.

f. The rule for sequence B is X minus 2. Everybody, read the sequence. Get ready. (Signal.) *12, 10, 8, 6, 4, 2.*
(Repeat step f until firm.)

g. Your turn: Write the function rule for sequence C and complete the sequence. Raise your hand when you're finished.
(Observe students and give feedback.)
Check your work. The function rule for sequence C is X plus 3. Everybody, read the sequence. Get ready. (Signal.) *3, 6, 9, 12, 15, 18.*

h. Raise your hand if you wrote the correct rules and numbers for these problems.

Teaching Notes

The rule that students write is simply the function for going from one number to the next number. The steps involved in determining the function are the same steps students use for writing functions for pairs of X and Y values. For sequence A in Lesson 100, there are two simple ways to go from 1 to 2.
The functions students write are:
$x \times 2$ and $x + 1$
Students figure out which rule holds for 2 and 4. Then they write $X \times 2$ in the rule box and complete the sequence.

The value of using functions to work these sequences is that it permits students to express the rule articulately and yet accurately.

In later lessons, students work with sequences that have fractional values, such as:

$$3, \ 3\frac{1}{2}, \ 4, \ \ldots$$

and

$$\frac{1}{5}, \ \frac{2}{10}, \ \frac{4}{20} \ \ldots$$

In Lesson 105, students plot fractional values on the coordinate system. They apply the rule that the denominator is the X value and the numerator is the Y value. By following the conventions for plotting fractions, students are able to graph lines that show equivalent fractions.

The final step is for students to draw a line from a ratio equation and use it to answer questions.

Here's the student material from Lesson 106:

a. A recipe calls for 3 cups of onions for every 2 tablespoons of garlic. A cook follows the same ratio, but uses 9 cups of onions. How many tablespoons of garlic will the cook need?

b. A set has winners and losers. For the set, if you took 4 trials, you would expect to get 1 winner. About how many trials would you have to take to get 3 winners?

To work each problem, students first write a ratio equation. For problem A, the ratio equation is:

$$\frac{\textbf{cups of onions}}{\textbf{tablespoons of garlic}} \qquad \frac{3}{2} \times \frac{3}{3} = \frac{9}{6}$$

Next, students plot the equivalent ratios. For the first fraction, X is 2 and Y is 3. For the equivalent fraction, X is 6 and Y is 9.

Students plot points for these values and connect them with a line that goes through zero on the coordinate system. The line shows a full range of fractions that are equivalent to $\frac{3}{2}$.

With this knowledge of equivalent fractions, students are ready for sophisticated applications involving ratios. If you present the material carefully, all students will learn these important relationships.

Word Problems

In addition to the work with tables, students also learn to solve various types of word problems by creating number families. Students work on several main problem types: comparison problems, classification problems, addition and subtraction problems, and problems involving fractions, including probability problems.

CLASSIFICATION PROBLEMS

Starting in Lesson 16, students work classification word problems. These problems tell about an entire class (the big number) and two subclasses (the small numbers). If the names of the subclasses are **boys** and **girls,** the class is **children.** If the names of the subclasses are **dirty cars** and **cars that are not dirty,** the entire class is **cars.**

To work the problems, students make number families with the names of the two subclasses for the small numbers and the word **all** for the big number. Below, students write the name of the class. The test for that name is whether it applies to all the names above the arrow.

Here's the number family for dirty cars and cars that are not dirty:

dirty**not dirty****all**
cars

Here's the number family for children:

boys**girls****all**
children

Here's the number family for large trees and small trees:

large**small****all**
trees

Here's part of the exercise from Lesson 16 (which follows a demonstration of how to construct a classification number family):

b. Find the problems for part 1. For each problem, you're going to make the number family with the names. Remember the name for everything in the family goes **under** the arrow. The name at the end of the arrow is **all.** That's another way of saying **total.**

c. Problem A: There were 61 black horses. There were 41 horses that were not black. How many horses were there in all?

• Make the number family with the names and numbers the problem gives. Remember to write the name for **everything** under the family. Raise your hand when you have a number family with the names and the numbers the problem gives. (Observe students and give feedback.)

• (Write on the board:)

black**not black****all**
a. 61 ———————→ 41
horses

• Here's what you should have. The name under the family is **horses.** The names above are **black, not black,** and **all.** Raise your hand if you wrote the correct names and put them where they go.

• The numbers are **61** for black and **41** for not black.

d. Problem B: There were 81 plants in all. 56 were alive. The rest were dead. How many plants were dead?

• Make the number family with the names and numbers the problem gives. Raise your hand when you have a family. (Observe students and give feedback.)

• (Write on the board:)

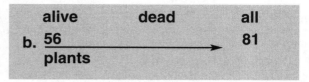

alive**dead****all**
b. 56 ———————→ 81
plants

• Here's what you should have. The name under the family is **plants.** The names above are **alive, dead,** and **all.** Raise your hand if you got the names right.

• The numbers are **56** for alive and **81** for all.

Teaching Notes

The biggest mistakes that students make are not writing the appropriate (or acceptable) names, not leaving enough space below each name to write a number, and not writing the name for the whole class below the family. If students are very sloppy in constructing their number families, show them how to make them and then have them re-do their families.

Some of these problems are easy enough for students to work without making a number family; however, the work with number families is a very good logic-language exercise. Also, students will have serious difficulty with some of the more complex problems scheduled later in the level if they do shortcuts on the early work.

Note that the wording is somewhat arbitrary. For problem A, acceptable wording would include: **black** horses; **not black** horses; and, **were black; were not black.**

When you display families on the board, always follow the rule that the first-named small number in the problem is the first name shown on the arrow. If black horses are mentioned in the problem first, you'll show them in the family first. When you check students' work, however, be careful because some students may show the names for the small numbers in the reverse order. That should not be considered a mistake.

Also in your displays, you'll generally not write the number students were to figure out in the family. This convention assures that students see the problem they were to work and understand that the question in the problem is answered by referring to the missing number in the family.

When students work problems, they write a column addition or a column subtraction problem and the answer. They are to box the answer. If they copy their answer in the family, they are to box it there also. A good practice, at least initially, is to direct students not to write their answer in the family, but to make sure that, when they do the addition or subtraction problem, they show it close to the number family or label it with the right letter.

Note that it is relatively easy for you to find the work for each problem if the answers are boxed.

Students work on classification number families through Lesson 22.

COMPARISON PROBLEMS

In Lesson 24, students start working on comparison problems. The first work is with sentences that name two values: Jan is taller than Mike. Students make a family with two names—Jan and Mike. Jan is the name for the big number. Mike is the name for a small number.

$$\text{Mike} \longrightarrow \text{Jan}$$

Students also make the same number family for the sentence: Mike is shorter than Jan. Mike still has the smaller number and Jan the bigger number.

In Lesson 25, students work with sentences that give the difference number. These sentences are similar to those presented in the preceding lesson, except that they tell how much taller, shorter, heavier, or lighter something is. The difference number is circled. For example:

Pile R weighed (120 pounds) less than pile B.

By reading the part of the sentence that is not circled, students determine that **pile B** is the big number.

Pile R weighed less than pile B.

$$\text{pile R} \longrightarrow \text{pile B}$$

The circled value (120 pounds) tells about the difference between the two piles. You could add that difference to go from the weight of pile R to the weight of pile B or you could subtract that value to go from the weight of pile B to the weight of pile R.

Here's the family with the name and number for the difference:

difference   pile R   pile B

$$\underset{120}{\longrightarrow}$$

Students construct families with three names and the difference number for a variety of sentences. Note that whether the sentence tells about something being greater or something smaller, the difference number is always a small number, and it's always the first small number in the family.

After students work on making number families for sentences for three days, students work comparison word problems, such as:

The elephant was 1800 pounds lighter than the trailer. If the elephant weighed 9900 pounds, how much did the trailer weigh?

The first sentence tells the difference number and gives the names:

difference   elephant   trailer

$$\underset{1800}{\longrightarrow}$$

The next sentence gives a value for the elephant:

difference   elephant   trailer

$$\underset{1800 \qquad\qquad 9900}{\longrightarrow}$$

Here's part of the exercise from Lesson 28:

a. Crow River is 259 miles shorter than Eagle River. Crow River is 416 miles long. How long is Eagle River?

b. The turtle is 47 years older than the mule. The turtle is 98 years old. How old is the mule?

c. There were 217 more green candies than red candies. There were 304 red candies. How many green candies were there?

d. A shark ate 570 fewer shrimp than a whale ate. The whale ate 742 shrimp. How many shrimp did the shark eat?

c. Problem A: Crow River is 259 miles shorter than Eagle River. Crow River is 416 miles long. How long is Eagle River?

- Raise your hand when you know which sentence tells about the two things that are compared.
- That sentence says Crow River is 259 miles shorter than Eagle River. Make the number family for the first sentence. You can use initials for Crow River and Eagle River. You can write **CR** and **ER**. Raise your hand when you've written the initials and the number for the difference.
- (Write on the board:)

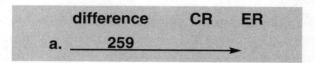

difference	CR	ER
a. 259 ⟶		

- Here's what you should have. 259 is the difference number. Crow River is shorter than Eagle River. So **Crow River** is a small number. **Eagle River** is the big number.
- You can't solve the problem because there are two missing numbers in the number family.
- Read the next sentence. It gives a number for one of the rivers. Write that number in the family. Raise your hand when you're ready.
- (Write to show:)

difference	CR	ER
a. 259 416 ⟶		

- Here's what you should have. Now you can figure out the missing number for Eagle River. You'll figure out that number later.
d. Read problem B to yourself and make the number family. Remember to start with the sentence that compares. Raise your hand when you've made your number family with names and two numbers.
- (Write on the board:)

difference	mule	turtle
b. 47 ⟶ 98		

- Here's what you should have. 47 is the difference number. The turtle is older than the mule. So **turtle** is the big number. **Mule** is a small number. The turtle is **98** years old. Raise your hand if you got everything right.
- You'll work the problem later.
e. Your turn: Make number families for the rest of the problems in part 3. Don't do the addition or subtraction. Just make the number families. Raise your hand when you're finished.

(Observe students and give feedback.)
f. (Write on the board:)

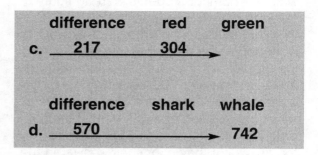

difference	red	green
c. 217 304 ⟶		

difference	shark	whale
d. 570 ⟶ 742		

- Check your work. Here's what you should have for each family.
g. Make sure your families are right. Then do the addition problem or subtraction problem to find the missing number in each family. Remember to box the answer. Raise your hand when you have an answer to all of the problems.

(Observe students and give feedback.)
h. Check your work.
- Everybody, say the number problem and the answer for A. (Signal.) *259 plus 416 equals 675.*
- How long is Eagle River? (Signal.) *675 miles.*
- Say the number problem and the answer for B. (Signal.) *98 minus 47 equals 51.*
- How old is the mule? (Signal.) *51 years.*
- Say the number problem and the answer for C. (Signal.) *217 plus 304 equals 521.*
- How many green candies were there? (Signal.) *521.*
- Say the number problem and the answer for D. (Signal.) *742 minus 570 equals 172.*
- How many shrimp did the shark eat? (Signal.) *172.*
i. Raise your hand if you got everything right.

Teaching Notes

Again, when students work problems, they write a column addition or a column subtraction problem and box the answer. If they copy their answer in the family (or near the family), they are to box it there also and label it with the right letter.

In Lesson 33, students work with a mix of sentences that tell either about a classification number family (no difference number) or a comparison family (a difference number). Make sure that students are very firm on this discrimination.

In Lesson 43, students work comparison problems that do not tell about the difference, but ask about the difference.

Here are the problems from Lesson 43:

a. Joan is 56 inches tall. Ted is 37 inches tall. What is the difference in their height?

b. The bike went 16 miles per hour. The car went 75 miles per hour. What was the difference in the speed of the vehicles?

c. A tub held 112 gallons. A tank held 256 gallons. What was the difference in the amounts held by the containers?

MONEY PROBLEMS

Some early word problems involve dollar-and-cent amounts and do not require number families. The general format for these problems is to present a "menu" or list of items and then to ask questions about how much was spent or how much a person ended up with. This work begins in Lesson 29, after students have practiced aligning dollar-and-cent values.

Here are the problems from Lesson 29:

a. A person purchased the hat, the cat and the bat. How much did the person spend in all?

b. Joan bought a tire and a ball. How much did Joan spend?

Students work each problem by aligning the amounts to be added, then adding and boxing the answer to the question. Note that students use the back of their paper, oriented so the lines form columns for the digits.

Starting in Lesson 32, students work price-tag problems that require subtraction.

Here's the problem set from Lesson 32:

a. A person had $20.00. The person purchased the hat. How much did the person end up with?

b. Joe started out with $14.87. He bought the bat. How much did Joe end up with?

c. A club had $56.80 in the cash box. The club purchased the phone. How much did the club end up with?

Starting in Lesson 47, students work a variation of comparison problems. This variation shows price tags for items and asks about the difference number. The wording of the question is: How much more does Jim need to buy the hat? or: How much less does the broom cost than the hat costs?

The wording of the sentence implies which costs more or less. Because the question asks "How much more" or "How much less," it asks about the difference number. Therefore, the number family is:

difference   broom   hat

———————————————————→

Again, these problems are more than math exercises. They focus on the implications and the logic of the information provided by the sentences.

In Lesson 53, students work problems that require them to identify the mystery object. They are shown prices for various objects. The problem gives information about the difference in price between the mystery object and one of the other objects, or the amount a person has. Students solve the problem and get a number answer. Then they check the list of items to find out which items cost that much. The answer to the problem is the name of the object, not a number.

Here's the set of problems from Lesson 53:

a. One of the items costs $3.78 more than the umbrella costs. What is the name of that item?

b. One of the items costs $5.90 less than the fishing pole. What is the name of that item?

c. The swimsuit costs $4.02 more than one item. What is the name of that item?

d. The boots cost $8.02 less than one of the items. Which item?

Starting in Lesson 59, another variation in wording is presented. The difference number is expressed as the amount of additional money somebody needs to buy an object or the amount of money somebody will have left after buying the object. Both types of problems imply which is the big number (whether the person has more than the price of the object or whether the person has less than the price of the object).

Here's part of the exercise from Lesson 59:

a. Find part 2. These problems are different from the ones you've worked, but they are not too difficult.

b. Problem A: Fran had more money than the price of the wallet. After Fran bought the wallet, she still had $4.44. How much money did she start out with?

- The problem compares the amount of money she started with and the price of the wallet. Which of those is the big number? (Signal.) *The amount she started with.*

- (Write on the board:)

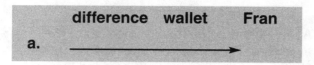

difference   wallet   Fran

a.

- The problem gives the difference number. How much is the difference? (Signal.) *$4.44.*
- Now put in the price of the wallet and figure out how much she started out with. Do it. Make the number family with two numbers. Then figure out the missing number and box the answer. Raise your hand when you're finished. (Observe students and give feedback.)
- Everybody, how much money did Fran start out with? (Signal.) *$13.38.*

c. Problem B. Sid didn't have enough money to buy the sunglasses. The sunglasses cost $5.30 more than he had. How much did Sid have?

- The problem compares the money Sid had with the cost of the sunglasses. Which is more? (Signal.) *The cost of the sunglasses.*
- Make the family. Figure out how much Sid had. Raise your hand when you're finished. (Observe students and give feedback.)
- (Write on the board:)

difference   Sid   sunglasses

b.   5.30   →   9.52

- Here's the number family you should have. To figure out the amount Sid had, you worked the problem $9.52 minus $5.30. What's the answer? (Signal.) *$4.22.*
- That's how much Sid had.
- Remember, when you work these problems, you find the sentence that compares two things. Make the number family for those two things. Then you put in the two numbers you know and figure out the missing number.

Teaching Notes

If students have trouble with these problems, don't try to give them a "word formula." Instead, require them to use the information the problem gives.

For example, "If Fran got money back after buying the wallet, which is more: the amount she started with or the price of the wallet?" If students do not answer this type of question correctly, point out the contradiction: "Do you mean that you could go to the store, buy something that costs more money than you have, and get **change?** If you get change, you must have more money than the cost of the item."

Once students have figured out which is the big number and which is the small number next to it, the difference number is easy to identify. That's the amount more or the amount less.

If students are having serious difficulty, present them with a simple series of problems in which they write two names in each family: **wallet** and **item**. The problems indicate whether or not there's change or not enough money. Students make number families with three names and the difference number.

Sample items:

a) You go to the store. Your wallet has $3.11 more than the cost of the items you want to buy. Make the family.

b) You go to the store. The item costs $11.30 less than the amount you have in your wallet.

c) You go to the store. You'd like to buy the item, but you need $15.60 more than you have in your wallet.

d) You go to the store. You buy an item and get $8.00 in change.

MULTI-STEP PROBLEMS

Students work a variety of problems that involve both addition and subtraction. These problems are typically troublesome for students, but are processed easily through number families.

For example:

Jane spends \$13. Then she spends another \$18. If she ends up with \$40, how much does she start with?

Frequently, students who do not know how to work these problems with number families make serious mistakes. Because the problem refers to "spending," these students only subtract. The number-family analysis buttresses against this kind of mistake.

Beginning in Lesson 74, students work basic problems. For each, they make a family that shows values for **in, out,** and **end up. In** is always the big number, **out** and **end up** are the small numbers.

end up	out	in

⟶

Here are the problems from Lesson 74:

a. A pocket is empty. \$342 goes into that pocket. Then some money goes out of that pocket. The pocket ends up with \$58. How much went out?

b. A woman starts without any roses. She picks 78 roses. She sells 45 roses. How many roses does she end up with?

c. Jill had an empty basket. She put some apples in the basket. Then she gave away 37 of those apples. The basket still had 14 apples in it. How many apples did Jill put in the basket?

These problems are more elaborately worded than later problems. The prompts provided by the early problems make it relatively easy for students to identify the values for **in, out,** or **end up.**

Teaching Notes

Students have worked problems of this type without using number families. Acknowledge that it is possible to work them without using number families. "You're using number families because, in a few days, you'll be working some much more difficult problems that use this same kind of number family."

Make sure that students **do** make number families, just as they are shown in the work checks.

In Lesson 79, a harder problem type is introduced. For this type, students are provided with more than one value for **in** or more than one value for **out**. They show these values on the number family as a "stack" that is to be added.

Here are the problems for Lesson 79 and part of the introduction:

a. Jan had \$17.00 in the bank. Later she put \$12.00 in the bank. The next day Jan went to the bank and took out \$11.50. How much money did Jan end up with in the bank?

b. A tank had some water in it. 250 gallons were taken from the tank. Then another 720 gallons were taken from the tank. The tank still had 1150 gallons in it. How many gallons were in the tank at the beginning?

c. A farmer had 534 bales of hay. She fed 247 bales to her cattle. She sold 85 bales to a neighbor. She threw 4 bales away because they were rotten. How many bales did she end up with?

b. Find problem A: Jan had \$17 in the bank. Later she put \$12 in the bank. The next day Jan went to the bank and took out \$11.50. How much money did Jan end up with in the bank?

• The first part of the problem tells about the two values that went in the bank. Write the number family. Leave two lines of space between the names and the arrow. Add the two amounts Jan put **in** and show the total for **in**. Show the amount she took out. Raise your hand when you have the number family with a total for **in** and a number for **out**.
(Observe students and give feedback.)

• (Write on the board:)

end up	out	in
a. ⟶	11.50	17.00 + 12.00 29.00

• Check your work. Here's what you should have. The total for **in** is \$29. The amount for **out** is \$11.50.

• Now write the addition or subtraction problem to figure out how much she **ended up** with. Raise your hand when you're finished.
(Observe students and give feedback.)

• The subtraction problem is: \$29 minus \$11.50. Everybody, what's the answer? (Signal.) *\$17.50.*

• Yes, Jan ended up with \$17.50.

c. Problem B: A tank had some water in it. 250 gallons were taken from the tank. Then another 720 gallons were taken from the tank. The tank still had 1150 gallons in it. How many gallons were in the tank at the beginning?

- Listen: Does the problem give two numbers for **in** or for **out**? (Signal.) *Out.*
- Write the number family with the names and the number for **end up**. Then add the two amounts that went **out** of the tank and show a total for **out**. Raise your hand when you have a number for **end up** and a total for **out**.
  (Observe students and give feedback.)
- (Write on the board:)

end up	out	in
	250	
	+ 720	
b. 1150	970 →	

- Check your work. Here's what you should have. A total of 970 gallons were taken from the tank. The tank ended up with 1150 gallons.
- Now write the addition or subtraction problem to figure out how many gallons were in the tank at the beginning. Raise your hand when you're finished.
  (Observe students and give feedback.)
- The addition problem is: 1150 plus 970. Everybody, what's the answer? (Signal.) *2120.*
- Yes, there were 2120 gallons in the tank before anything was removed.

Teaching Notes

Problems such as B would be very difficult for many students if they were not able to organize the information in a number family. The number family, although seemingly mechanical, is based on the logic of "stacking problems." Given that the amount a person ends up with is a positive number, the amount that goes in is always more than the amount that goes out. The **end-up** value is the difference between the amount that goes in and the amount that goes out. We can enlarge either **in** or **out** by adding more than one value.

In Lesson 84, students work a variation of stacking problems that indicate more than one stack.

Here's a problem of that type:

a. There were no people on an elevator. Then 2 people got on the elevator. On the next floor, 5 more people got on the elevator. On the next floor, 4 people got off the elevator. On the next floor, 7 people got on the elevator, and 9 people got off the elevator. How many people were still on the elevator?

For this problem, students would make a stack for **in** and a stack for **out**.

end up	out	in
	4	2
	+ 9	5
	13	+ 7
		14

FRACTION PROBLEMS

Starting in Lesson 77, students work a new kind of classification problem that involves fractions. For these problems, the big number is always the whole thing. The big number is 1. The small numbers are for the two subsets that make up the whole.

For this unit from Lesson 72:

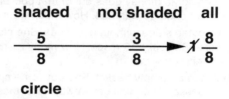

students make this number family:

shaded	not shaded	all
$\frac{5}{8}$	$\frac{3}{8}$	✗ $\frac{8}{8}$

circle

Teaching Notes

The name under the family tells about all the values in the family. The denominators suggest the relationship between the parts of the unit. All are expressed as eighths.

Working these problems is not particularly difficult for students. They must look at the diagram to determine the number of parts that are in the whole unit. That's the denominator for all the fractions, including the big number. The procedures for adding or subtracting the fractions in the number family are the same as those that students have used for working with "mixed numbers."

Beginning in Lesson 79, students work from word problems that describe fractional relationships. For these problems, students make a number family and figure out the fraction for the missing number.

Here are the problems from Lesson 79:

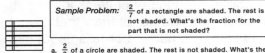

Sample Problem: $\frac{2}{7}$ of a rectangle are shaded. The rest is not shaded. What's the fraction for the part that is not shaded?

a. $\frac{2}{3}$ of a circle are shaded. The rest is not shaded. What's the fraction for the part that is not shaded?

b. $\frac{11}{15}$ of a triangle were not shaded. What fraction of the triangle was shaded?

c. $\frac{3}{10}$ of a board were not shaded. What fraction of the board was shaded?

d. $\frac{4}{9}$ of a ruler were shaded. What fraction of the ruler was not shaded?

To work each problem, students make a family that has the names **shaded, not shaded,** and **all**. The name of the particular object appears below the family.

Here's the number family for problem A:

shaded   not shaded   all

$$\frac{2}{3} \longrightarrow \chi \frac{3}{3}$$

circle

The whole circle is $\frac{3}{3}$. The shaded part is $\frac{2}{3}$.

To find the part that is not shaded, students work the problem. $\frac{3}{3} - \frac{2}{3}$.

In Lesson 84, students are introduced to a type of fraction problem that parallels a whole-number word problem type:

2 berries are ripe. 5 berries are not ripe. What fraction of the berries are ripe? What fraction of the berries are not ripe?

The only difference between this problem and one that requires whole-number operations is that the problem asks about the **fraction** of ripe and unripe berries, not about the number.

To work the problem, students write the names, put in the numbers the problem gives, and figure out the missing number in the family. Then they construct the fractions:

ripe   not ripe   all

$$2 \qquad 5 \longrightarrow 7$$

Therefore:

ripe   not ripe   all

$$\frac{2}{7} \qquad \frac{5}{7} \longrightarrow \frac{7}{7}$$

For this type of problem, the whole is the entire aggregate. If there is a total of 7 berries, the fraction for the whole is $\frac{7}{7}$.

Probability

The probability exercises in Level D are extensions of the basic properties of ratio numbers. The ripe/not ripe fraction problem just mentioned could be expressed as a probability question by asking, "What are the chances of picking a berry from the set of 7 that is ripe?" or "What is the probability of picking a berry that is not ripe?" The chances are governed by the ratio numbers. The entire set consists of 7 entities, or 7 opportunities. Given that each is equally probable, the chances of picking a ripe berry are expressed as $\frac{2}{7}$.

The work that students do with probability in Level D focuses first on the composition of the set that is being analyzed. Later, the focus switches to "taking trials" and predicting outcomes that are based on the composition of the set.

The first exercise in Lesson 91 presents students with the rule that the closer a fraction is to 1, the greater the probability that fraction expresses.

Here's part of the initial exercise:

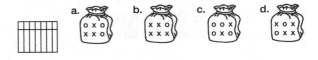

e. Which fraction gives you the best chance of drawing an X?

f. Which fraction gives you the second-best chance of drawing an X?

g. Which fraction gives you the worst chance of drawing an X?

b. Find part 3.
• Which fraction is closer to 1 whole, 2-fifths or 2-eighths? (Signal.) *2-fifths.*
• So 2-fifths tells about a better chance of drawing an X.

c. For each bag, you're going to write the fraction that tells your chances of pulling an X out. Remember, the denominator tells about all the things in the bag. The numerator tells about the number in X's.

d. Write the fraction for bag A. Raise your hand when you're finished.

(Observe students and give feedback.)
- (Write on the board:)

a. $\dfrac{3}{6}$

- Here's the fraction for bag A. There are 6 things in the bag and there are 3 X's. The fraction is 3-sixths.
e. Your turn: Write fractions for the other bags. Remember, the number of all the things goes in the denominator. The number of X's goes in the numerator. Raise your hand when you're finished. **(Observe students and give feedback.)**
f. Check your work.
- What's the fraction for bag B? (Signal.) *5-sixths.*
- What's the fraction for bag C? (Signal.) *2-sixths.*
- What's the fraction for bag D? (Signal.) *4-sixths.*
g. Now you're going to rank the bags. For item E, you're going to write the fraction for the bag that gives you the best chance of drawing an X without looking into the bag. Remember, that's the bag with the fraction that is closest to 1. Write the fraction for the bag that gives you the best chance. Raise your hand when you're finished. **(Observe students and give feedback.)**
- Everybody, which fraction gives you the best chance of pulling out an X? (Signal.) *5-sixths.*
- That's the fraction for bag B.
h. For item F, write the fraction that gives you the second-best chance of getting an X. Then for item G, write the fraction that gives you the worst chance. Remember, the worst chance is the fraction that's farthest from 1. It's the smallest fraction. Raise your hand when you're finished. **(Observe students and give feedback.)**
i. Check your work. Everybody, which fraction gives you the second-best chance of drawing an X? (Signal.) *4-sixths.*
  Which bag gives you the second-best chance of drawing an X? (Signal.) *Bag D.*
  Which fraction gives you the worst chance of drawing an X? (Signal.) *2-sixths.*
- What **bag** gives you the worst chance of drawing an X? (Signal.) *Bag C.*
j. Remember, you can write fractions that tell about your chances.

Teaching Notes

The composition of the set determines the probability. For the exercise above, students are simply writing fractions that tell about that composition. The denominator is the total number of things in the set. The numerator is the number of "winners," (in this case, Xs).

When students work with actual probability, the number of items in the set tells about the number of trials that they would take. The numerator tells about the number of winners they would expect.

In Lesson 94, students are taught to "translate" information about the number of things in the set and the number of "winners" in the set to a statement of probability. For example, if the fraction is 4/6, students would say: "If I took 6 trials, I would expect to get 4 winners."

Following this exercise, the basic procedure for confirming probability is demonstrated.

Here's the demonstration from Lesson 94:

Note: **For this exercise, you will need a paper bag and 6 one-inch squares of paper (4 with triangles drawn on them and 2 that are blank.)**

a. We're going to see how close we actually come to the fraction for one of these sets.
b. Touch bag C.
- How many things are in that set? (Signal.) *6.*
- How many winners are in that set? (Signal.) *4.*
- I have 6 pieces of paper. 4 of them show triangles. The rest are blank. I'm going to put them in the bag and mix them up. Then I'm going to take some trials and see how many winners I get.
c. How many trials am I going to take? (Signal.) *6.* When I take 6 trials, how many winners should I expect to get? (Signal.) *4.*
  (Repeat step c until firm.)
d. (Write on the board:)

winners _____
trials

- Each time I take a trial, I'll make a tally mark in the denominator. Each time I get a winner, I'll put a tally in the numerator.
- (Put squares in bag.)
e. Here's the first trial.
- (Make tally on bottom of fractions.)
- (Shake the bag. Draw square from bag. Tell if it is a winner or loser. If it's a winner, make tally on top.)
- I have to put that square back in the bag before I take the next trial.
- (Return square.)
f. Here's the next trial.
- (Make tally on the bottom.)

- (Shake bag. Draw square from bag. Tell if it is a winner or loser. If it's a winner, make tally on top.)
- (Return square to bag.)
g. (Repeat until you have taken 6 trials.)
h. (Count tallies for top and write the fraction for the results.)
i. (If the fraction is not 4-sixths, say:) We didn't get the fraction we expected, but if we did this experiment again and again, we would come very close to our expected fraction of 4-sixths.
- (If the fraction is 4-sixths, say:) We got the fraction we expected, but if we did this experiment again and again, we wouldn't get the expected fraction every time. We would come very close to it.

Teaching Notes

When you take a trial, you always make a tally for the denominator. If you get a winner, you also make a tally for the numerator.

Remember to return the paper to the bag following each trial and shake the contents of the bag.

It's a good idea to practice this type of experiment so that you can move quickly.

In Lesson 98, students connect what they have learned about probability to what they know about equivalent fractions. In the experiment above, students learn that if the ratio of winners to things in the set is 4 to 6, you would expect to get 4 winners for every 6 trials. In Lesson 98, students learn that this ratio can be expanded to any fraction that equals $\frac{4}{6}$.

Here is a problem:

The winners for this set are circles. How many winners would you expect if you took 42 trials?

To work the problem, students first write the information about the composition of the set:

$$\frac{\text{winners}}{\text{trials}} \quad \frac{2}{7}$$

Next, they complete the equivalent fraction that tells about 42 trials.

$$\frac{\text{winners}}{\text{trials}} \quad \frac{2}{7} = \frac{\boxed{}}{42}$$

Students figure out the missing fraction that equals 1 (6/6), multiply on top, and conclude that they would expect about twelve winners.

With this information about probability, students are prepared for the last part of the program, which presents a series of extended problems and experiments involving probability. (See Projects with Probability, page 117.)

Geometry and Measurement

The work on geometry and measurement presented in Level D includes finding the area of rectangles, finding the perimeter of various polygons, finding the length of unknown sides (given additional information about the figure), finding the volume of rectangular prisms (boxes), drawing inferences based on information about lines that are parallel and those that intersect, and performing unit conversions. Students also learn about the coordinate system. (See Coordinate System and Functions.)

AREA

The first work is a review of the area of rectangles. Students write the multiplication equation and the repeated addition equation for finding the area of rectangles. Here's part of the initial exercise (following a textbook demonstration):

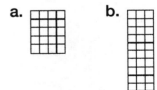

b. You're going to find the number of squares for each rectangle by writing the addition problem and the multiplication problem. Remember, you should get the same answer. Multiplication is just a fast way of adding the same number again and again.
c. Problem A. Count the number of squares in the first column.
- Everybody, how many? (Signal.) 5.

- Each column has 5, so you'll just add 5 for each column. Use your lined paper. Write the addition problem and the answer. Raise your hand when you're finished.
  (Observe students and give feedback.)
- (Write on the board:)

a. 5 + 5 + 5 + 5 = 20

- Here's what you should have. There are 4 columns. So you should have added 5 plus 5 plus 5 plus 5. The answer is 20.
d. Now do the multiplication. Start with the number of squares in the first column. Then multiply by the number of columns. Remember, the second number you write tells the total number of columns. Be careful. You should get exactly the same answer you got when you added. Raise your hand when you're finished. √
- (Write on the board:)

5 × 4 = 20

- Here's what you should have for the multiplication. There are 5 squares in each column. You multiply by 4 because there are 4 columns. The answer is 20. There are 20 squares in rectangle A.
e. Your turn: Write the addition for rectangle B. Raise your hand when you're finished. √
- (Write on the board:)

b. 10 + 10 + 10 = 30

- Here's what you should have. 10 plus 10 plus 10. The answer is 30.
f. Now write the multiplication problem and the answer. Write the number of squares in the first column. Multiply by the number of columns. Raise your hand when you're finished. √
- (Write on the board:)

10 × 3 = 30

- Here's what you should have. 10 times 3. The answer is 30. There are 30 squares in rectangle B.
g. Remember, multiplication works just like addition that uses the same number again and again.

Teaching Notes

Make sure that students write proper equations. Do not accept equations if signs are omitted. Remind students that if signs are missing, their equations are wrong.

Beginning in Lesson 17, students work area problems that involve 2-digit numbers. The rule that students learn is that, if they have to solve a multiplication problem involving a 2-digit value, they write the 2-digit value on top.

Here are the problems from Lesson 17:

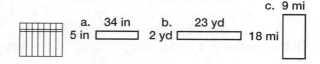

Teaching Notes

Be very picky about how students write their answers. By Lesson 17, students have learned the abbreviation for square: **sq.** They have also learned that they are to write the answer to area problems with a number and a unit name (such as **sq in.**). Remind them that you'll consider answers wrong if they do not include the number and the unit name. This convention is not arbitrary. Later, students will work with perimeter. If students are well-practiced in working area problems, they can more easily master the discrimination between area problems and perimeter problems. Their understanding will be greatly facilitated if they are practiced in associating area with square units. Students will receive sufficient practice if you make sure that they write the appropriate answers.

In Lesson 19, students draw rectangles from descriptions. The conventions for drawing diagrams are:

Width tells about this dimension: ⟷

Length or height tells about this dimension: ↕

Here's the kind of description students work from:

The floor of a room is 8 feet long and 5 feet wide. What is the area of the floor?

Teaching Notes

When you observe students' work, make sure that the proportions of their drawings are correct and that the rectangle is properly oriented: The rectangle described above should be higher than it is wide, but not 2 times or more higher than wide. If students make silly diagrams, respond to them as if they are silly:

"Your diagram is supposed to be 3 feet longer than it is wide, but look at your diagram. It's about as wide as it is high."

Do not require students to use rulers or to measure. These steps defeat the main purpose of the exercise, which is to give students practice in quickly constructing a diagram that is "reasonable" in proportion.

PERIMETER

After students have worked area problems independently, they begin working perimeter problems. This work is presented so that it relates to what students have learned about area and about area units.

Perimeter is introduced in Lesson 85. Diagrams of rectangles show the length of two adjacent sides. Students infer the length of the other two sides, and then write the addition problem and the answer. The answer consists of a number and a unit name.

Here's the exercise that follows a textbook demonstration in Lesson 85:

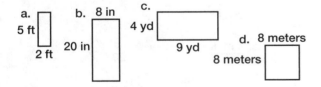

b. Find problem A. To find the perimeter of each rectangle, you just add the length of each side.
c. Rectangle A. Start with the bottom edge. How long is that edge? (Signal.) *2 feet.*
- How long is the left side? (Signal.) *5 feet.*
- How long is the top? (Signal.) *2 feet.*
- How long is the right side? (Signal.) *5 feet.*
- (Write on the board:)

a.	2
	5
	2
	+ 5

- So here's what you could write to figure out the perimeter.
- Figure out the perimeter of figure A and write the answer. The unit for the answer is **feet**, not **square feet**. Raise your hand when you're finished. (Observe students and give feedback.)
- Everybody, what's the perimeter of rectangle A? (Signal.) *14 feet.*
d. Your turn: Figure out the perimeter of the other rectangles in part 1. Remember the unit name. Raise your hand when you're finished. (Observe students and give feedback.)
e. (Write on the board:)

b.	20	c.	4	d.	8
	8		9		8
	20		4		8
	+ 8		+ 9		+ 8
	56 in		**26 yd**		**32 meters**

f. Check your work. Here are the numbers you should have for each rectangle. You can have them in a different order, but you must have all of them.
- What's the perimeter of rectangle B? (Signal.) *56 inches.*
- What's the perimeter of rectangle C? (Signal.) *26 yards.*
- What's the perimeter of rectangle D? (Signal.) *32 meters.*
g. Raise your hand if you got everything right.
h. Remember, the perimeter is the **distance around** the rectangle. To find the perimeter, you **add up** the lengths of all the sides.

Teaching Notes

If students write **square in** for the unit name, tell them, "The perimeter is just the distance around the whole rectangle. Take your finger and trace the distance around figure B. That's the perimeter. If that rectangle were true size, your finger would have gone 56 inches. There are no squares for perimeters."

Starting in Lesson 86, students work problems in which they figure out both the area and the perimeter of rectangles. Here's the exercise from Lesson 86:

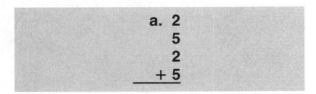

a. Find part 5. For each rectangle, you're going to figure the area and then figure the perimeter.
- Remember, the area is the number of **square** units inside the rectangle. The perimeter is the **distance around** the figure.
- You figure out the perimeter by adding up the lengths of all the sides. The units for the perimeter are not square units—just units of length.

b. Your turn: Figure out the area for rectangle A, and figure out the perimeter. Remember to write the unit name in each answer. Raise your hand when you're finished.
(Observe students and give feedback.)
- (Write on the board:)

a. area	perimeter
3	3
× 7	7
21 sq mi	3
	+ 7
	20 mi

- Check your work. Here's what you should have. The area is 3 times 7. That's 21 square miles. The perimeter is 3 plus 7 plus 3 plus 7. That's 20. The distance around the rectangle is 20 miles.

c. Figure out the area for rectangle B and figure out the perimeter. Remember the unit names for the answers. Raise your hand when you're finished.
(Observe students and give feedback.)
- (Write on the board:)

b. area	perimeter
4	4
× 5	5
20 sq in	4
	+ 5
	18 in

- Check your work. Here's what you should have. The area is 4 times 5. That's 20 square inches. The perimeter is 4 plus 5 plus 4 plus 5. That's 18 inches. The distance around the rectangle is 18 inches.

d. Figure out the area for rectangle C, and figure out the perimeter. Remember the unit names for the answers. Raise your hand when you're finished.
(Observe students and give feedback.)

- (Write on the board:)

c. area	perimeter
30	30
× 12	12
60	30
+ 300	+ 12
360 sq ft	84 ft

- Check your work. Here's what you should have. The area is 30 times 12. That's 360 square feet. The perimeter is 30 plus 12 plus 30 plus 12. That's 84 feet.

Teaching Notes

If students have trouble with the unit names, remind them, "When you figure out the area, you're trying to figure out how many squares there are inside the rectangle. The units are always squares. When you figure out the perimeter, you're just figuring out the distance around the outside of the rectangle."

Starting in Lesson 88, students compute the perimeters of figures that are not rectangles. The length of each side is shown. Students add the lengths and write the answer as a number and a unit name. Here's the set of problems from Lesson 88:

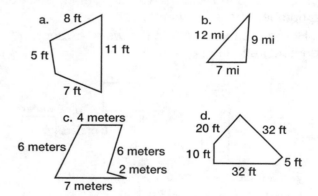

In Lesson 90, students work problems that tell about the length of all sides of a polygon but one, and indicate the perimeter. They use a variation of a classification number family to figure out the length of the unknown side.

Here's the family they use:

shown   not shown   all

————————————————▶

perimeter

Students add the sides that are shown. The total gives them the first small number. Then they work the problem that subtracts the total of the sides that are shown from the big number. That gives the length of the missing side.

Here's a problem and the solution:

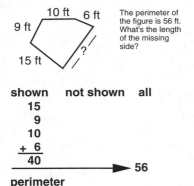

The problem and the answer for the missing number is 56 minus 40 equals 16 feet.

In the following lessons, students work mixed sets of problems that include those that ask about the length of an unknown side and those that ask about the perimeter.

VOLUME

In Lesson 98, students find the volume of rectangular prisms. Students use the equation: Volume = area of base × height.

Here's part of the introduction from Lesson 98:

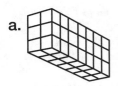

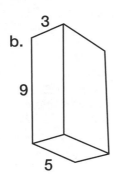

b. Find part 4.
c. For each problem, you'll find the volume. The unit name for the answer is **cubes.** First, you find the area of the base. The base is shaded for both figures. Raise your hand when you know the numbers you multiply to find the area of the base for box B.
• Everybody, what are the numbers you multiply to find the area of the base? (Signal.) *2 and 7.*
• What is the area? (Signal.) *14 squares.*
d. Copy the equation. Below, write the equation with the number for the area of the base and the height. Then find the volume. Raise your hand when you're finished.
   (Observe students and give feedback.)
• (Write on the board:)

Volume = area of base x height		
a. Volume =	14	x 3 = 42 cubes

• Check your work. Here's what you should have. The area of the base is 14. The height is 3. So the volume is 42 cubes. Raise your hand if you got it right.
e. Only the numbers for the width, the length and the height are written for box B. Everybody, how many units wide is box B? (Signal.) *3.*
• How many units long is box B? (Signal.) *5.*
• How many units high is box B? (Signal.) *9.*
• (Repeat step e until firm.)
f. Your turn: Find the volume of box B. Remember; first find the area of the base. Then multiply by the height. Remember to write the unit name in the answer. Raise your hand when you're finished.
   (Observe students and give feedback.)
• (Write to show:)

a. Volume =	14	x 3 = 42 cubes
b. Volume =	15	x 9 = 135 cubes

• Here's what you should have. The area of the base is 15 square units. The height is 9 units. So the volume is 135 cubes. Raise your hand if you got it right.

Teaching Notes

Students might have trouble writing the area of the base. Refer them to the figure. Point out that they have to find the number of squares on that shaded bottom surface. "Say the multiplication problem for the area of the base. . . . And you'll multiply that number by the height. Remember, first you have to figure out the area of the base."

If students have a lot of trouble with the introductory set, tell them to start with a new sheet of paper. Repeat the exercise.

LINES

Students learn to identify pairs of lines that are parallel and lines that are not (starting on Lesson 99). They also learn to identify pairs of lines that intersect or do not intersect. The problem sets that students work from show pairs of lines that are either parallel or not, that either intersect or don't. Students classify the lines as parallel or not, intersecting or not.

MEASUREMENT

Measurement activities begin in Lesson 3 with telling time and continue throughout Level D. The early work reviews time and units of length.

In Lesson 83, students begin work on equivalent measures. Students refer to the table of measurement facts, which appears on the inside-back cover of the textbook. Measurement facts are shown for U.S. and metric systems. Each measurement fact names the larger unit first.

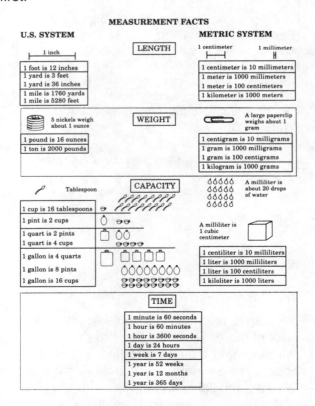

The first equivalence problems involve length conversions with U.S. units of length.

Here's part of the exercise from Lesson 83:

Note: You will need a ruler for this exercise.

a. Find the table of measurement facts on the inside back cover of your textbook. These facts tell about different measurement units. Each fact names two units, a larger one and a smaller one. The larger unit is named first.

b. Find the heading **length**. That's the first heading. √
• The first fact is: 1 foot is 12 inches. Remember, the larger unit is named first. What's the name of the larger unit? (Signal.) *Foot.*
• What's the name of the smaller unit? (Signal.) *Inches.*
• How many inches does it take to make 1 foot? (Signal.) *12.*

c. (Show ruler.)
• This ruler is 1 foot long. How many inches long is it? (Signal.) *12.*
• Hold up your hands to show me a space about 1 foot wide.
• Show me a space that is about 1 inch wide.
• Everybody, hold up your hands and show me a space that is about three feet wide. That space is about 1 yard wide.

d. Next fact: 1 yard is 3 feet.
• Which is the larger unit? (Signal.) *Yard.*
• Which is the smaller unit? (Signal.) *Feet.*
• How many feet does it take to make 1 yard? (Signal.) *3.*

e. Next fact: 1 yard is 36 inches.
• Which is the larger unit? (Signal.) *Yard.*
• Which is the smaller unit? (Signal.) *Inches.*
• How many inches does it take to make 1 yard? (Signal.) *36.*

f. Next fact. Read it. (Signal.) *1 mile is 1760 yards.*
• There's no picture for that fact.
• Which is the larger unit? (Signal.) *Mile.*
• Which is the smaller unit? (Signal.) *Yards.*
• How many yards does it take to make 1 mile? (Signal.) *1760.*

g. Last fact. Read it. (Signal.) *1 mile is 5280 feet.*
• Which is the larger unit? (Signal.) *Mile.*
• Which is the smaller unit? (Signal.) *Feet.*
• How many feet does it take to make 1 mile? (Signal.) *5280.*

h. You're going to work ratio problems based on the facts in the table. I'll say the problems. If you don't remember them, you can turn back to part 4 of lesson 83.

i. Problem A: A board is 5 feet long. How many inches long is it?
• The problem names two units of length. One unit is feet. What's the other unit? (Signal.) *Inches.*
• Touch the fact that tells about feet and inches. √

- Everybody read the fact about feet and inches. (Signal.) *1 foot is 12 inches.*
- You'll write that fact as a ratio starting with the name for the larger unit.
- (Write on the board:)

$$a. \quad \frac{feet}{inches} \quad \frac{1}{12} \quad = -$$

- Here it is. The names are **feet** and **inches**. The numbers are 1 and 12.
- The problem gives another number for feet or for inches. Which unit? (Signal.) *Feet.*
- What's the number of feet? (Signal.) *5.*
- So I write **5** for **feet.**
- (Write to show:)

$$a. \quad \frac{feet}{inches} \quad \frac{1}{12} \quad = \frac{5}{}$$

j. Your turn: Copy what's on the board. Figure out the fraction that equals 1. Then figure out how many inches long that board is. Remember to box your answer. Raise your hand when you're finished. (Observe students and give feedback.)
- (Write to show:)

$$a. \quad \frac{feet}{inches} \quad \frac{1}{12} \times \frac{5}{5} \quad = \frac{5}{\boxed{60}}$$

- Here's what you should have. You multiply 12 times 5. That's 60. So the board is 60 inches long. Raise your hand if you got it right.

Teaching Notes

Although students should not have trouble with most of the problems involving equivalencies, there is a potential for problems. The larger unit has the smaller number. For the fact 1 foot is 12 inches, the number for foot is smaller; yet, foot is the larger unit.

In the following lessons, students work with equivalent units of time (starting in Lesson 85), units of capacity (starting in Lesson 86), units of weight (starting in Lesson 87), and metric units (starting in Lesson 89).

Projects

Projects are introduced in Lesson 101 and continue through Lesson 120. Projects are different from the other exercises in the program in that they require students to combine information in new ways and take problem-solving steps that are unique to the particular project.

PROJECTS WITH PROBABILITY

In Lessons 101–110, students work on projects that involve the probability of drawing a member of a particular subset of cards, rolling a die or dice to get a particular number, or flipping one or more coins.

The first probability project occurs in Lesson 101. Students figure out about how many trials it would take to get twenty winners when flipping a coin. (Heads are winners; tails are losers.) Students then conduct an experiment and compare their results with the "ideal" or predicted number of trials.

> *Note:* **For this exercise, you will need a small paper bag, a coin, and a calculator.**

- Part of each lesson until the end of the program will be a project. For projects, we'll work together on math experiments or problems that require a lot of work to solve. We'll work in teams for some projects. Remember which team you're on. (Form 5 teams: Teams A, B, C, D, and E. Each team should have some higher performing students and some lower performers.)
a. We're going to do an experiment with coins. A coin is only one thing, but it has two sides. We can call one of the sides the winner and the other side the loser. Then we'll flip the coin and see which side comes up. For our experiment, we'll call the side of the coin with the person's head the **winner.** The other side is the **loser.**
b. First we'll write a ratio equation to show the ratio of winners to trials. There are two possibilities when we flip a coin. It will either land with the head side showing or the other side showing. On each coin, there is only one winner—the head side.
- (Write on the board:)

$$\frac{winner}{trials} \quad \frac{1}{2}$$

- Here's the ratio numbers for flipping a coin. Your turn: Use lined paper. Figure out the expected number of trials needed for 20 winners. Raise your hand when you're finished.
(Write to show:)

$$\frac{\text{winners}}{\text{trials}} \quad \frac{1}{2} \times \frac{20}{20} = \frac{20}{40}$$

- Here's what you should have. If there are 2 trials for every 1 winner, you'd expect to take 40 trials to get 20 winners. Raise your hand if you got it right.

c. Each team is going to do an experiment to see how many trials it takes the team to get 20 winners. To take a trial, you put the coin in the bag. You shake the bag well. You turn the bag over and dump the coin out. Two members of each team will keep count. One will make tallies for the number of trials on lined paper. The other will make tallies for the number of winners. That member will indicate when the team has 20 winners.

d. (Write on the board:)

winners ☐
trials ☐

- Raise your hand when your team is ready to go and you know who will make the tallies and who will take the trials.
- Take your trials. Raise your hand when you have 20 winners.
(Observe students and give feedback.)
- (Tell one member of each team to write the numbers of winners and trials on the board.)
- If we add up the winners and trials for each of the teams, we should get a fraction that is pretty close to what we would expect.
- (Write on the board:)

winners | 20 +20 +20 +20 +20 | = ☐
trials | + + + + | ☐

- (For each team, write **20** in the box for **winners**. Write the number of trials in the box for trials.)
- Use your calculator. Enter the numbers for the trials. Figure out the total number of trials we took. Then figure out the total winners. When you get the totals, write the fraction for the class. Raise your hand when you know the fraction for the entire class.
(Observe students and give feedback.)
- (Call on a student to write the fraction on the board.)

- If you just saw that fraction, you'd know the ratio of winners to trials is 1-half. The fraction we ended up with is closer to 1-half then it is to any other fraction with a denominator of 2.

Teaching Notes

This activity calls for students to use a paper bag. It is also possible for them to use a paper cup. Students, however, **must** keep the cup covered while shaking it. If students are careful about keeping the cup covered with their hand, permit them to use paper cups.

Monitor the groups carefully in step d. The scorekeepers should work systematically. As soon as the experimenter takes a trial, that scorekeeper should make a tally mark. If the result is a winner, the other scorekeeper should also make a tally mark. If scorekeepers are not well organized, assign several members of the group to prompt them. "Remember, as soon as ____ takes a trial, remind ____ to make a tally."

At the end of step d, you get the final fraction for the class. Since there are five groups in the class, the numerator of the fraction should be close to 100 and the denominator close to 200.

In Lesson 102, students figure out the chances of two coins both being heads. To figure out the chances, they write ratio equations based on the possibility that the ratio of winners to trials is 1 to 4, 1 to 3, or 1 to 2.

They then run an experiment and identify the correct ratio on the basis of the outcome (1 to 4).

In Lesson 106, students figure out the ratio of winners to trials for three coins, all being heads. Again, they write possible ratio numbers and then determine the correct ratio by the outcome of their experiment.

In Lesson 107, students apply what they have learned about determining possibilities to figure out the probability of five coins all showing heads:

$$\frac{1}{2} \times \frac{1}{2} \times \frac{1}{2} \times \frac{1}{2} \times \frac{1}{2} = \frac{1}{32}$$

Starting in Lesson 103, students determine the probability of drawing a member of a subset. For the first experiment, you put four cards in a bag. Three of the cards display a blue triangle. (The cards should be about 2 inches by 2 inches. Make them out of index-card stock. Draw a blue triangle on both sides of three cards. Leave the fourth card blank or draw a black line on each side.)

You tell the students that there are four cards in the bag and that at least one of them is a winner with a blue triangle on it. Students write the ratio for the various possibilities of winners and trials: $\frac{1}{4}, \frac{2}{4}, \frac{3}{4}, \frac{4}{4}$.

Next, you draw cards from the bag one at a time and announce whether each is a winner or a loser. Have two students make tallies (one student for the trials, the other for the winners). Then you put the card back in the bag.

After you get 24 winners, students determine which ratio the results are closest to by working a ratio problem for each possibility:

$$\frac{\text{winners}}{\text{trials}} \quad \frac{1}{4} = \frac{24}{\square} \qquad \frac{\text{winners}}{\text{trials}} \quad \frac{3}{4} = \frac{24}{\square}$$

$$\frac{\text{winners}}{\text{trials}} \quad \frac{2}{4} = \frac{24}{\square} \qquad \frac{\text{winners}}{\text{trials}} \quad \frac{4}{4} = \frac{24}{\square}$$

They select the ratio that has the number of trials closest to the number of trials you took during the experiment.

Teaching Notes

When you do this experiment, remember to return the card to the bag and shake well before drawing the card for the next trial.

In Lessons 104, 105, and 110, students do similar projects.

In Lesson 105, students learn the difference between probability and certainty. For this project, there are four cards, all of which are winners.

In Lesson 108, students conduct their first experiment involving dice. A die is like a coin in that one of the sides is a winner. The die is unlike a coin because there are six possibilities for each die, rather than two. In this lesson, students first determine the number of trials that would be needed to get five winners. (Winners

have three dots showing on top). Then they conduct an experiment to see how many trials their group requires to get five winners.

In Lesson 109, students run an experiment to figure out the ratio numbers for getting the same particular number on a pair of dice. Students run the experiment until they get three winners. Then they figure out the ratio.

Here's a possible ratio equation that one team might write:

$$\frac{\text{winners}}{\text{trials}} \quad \frac{1}{\square} \times \frac{3}{3} = \frac{3}{102}$$

The ratio is $\frac{\frac{1}{102}}{3}$ or $\frac{1}{34}$. That's close to $\frac{1}{36}$.

And $\frac{1}{36}$ is the ratio that follows the same function rule as the rule for more than one coin showing heads. Each denominator in the sequence is multiplied by the number of possibilities for one die.

1 die	2 dice	3 dice
$\frac{1}{6}$	$\frac{1}{36}$	$\frac{1}{216}$

The final probability experiment is a survey. Students ask four different people, "Does somebody in your family golf (or bowl) more than three times a year?" Students use the data they have collected to predict results of larger samples. Then they combine their data with data other students have obtained to create larger samples and test their predictions.

PROJECTS WITH GEOMETRY

The projects at the end of Level D include a variety of geometry problems. Some of these projects relate the area of a triangle to the area of a rectangle with the same base and same height. In Lesson 111, students construct a right triangle using a coordinate grid. They cut the triangle in half (two parts will have the same height). Then they piece the parts together to form a rectangle that has the same base as the original triangle and 1-half the height.

In Lesson 112, students do a variation of this project in which they start with several rectangles of different sizes. They divide each rectangle into two right triangles by cutting diagonally from one corner to the other. Each triangle has the same base as the rectangle. Each has 1-half the area. Students prove that the triangle is 1-half the area of the original rectangle by cutting one of the triangles in half (horizontally) and fitting the two parts together to make a rectangle that has the same base and half the height of the original rectangle.

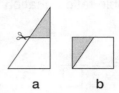

a   b

In Lesson 113, students construct a triangle that is not a right triangle. They enclose it in a rectangle and make two diagonal cuts from the apex, creating three triangles.

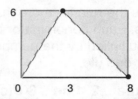

The largest triangle has the same base and height as the original rectangle. The proof that it has half the area of the original rectangle is provided by positioning the two smaller triangles to cover the largest triangle.

Students work the final triangle project in Lesson 116. Students draw three rectangles on a coordinate grid. Dimensions of the triangles are specified.

Students then construct a non-right triangle inside each rectangle. They figure the area of each triangle and each rectangle. Finally, they cut out each rectangle and triangle to demonstrate that the equation for the area of the triangle works by piecing together the three cutouts from each rectangle.

Beginning in Lesson 114, students do a series of projects that involve the relationship between area and perimeter. In Lesson 114, students measure the classroom and compute its area and perimeter. Then they use the area and perimeter to find the cost of installing carpeting and molding in the room.

In Lesson 115, students work problems involving the relationship between the perimeter and area of rectangles having different dimensions. The problem students work involves two farmers who argue about the relative efficiency of fencing fields. One farmer contends that the cost of fencing is relatively lower if the field is small. The other farmer argues that a larger field is more efficient to fence. Students settle the debate by figuring out the ratio of fencing to the area fenced for both farmers.

Here are the fractions for each farmer:

$$\frac{\text{Jones' fencing}}{\text{Jones' area fenced}} \quad \frac{12}{9}$$

$$\frac{\text{Blacks' fencing}}{\text{Blacks' area fenced}} \quad \frac{36}{81}$$

Students compare the fractions by starting with the one with smaller numbers and including one number from the larger fraction:

$$\frac{\text{Jones' area fencing}}{\text{Jones' area fenced}} \quad \frac{12}{9} = \frac{\boxed{36}}{27}$$

If Black were as inefficient as Jones, he would have fenced only 27 square rods. Instead, Black fenced 81 square rods using 36 rods of fencing.

In Lesson 117, students construct a line on a coordinate system that shows the diagonal for a series of possible rectangles:

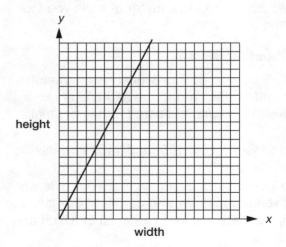

They then use clues to figure out the mystery rectangle.

Some clues tell students that the mystery rectangle is larger than another rectangle: The height of the mystery rectangle is more than 2. Students rule out rectangles that do not have a height of more than 2 by shading in the rectangle that has a height of 2:

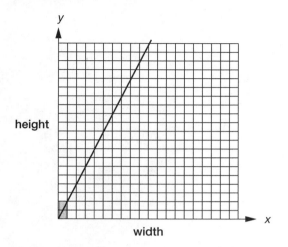

Some clues tell students that the mystery rectangle is smaller than other rectangles: The mystery rectangle has an area that is smaller than 72 square units.

Students use a function table to figure out the area of rectangles that have different heights. They then shade the part of the coordinate grid that includes rectangles that have an area of more than 72 square units:

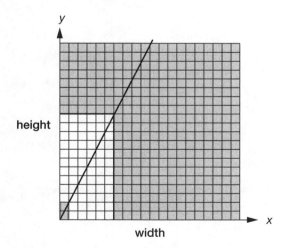

By applying the third clue, students can identify the rectangle. The area of the mystery rectangle has 8 more units than the perimeter. This mystery rectangle has a width of 4 units and a height of 8 units.

In Lessons 118 and 119, students do sighting projects in which they apply what they have learned about ratios. For these experiments, students need a distance of 24 feet and two desks that are the same height.

For Lesson 118, the students stand at a "sighting line" and set a card that is 4 inches high on a desk 6 feet from them. They place an 8-inch card on the second desk and adjust its position so that, when the two cards are viewed from the sighting line, they appear to be identical in height. (They are superimposed.)

Students record the distance for the placement of the card in a ratio equation that relates the height of the card to its distance from the sighting line:

height of card
distance of card

Students use these ratios to predict how far from the sighting line the 16-inch card should be placed so it appears to be the same height as the 4-inch card. They then confirm their prediction by sighting.

In Lesson 119, students do a similar sighting experiment using the set up from Lesson 118, with two new cards. Students figure out where the cards should be placed by using ratio numbers. They confirm their predictions by sighting, then measuring the height of the card and the distance from the sighting line.

Appendix A

Connecting Math Concepts

Level D Cumulative Test 1
(Lessons 1–30)

EXERCISE 1

a. Find Part 1. √
- You're going to write answers for all the items in Part 1. Don't start until I tell you to go. You'll have 1 minute. I'll tell you when to stop. Get ready. Go.
- (After 1 minute, say:) Stop writing.

b. Find Part 2. √
- You're going to write thousands numerals with a comma to show where the thousands end. The columns for thousands and hundred thousands are marked.
- Item A: 5 thousand 60. 5 thousand 60. Write item A.
- Item B: 16 thousand 2 hundred. 16 thousand 2 hundred. Write item B.
- Item C: 36 thousand 29. 36 thousand 29. Write item C.
- Item D: 69 thousand 6 hundred 2. 69 thousand 6 hundred 2. Write item D.

c. Find Part 3. √
- For Parts 3 through 12, read the directions for each part and work the problems.
- Raise your hand when you're finished.
- (Observe but do not give feedback.)

PART	SCORE			POSSIBLE SCORE	PASSING SCORE
	CUMULATIVE TEST 1 SCORING CHART				
1	1 for each item			12	10
2	1 for each item			4	4
3	2 for each item			6	Parts 3, 4, combined
4	Each Correct Equation	Total	Deductions For Each Equation Written For Fractions Not Equal To Whole Numbers	6	10
	3	6	2		
5	1 for each cell			3	3
6	EACH ITEM			6	6
	Problem	Answer	Total		
	2	1	3		
7	2 for each item			4	Parts 7, 8 combined
8	2 for each item			8	10
9	EACH ITEM			6	6
	Problem	Answer and Unit Name	Total		
	2	1	3		
10	1 for each item			6	5
11	2 for each cell			6	3
12	1 for each sign			4	3
	TOTAL			71	

CUMULATIVE TEST 1 PERCENT SUMMARY					
SCORE	%	SCORE	%	SCORE	%
71	100	63	89	56	78
70	99	62	87	55	77
69	97	61	86	54	76
68	96	60	85	53	75
67	94	59	83	52	73
66	93	58	82	51	71
65	92	57	80	50	70
64	90				

CUMULATIVE TEST 1 REMEDIES	
PART	**LESSON and (EXERCISE)**
1 a, b, c, f, k, l	1 (6), 4 (5), 5 (3), 6 (3), 7 (5), 8 (2), 10 (2)
1 d, e, g, h, i, j	5 (6), 6 (6), 7 (2), 8 (7), 9 (8), 13 (4)
2	1 (4), 2 (2), 3 (5), 4 (8), 7 (6), 9 (1), 12 (1), 13 (2), 14 (6), 15 (2), 16 (8), 17 (7), 21 (7)
3	1 (2), 2 (4), 6 (4), 7 (1), 8 (1), 9 (4)
4	1 (2), 2 (4), 3 (3), 4 (3), 5 (2)
5	1 (5), 2 (3), 3 (2), 4 (6), 5 (4), 6 (2, 7), 7 (3, 7), 11 (4), 12 (6), 13 (1), 14 (8), 17 (5), 18 (6), 19 (2), 21 (8), 22 (7), 23 (3), 25 (5)
6	16 (1), 17 (1), 18 (4), 19 (6), 22 (4)
7	1 (3), 2 (6), 3 (1), 4 (1)
8	1 (7), 2 (5), 3 (6), 5 (7), 6 (5), 8 (5)
9	9 (2), 12 (3), 13 (9), 14 (5), 15 (7), 16 (5), 18 (3)
10	11 (3), 12 (5), 13 (6), 14 (7), 15 (4), 16 (3), 17 (4), 18 (5), 19 (7)
11	1 (5), 2 (3),3 (2), 4 (6), 5 (4), 6 (2), 7 (7), 9 (9), 11 (4), 12 (6), 13 (1), 14 (8), 17 (5), 18 (6), 19 (2), 21 (8), 22 (7), 23 (3), 25 (5)
12	21 (6), 22 (8), 23 (8 part 4), 28 (7 part 3)

Connecting Math Concepts

Level D Cumulative Test 2
(Lessons 1–60)

EXERCISE 1

a. Find Part 1. √
- Write answers to the division and multiplication problems. You have 2 minutes. Get ready. Go.
- (At the end of 2 minutes, say:) Stop writing.

b. Find Part 2. √
- These are mixed numbers. Each goes on one of the number lines. You're going to write the correct mixed number in each circle. Raise your hand when you've written each mixed number where it goes.

c. Find Part 3. √
- For Parts 3 through 13, read the directions for each part and work the problems.
- Raise your hand when you're finished.
- (Observe but do not give feedback.)

CUMULATIVE TEST 2 PERCENT SUMMARY					
SCORE	**%**	**SCORE**	**%**	**SCORE**	**%**
96	100	86	90	76	79
95	99	85	89	75	78
94	98	84	88	74	77
93	97	83	86	73	76
92	96	82	85	72	75
91	95	81	84	71	74
90	94	80	83	70	73
89	93	79	82	69	72
88	92	78	81	68	71
87	91	77	80	67	70

CUMULATIVE TEST 2 SCORING CHART			
PART	**SCORE**	**POSSIBLE SCORE**	**PASSING SCORE**
1	1 for each item	22	18
2	2 for each item	10	8
3	EACH ITEM Problem 2 / Answer 1 / Total 3	6	5
4	2 for each item	6	Parts 4, 5 combined 10
5	2 for each item	6	
6	EACH ITEM Problem 1 / Answer and unit name 1 / Total 2	4	Parts 6, 7 combined 8
7	2 for each item	6	
8	2 for each item Each correct fraction 3 / Total 6 / Deduction for incorrect fraction 1	6	Parts 8, 9 Combined 10
9	2 for each item	6	
10	3 for each item	9	Parts 10, 11 combined
11	EACH ITEM Problem 2 / Answer 1 / Unit Name 1 / Total 4	8	
12	1 for each item	3	14 3
13	2 for each item	4	4
	TOTAL	**96**	

<table>
<tr><th colspan="2">CUMULATIVE TEST 2
REMEDIES</th></tr>
<tr><th>PART</th><th>LESSON and (EXERCISE)</th></tr>
<tr><td>1 a – l</td><td>21 (5), 22 (6), 23 (4), 24 (4), 25 (3), 26 (8), 27 (1), 28 (1), 31 (2), 32 (2, 3), 33 (4), 34 (3, 6), 35 (5), 36 (2),</td></tr>
<tr><td>1 m, p, r</td><td>38 (1), 42 (2), 43 (6), 44 (5), 45 (7), 58 (5), 59 (7)</td></tr>
<tr><td>1 n, o, q, s, u</td><td>28 (5), 29 (1), 31 (1), 32 (5), 36 (5), 37 (7), 56 (5)</td></tr>
<tr><td>1 t, v</td><td>48 (4), 50 (2), 49 (5), 51 (5), 52 (1), 55 (2), 56 (5), 57 (1), 58 (3), 59 (3) 13 (6), 14 (7), 15 (4), 16 (3), 18 (5), 19 (7)</td></tr>
<tr><td>2</td><td>1 (2), 2 (4), 3 (3), 4 (3), 5 (2), 6 (4), 7 (1), 8 (1), 9 (4), 22 (5), 23 (2), 24 (6), 34 (4), 35 (7), 36 (4), 37 (6, 8), 38 (3), 39 (6), 41 (4), 46 (6), 47 (6), 48 (7)</td></tr>
<tr><td>3</td><td>16 (1), 17 (1), 18 (4), 19 (6), 22 (4)</td></tr>
<tr><td>4</td><td>33 (7), 34 (7), 35 (6), 36 (3), 37 (3), 38 (4), 39 (1), 41 (6), 42 (6), 44 (6), 45 (3, 4), 49 (3), 50 (3), 51 (1, 6), 52 (6), 53 (5), 54 (2), 55 (7), 56 (7)</td></tr>
<tr><td>5</td><td>16 (6), 17 (6), 18 (7), 19 (1), 20 (2), 21 (1), 22 (3), 23 (6), 24 (3), 25 (1), 26 (7), 28 (6), 35 (4), 36 (7), 39 (4), 40 (3), 41 (1), 43 (1)</td></tr>
<tr><td>6</td><td>29 (7), 31 (4), 35 (9 part 10), 39 (8 part 9), 45 (8 part 4), 51 (7 part 9)</td></tr>
<tr><td>7</td><td>10 (3), 14 (1, 3), 15 (3, 5), 16 (2), 18 (2), 27 (6), 29 (5), 31 (5), 32 (4), 45 (5), 46 (4), 47 (4), 48 (5), 49 (7), 52 (7), 53 (4), 56 (9), 58 (6)</td></tr>
<tr><td>8</td><td>1 (2), 2 (4), 3 (3), 4 (3), 5 (2), 6 (4), 7 (1), 8 (1), 9 (4), 16 (6), 17 (6), 18 (7), 19 (1), 20 (2), 21 (1), 22 (3), 42 (4), 43 (5), 44 (3)</td></tr>
<tr><td>9</td><td>1 (5), 2 (3), 3 (2), 4 (6), 5 (4), 6 (2, 7), 7 (3, 7), 11 (4), 12 (6), 13 (1), 14 (8), 17 (5), 18 (6), 19 (2), 21 (8), 22 (7), 23 (3), 25 (5)</td></tr>
<tr><td>10</td><td>34 (8), 35 (8), 36 (1), 38 (7), 41 (5), 42 (5), 43 (4), 44 (4), 45 (6), 46 (5), 47 (5), 48 (1)</td></tr>
<tr><td>11</td><td>9 (2), 12 (3), 13 (9), 14 (5), 15 (7), 16 (5), 18 (3)</td></tr>
<tr><td>12</td><td>21 (6), 22 (8), 23 (8 part 4), 28 (7 part 3)</td></tr>
<tr><td>13</td><td>1 (3), 2 (6), 3 (1), 4 (1), 8 (8), 9 (3), 11 (5)</td></tr>
</table>

Connecting Math Concepts

Level D Cumulative Test 3
(Lessons 1–90)

EXERCISE 1

a. Find Part 1. √
- Write answers to the problems. You have 1 minute. Get ready. Go.
- **(After 1 minute, say:)** Stop writing.

b. Find Part 2. √
- For each row, the **X** value is shown. You'll write the function and the **Y** value for the row.
- Raise your hand when you're finished.

c. Find Part 3. √
- For Parts 3 through 14, read the directions for each part and work the problems.
- Raise your hand when you're finished.
- **(Observe but do not give feedback.)**

<table>
<tr><th colspan="6">CUMULATIVE TEST 3
PERCENT SUMMARY</th></tr>
<tr><th>SCORE</th><th>%</th><th>SCORE</th><th>%</th><th>SCORE</th><th>%</th></tr>
<tr><td>132</td><td>100</td><td>118</td><td>89</td><td>105</td><td>79.5</td></tr>
<tr><td>131</td><td>99</td><td>117</td><td>88.5</td><td>104</td><td>79</td></tr>
<tr><td>130</td><td>98</td><td>116</td><td>88</td><td>103</td><td>78</td></tr>
<tr><td>129</td><td>97.5</td><td>115</td><td>87</td><td>102</td><td>77</td></tr>
<tr><td>128</td><td>97</td><td>114</td><td>86</td><td>101</td><td>76.5</td></tr>
<tr><td>127</td><td>96</td><td>113</td><td>85.5</td><td>100</td><td>76</td></tr>
<tr><td>126</td><td>95</td><td>112</td><td>85</td><td>99</td><td>75</td></tr>
<tr><td>125</td><td>94.5</td><td>111</td><td>84</td><td>98</td><td>74</td></tr>
<tr><td>124</td><td>94</td><td>110</td><td>83</td><td>97</td><td>73</td></tr>
<tr><td>123</td><td>93</td><td>109</td><td>82.5</td><td>96</td><td>72.5</td></tr>
<tr><td>122</td><td>92</td><td>108</td><td>82</td><td>95</td><td>72</td></tr>
<tr><td>121</td><td>91.5</td><td>107</td><td>81</td><td>94</td><td>71</td></tr>
<tr><td>120</td><td>91</td><td>106</td><td>80</td><td>93</td><td>70</td></tr>
<tr><td>119</td><td>90</td><td></td><td></td><td></td><td></td></tr>
</table>

	CUMULATIVE TEST 3 SCORING CHART			
PART	**SCORE**		**POSSIBLE SCORE**	**PASSING SCORE**
1	1 for each item		12	10
2	2 for each cell		12	10
3	2 for each item		6	Parts 3, 4, 5 combined
4	3 for each item		6	
5	2 for each item		4	13
6	2 for each item		8	6
7	2 for each cell		16	12
8	1 for each item		3	3
9	EACH ITEM		9	7
	Answer 2 / Unit Name 1 / Total 3			
10	3 for each item		15	12
11	3 for each item		9	6
12	3 for each item		12	9
13	2 for each item		12	10
14	2 for each item		8	6
	TOTAL		**132**	

CUMULATIVE TEST 3 REMEDIES	
PART	**LESSON and (EXERCISE)**
1 d, j	5 (6), 6 (6), 7 (2), 8 (7), 9 (8)
1 b, e	9 (6)
1 g, l	11 (3), 12 (5), 13 (6), 14 (7), 15 (4), 16 (3), 17 (4), 18 (5), 19 (7)
1 a, c, f, i, k	58 (3), 59 (3), 61 (7 part 5), 62 (8 part 3), 63 (9 part 4)
2	77 (5), 78 (5), 79 (5), 81 (8), 82 (7), 83 (8 part 8), 84 (8 part 7)
3	71 (3), 72 (2), 73 (7), 74 (7), 75 (5), 77 (6), 78 (6), 79 (6), 80 (3), 83 (1), 84 (2)
4	46 (2), 47 (1), 48 (2), 49 (2), 55 (6, 8), 56 (3, 8), 57 (7), 58 (2), 59 (6), 60 (4), 61 (4), 63 (6), 64 (5), 66 (3), 67 (6), 68 (6), 69 (6), 73 (3), 75 (1)
5	1 (2), 2 (4), 3 (3), 4 (3), 5 (2), 42 (4), 43 (5), 44 (3), 49 (8 part 7)
6	72 (5), 73 (4), 74 (5), 75 (4), 76 (5), 78 (8 part 8), 82 (8 part 5)
7	1 (5), 2 (3), 3 (2), 4 (6), 5 (4), 6 (2, 7), 7 (3, 7), 9 (9), 11 (4), 12 (6), 13 (1), 14 (8), 17 (5), 18 (6), 19 (2), 21 (8), 22 (7), 23 (3), 25 (5), 48 (8), 53 (3), 54 (1), 55 (4), 56 (6), 57 (4), 59 (4), 61 (2), 62 (4), 63 (3), 64 (8), 65 (7), 66 (2), 67 (2)

CUMULATIVE TEST 3 REMEDIES *(cont'd)*	
PART	**LESSON and (EXERCISE)**
8	7 (4), 8 (4), 9 (7), 10 (1), 11 (2), 13 (5), 15 (6), 16 (4), 17 (9 part 8), 25 (8 part 9), 31 (8 part 11), 74 (2)
9	9 (2), 12 (3), 13 (9), 14 (5), 15 (7), 16 (5), 18 (3), 79 (3), 81 (1), 83 (2), 84 (5)
10	33 (7), 34 (7), 35 (6), 36 (3), 37 (3), 38 (4), 39 (1), 41 (6), 42 (6), 44 (6), 45 (3, 4, 5), 46 (4), 47 (4), 48 (5), 49 (3, 7), 50 (3), 51 (1, 6), 52 (6, 7), 53 (4, 5), 54 (2), 55 (7), 56 (7, 9), 58 (6), 63 (2), 68 (1, 5), 69 (4, 7), 70 (4), 71 (5), 72 (1), 73 (6), 74 (6), 75 (6), 76 (6)
11	1 (3), 2 (6), 3 (1), 4 (1), 8 (8), 9 (3), 11 (5), 82 (5), 83 (6), 84 (4), 85 (3), 86 (4), 87 (3)
12	34 (8), 35 (8), 36 (1), 38 (7), 41 (5), 42 (5), 43 (4), 44 (4), 45 (6), 46 (5), 47 (5), 48 (1), 49 (1), 51 (2)
13 c – f	27 (5), 28 (3), 29 (6), 30 (3), 32 (8)
13 a, b	46 (2), 47 (1), 48 (2), 49 (2)
And 13 a – f	51 (4), 52 (2)
14	57 (6), 58 (4), 59 (5), 61 (3), 62 (5), 63 (5), 64 (4), 65 (1), 66 (4), 67 (1)

Connecting Math Concepts

Level D Final Cumulative Test
(Lessons 1–120)

EXERCISE 1

- Work the problems in Parts 1 through 25 on your own.
- Raise your hand when you're finished.

FINAL CUMULATIVE TEST PERCENT SUMMARY					
SCORE	%	SCORE	%	SCORE	%
237	100	213	89.8	189	79.7
236	99.5	212	89.5	188	79.3
235	99	211	89	187	79
234	98.5	210	88.5	186	78.5
233	98	209	88	185	78
232	97.8	208	87.8	184	77.5
231	97.5	207	87.3	183	77
230	97	206	87	182	76.7
229	96.5	205	86.5	181	76.4
228	96	204	86	180	76
227	95.7	203	85.7	179	75.5
226	95.3	202	85	178	75
225	95	201	84.8	177	74.7
224	94.5	200	84.3	176	74.3
223	94	199	84	175	74
222	93.7	198	83.5	174	73.4
221	93.2	197	83	173	73
220	93	196	82.7	172	72.5
219	92.5	195	82	171	72
218	92	194	81.8	170	71.7
217	91.5	193	81.4	169	71.3
216	91	192	81	168	71
215	90.7	191	80.5	167	80.5
214	90	190	80	166	70

FINAL CUMULATIVE TEST SCORING CHART			
PART	SCORE	POSSIBLE SCORE	PASSING SCORE
1	3 for each item	18	15
2	3 for each item	12	9
3	3 for each item	12	9
4	1 for each number	7	6
5	2 for each item	16	Parts 5, 6 combined
6	2 for each item	6	18
7	2 for each item	20	18
8	2 for each item	10	8
9	3 for each item	12	Parts 9, 10 combined
10	2 for each item	8	17
11	2 for each item	6	6
12	1 for each item	3	Parts 12, 13 combined
13	1 for each item	2	4
14	EACH ITEM — Problems 2 · Answer 1 · Total 3	9	8
15	2 for each item	8	6
16	4 for the function	4	4
17	1 for each item	4	4
18	Each Point 2 · Total 6 · Line 1	7	Parts 18, 19 combined
19	2 for each point	6	11
20	1 for each cell	9	7
21	2 for each question	8	6
22	EACH ITEM — Problem 1 · Answer 1 · Unit 1 · Total 3	21	17
23	2 for each item	8	8
24	EACH ITEM — Problem 2 · Answer 1 · Total 3	12	9
25	3 for each item	9	6
	TOTAL	237	

PART	LESSON and (EXERCISE)
FINAL CUMULATIVE TEST REMEDIES	
1 a – c	33 (7), 34 (7), 35 (6), 36 (3), 37 (3), 38 (4), 39 (1), 41 (6), 42 (6), 44 (6), 44 (6), 45 (3, 4), 49 (3), 50 (3), 51 (1, 6), 52 (6), 53 (5), 54 (2), 55 (7), 56 (7)
1 d – f	45 (5), 46 (4), 47 (4), 48 (5), 49 (7), 52 (7), 53 (4), 56 (9), 58 (6), 63 (2), 68 (1, 5), 69 (4, 7), 70 (4), 71 (5), 72 (1), 73 (6), 74 (6), 75 (6), 76 (6), 106 (2), 107 (1), 108 (1), 109 (1), 110 (1)
2	1 (3), 2 (6), 3 (1), 4 (1), 8 (8), 9 (3), 11 (5), 82 (5), 83 (6), 84 (4), 85 (3), 86 (4), 87 (3)
3 a – c	34 (8), 35 (8), 36 (1), 38 (7), 41 (5), 42 (5), 43 (4), 44 (4), 45 (6), 46 (5), 47 (5), 48 (1), 49 (1), 51 (2)
3 d	49 (1), 51 (2), 49 (1), 51 (2), 53 (7 part 10), 54 (7 part 8), 56 (10 part 11), 57 (9 part 5)
4 a – d	16 (6), 17 (6), 18 (7), 19 (1), 20 (2), 21 (1), 22 (3), 23 (6), 24 (3), 25 (1), 26 (7), 28 (6), 35 (4), 36 (7), 39 (4), 40 (3), 41 (1), 43 (1)
4 e	29 (2), 30 (2), 31 (3), 32 (6), 33 (3), 36 (7), 43 (1)
5 a, b, d, f, h	27 (5), 28 (3), 29 (6), 30 (3), 32 (8)
5 c, e, g	46 (2), 47 (1), 48 (2), 49 (2)
And 5 a – h	51 (4), 52 (2), 61 (1), 62 (7), 63 (7)
6	55 (6, 8), 56 (3, 8), 57 (7), 58 (2), 59 (6), 60 (4), 61 (4), 63 (6), 64 (5), 66 (3), 67 (6), 68 (6), 69 (6), 73 (3), 75 (1)
7 a – g, i	1 (2), 2 (4), 3 (3), 4 (3), 5 (2), 33 (2), 34 (1), 35 (1), 37 (6), 38 (3), 39 (6), 41 (4), 46 (6), 47 (6), 48 (7), 57 (3), 72 (3), 74 (1), 99 (2), 100 (5), 101 (1)
7 h, j	89 (5), 90 (2), 91 (1), 92 (1), 93 (3), 94 (2), 95 (3), 106 (3), 107 (2), 111 (2 part 1)
8	89 (5), 90 (2), 91 (1, 4), 92 (3), 93 (8), 96 (5, 7), 97 (6), 98 (5), 99 (7), 105 (2)
9 a, c, d	57 (6), 58 (4), 59 (5), 61 (3), 62 (5), 63 (5), 64 (4), 65 (1, 5), 66 (4), 67 (1)
9 b	89 (5), 90 (2), 91 (1, 4), 92 (3), 93 (8), 96 (7), 97 (6)
10 a, c	38 (5), 39 (7), 40 (2), 41 (3), 52 (4), 70 (3), 96 (7), 97 (6), 100 (3)

PART	LESSON and (EXERCISE)
FINAL CUMULATIVE TEST REMEDIES (cont'd)	
10 b, d	89 (5), 90 (2), 91 (1, 4), 92 (3), 93 (8), 96 (7), 97 (6)
11	1 (2), 2 (4), 6 (4), 7 (1), 8 (1), 9 (4)
12	7 (4), 8 (4), 9 (7), 10 (1), 11 (2), 13 (5), 15 (6), 16 (4), 17 (9 part 8), 25 (8 part 9), 31 (8 part 11), 74 (2)
13	74 (2), 81 (6)
14	32 (7), 33 (1), 46 (1), 47 (2), 48 (3), 52 (3), 53 (1), 54 (6), 59 (2), 61 (6), 62 (2)
15	100 (4), 101 (4), 102 (1), 103 (1), 104 (2), 105 (3)
16	77 (5), 78 (5), 79 (5), 81 (8), 82 (7), 88 (1), 89 (7), 91 (5), 92 (6), 93 (6), 94 (4)
17	99 (1), 100 (2), 101 (6 part 2), 105 (6 part 4)
18	77 (5), 78 (5), 79 (5), 81 (8), 82 (7), 83 (7), 84 (7), 85 (4), 86 (7), 87 (8)
19	72 (5), 73 (4), 74 (5), 75 (4), 76 (5)
20, 21	6 (2, 7), 7 (3, 7), 9 (9), 11 (4), 12 (6), 13 (1), 14 (8), 17 (5), 18 (1, 6), 19 (2, 5), 21 (4, 8), 22 (7), 23 (7), 24 (2), 25 (4), 26 (5), 27 (3), 28 (2), 29 (3), 53 (3), 54 (1), 55 (4), 56 (6), 57 (4), 59 (4), 61 (2), 62 (4), 63 (3), 64 (8), 65 (7), 66 (2), 67 (2)
22 a, g	9 (2), 12 (3), 13 (9), 14 (5), 15 (7), 16 (5), 18 (3), 19 (4), 21 (2), 22 (2)
22 e	79 (3), 81 (1), 83 (2), 84 (5)
22 b, c, d	85 (1), 88 (6), 89 (4), 90 (3), 91 (3), 92 (4), 93 (4)
22 f	98 (3), 99 (4)
23	91 (2), 92 (2), 93 (1), 94 (6), 95 (4), 96 (4), 97 (2), 98 (1), 99 (3), 101 (2), 102 (3)
24 a, b	79 (4), 81 (2), 82 (3), 83 (5), 84 (6), 85 (2), 86 (1), 87 (2), 88 (4), 89 (6)
24 c, d	1 (5), 2 (3), 3 (2), 4 (6), 5 (4), 74 (4), 75 (2), 76 (2), 77 (1), 78 (4), 79 (1), 81 (3), 82 (2), 83 (3), 84 (3), 88 (2), 89 (1)
25	64 (6), 65 (3), 68 (3), 69 (1), 71 (4), 72 (4), 73 (5), 74 (3), 75 (3), 76 (1), 77 (3), 78 (3), 81 (5), 95 (1), 96 (3), 97 (1)

Part 1

a. $5 \times 9 =$ ____

b. $6 \times 5 =$ ____

c. $7 \times 5 =$ ____

d. $0 \times 9 =$ ____

e. $8 \times 9 =$ ____

f. $5 \times 5 =$ ____

g. $6 \times 9 =$ ____

h. $3 \times 9 =$ ____

i. $1 \times 9 =$ ____

j. $7 \times 9 =$ ____

k. $5 \times 8 =$ ____

l. $5 \times 4 =$ ____

Part 2

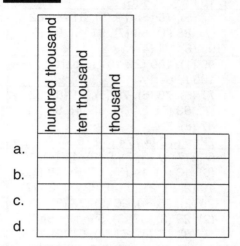

a.

b.

c.

d.

Part 3   Write the fraction for each item.

a.

b.

c.

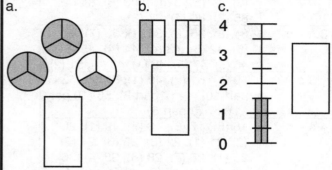

Part 4   Some of these fractions equal whole numbers. For each of these fractions complete an equation to show the whole number it equals.

a. $\dfrac{12}{5} =$

c. $\dfrac{12}{6} =$

b. $\dfrac{12}{9} =$

d. $\dfrac{12}{4} =$

Part 5   Write the addition or subtraction problem and answer for each row. Complete the table.

		TOTAL
	59	**236**
19		**62**
196	**102**	

Part 6   For each item, write the column problem and answer the question.

a. A car lot had 95 used cars. There were a total of 137 cars on the lot. How many new cars were there? _____

b. 35 kids were on the field, and the rest were in the gym. 96 kids were in the gym. How many kids were there in all? _____

© SRA/McGraw-Hill. Permission is granted to reproduce for school use.

Part 7	Work the problems.

a. 6 5 9
  − 5 8 9

b. 4 9 3
  − 2 3 6

Part 8	Work the problems.

a. 6 2 4
  × 5

b. 2 6 8
  × 2

c. 4 2 9
  × 9

d. 4 9 4
  × 5

Part 9	Find the area of each rectangle. Write the multiplication problem and the answer with the unit name.

a.   4 ft

36 ft

b.   8 in

5 in

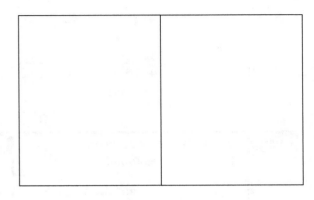

Part 10	Work the problems.

a.   9
  × 3

b.   4
  × 3

c.   3
  × 0

d.   7
  × 3

e.   3
  × 6

f.   8
  × 3

Part 11	Write the problem and answer for each column. Complete the table.

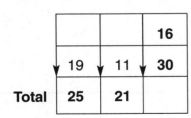

			16
↓ 19	↓ 11	↓ 30	
Total	25	21	

Part 12	Complete the sign to show >, <, or =.

a. 49 _____ 30

b. 16 _____ 12

c. 119 _____ 119

d. 59 _____ 84

© SRA/McGraw-Hill. Permission is granted to reproduce for school use.

Part 1

a. $5\overline{)45}$ e. $7\overline{)21}$ i. $5\overline{)40}$ m. $6 \times 4 =$ _____   r. $5 \times 4 =$ _____

b. $5\overline{)30}$ f. $7\overline{)56}$ j. $7\overline{)35}$ n. $3 \times 7 =$ _____   s. $6 \times 7 =$ _____

c. $3\overline{)12}$ g. $4\overline{)32}$ k. $3\overline{)24}$ o. $9 \times 7 =$ _____   t. $3 \times 6 =$ _____

d. $3\overline{)18}$ h. $4\overline{)16}$ l. $4\overline{)12}$ p. $8 \times 4 =$ _____   u. $0 \times 7 =$ _____

q. $7 \times 7 =$ _____   v. $8 \times 3 =$ _____

Part 2   Write the correct mixed number in each circle.

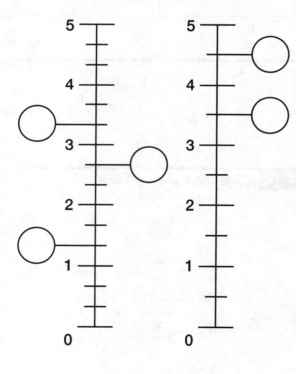

$3\frac{1}{3}$ $4\frac{1}{2}$ $1\frac{1}{3}$

$3\frac{1}{2}$ $2\frac{2}{3}$

Part 3   For each item, write the column problem and answer the question.

a. Meg ate 12 grapes. Ryan ate 15 more grapes than Meg. How many grapes did Ryan eat in all?

_____

b. Toni read 131 books. Dawn read 96 books. How many more books did Toni read? _____

Part 4   Work each problem.

a. $3\overline{)189}$ b. $4\overline{)3284}$ c. $2\overline{)608}$

© SRA/McGraw-Hill. Permission is granted to reproduce for school use.

Part 5   Complete each equation.

a. $4 = \dfrac{}{9}$

b. $\dfrac{}{8} = 64$

c. $\dfrac{12}{3} =$

Part 6   Write each problem and the answer with a unit name.

a. Brett buys the paper and the pen set. How much does Brett spend? _____

b. Candi buys the scissors and the paper. How much does Candi spend? _____

Part 7   Complete each equation.

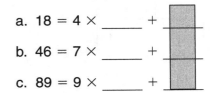

a. $18 = 4 \times$ _____ $+$

b. $46 = 7 \times$ _____ $+$

c. $89 = 9 \times$ _____ $+$

Part 8   Refer to the pictures and complete the equation.

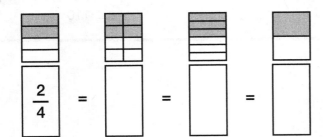

$$\dfrac{2}{4} = \quad = \quad =$$

© SRA/McGraw-Hill. Permission is granted to reproduce for school use.

Part 9	Write the addition or subtraction problem and answer for each row. Complete the table.

Total

		Total
	13	**65**
196	10	
248		**271**

Part 10	Work the problems.

a.

b.

c.

$$\begin{array}{r} 39 \\ \times\ 62 \end{array}$$

$$\begin{array}{r} 68 \\ \times\ 43 \end{array}$$

$$\begin{array}{r} 26 \\ \times\ 59 \end{array}$$

Part 11	Write the problem and find the area of each figure.

a.

10 in

3 in

_____

b.

6 ft

5 ft

_____

Part 12	Complete the sign to show $>$ or $<$ or $=$.

a. 65 _____ 27

b. 14 _____ 14

c. 96 _____ 110

Part 13	Work the problems.

a.

$$\begin{array}{r} 543 \\ -299 \end{array}$$

b.

$$\begin{array}{r} 105 \\ -92 \end{array}$$

© SRA/McGraw-Hill. Permission is granted to reproduce for school use.

Part 1

a. $4 \times 4 =$ ____

b. $1 \times 6 =$ ____

c. $6 \times 6 =$ ____

d. $2 \times 9 =$ ____

e. $5 \times 0 =$ ____

f. $7 \times 7 =$ ____

g. $3 \times 8 =$ ____

h. $6 \times 7 =$ ____

i. $3 \times 3 =$ ____

j. $9 \times 6 =$ ____

k. $8 \times 8 =$ ____

l. $3 \times 7 =$ ____

Part 2

	x	$\frac{x}{6}$	**y**
		Function	
A	54	$\frac{54}{6}$	9
B	24		
C	36		
D	18		

Part 3

Circle *more than 1*, *= 1*, or *less than 1* for each missing number.

a. $2 \times \blacksquare = \frac{12}{4}$

more than 1
= 1
less than 1

b. $\frac{4}{5} \times \blacksquare = \frac{16}{20}$

more than 1
= 1
less than 1

c. $\frac{14}{9} \times \blacksquare = \frac{6}{6}$

more than 1
= 1
less than 1

Part 4

Complete each equation to show the equivalent fractions.

a. $\frac{9}{4} = \frac{63}{\boxed{}}$

b. $\frac{6}{13} = \frac{\boxed{}}{39}$

Part 5

For each pair of pictures, complete each equation to show the equivalent fractions.

a.

$\boxed{} = \boxed{}$

b.

$\boxed{} = \boxed{}$

© SRA/McGraw-Hill. Permission is granted to reproduce for school use.

Part 6 Write the X value and the Y value for each point.

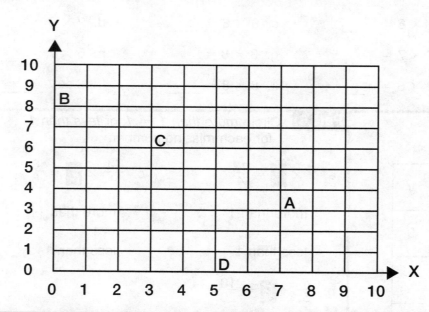

- Letter A. (X = ___, Y = ___
- Letter B. (X = ___, Y = ___
- Letter C. (X = ___, Y = ___
- Letter D. (X = ___, Y = ___

Part 7 Write a number in the table for each fact. Then figure out the missing numbers.

> The table is supposed to show the number of fish in Blue River and Snake River.

	Trout	Perch	**Total Fish**
Blue River	61		
Snake River			
Total for both rivers			

Fact 1: 132 fish were in the Blue River.

Fact 2: 59 trout were in the Snake River.

Fact 3: In the Snake River, there were 38 fewer perch than trout.

Part 8 Write the fraction for each description.

a. The numbers are 8 and 12. The fraction is less than 1.

b. The numbers are 6 and 9. The denominator is 6.

c. The numbers are 8 and 4. The fraction is more than 1.

© SRA/McGraw-Hill. Permission is granted to reproduce for school use.

Part 9 Write the problem and answer the question for each item.
Write the unit name in each answer.

a.

7 in

What's the height?

_____

b.

8 ft

3 ft

What's the area?

_____

c.

  2 in

What's the width?

_____

Part 10 Work the problems.

a. $5\overline{)155}$ b. $7\overline{)6328}$

c. $3\overline{)105}$ d. $2\overline{)178}$

e. $5\overline{)165}$

Part 11 Work the problems.

a. $\begin{array}{r} 9007 \\ -2495 \end{array}$ b. $\begin{array}{r} 4006 \\ -1248 \end{array}$ c. $\begin{array}{r} 5007 \\ -4316 \end{array}$

Part 12 Work the problems.

a. $\begin{array}{r} 534 \\ \times 49 \end{array}$ b. $\begin{array}{r} 629 \\ \times 32 \end{array}$

c. $\begin{array}{r} 29 \\ \times 46 \end{array}$ d. $\begin{array}{r} 215 \\ \times 29 \end{array}$

Part 13 Work the problems.

a. $\dfrac{3}{4} \times \dfrac{6}{3} =$ ☐   b. $\dfrac{8}{3} \times \dfrac{6}{5} =$ ☐

c. $\dfrac{6}{12} + \dfrac{9}{12} =$ ☐   d. $\dfrac{14}{16} - \dfrac{8}{6} =$ ☐

e. $\dfrac{18}{8} - \dfrac{13}{8} =$ ☐   d. $\dfrac{7}{10} + \dfrac{8}{10} =$ ☐

Part 14 Write the mixed number for each item.

a. $\dfrac{9}{12} =$ ☐   b. $6\overline{)45} =$ ☐

c. $\dfrac{33}{4} =$ ☐   d. $5\overline{)32} =$ ☐

© SRA/McGraw-Hill. Permission is granted to reproduce for school use.

Part 1 Work the problems.

a. $3\overline{)1209}$

b. $4\overline{)488}$

c. $9\overline{)936}$

d. $2\overline{)156}$

e. $5\overline{)950}$

f. $4\overline{)87}$

Part 2 Work the problems.

a. $\begin{array}{r} 846 \\ -\ 38 \\ \hline \end{array}$

b. $\begin{array}{r} 7062 \\ -6850 \\ \hline \end{array}$

c. $\begin{array}{r} 7003 \\ -2749 \\ \hline \end{array}$

d. $\begin{array}{r} 4008 \\ -\ 927 \\ \hline \end{array}$

Part 3 Work the problems.

a. $\begin{array}{r} 74 \\ \times\ 5 \\ \hline \end{array}$

b. $\begin{array}{r} 36 \\ \times 40 \\ \hline \end{array}$

c. $\begin{array}{r} 92 \\ \times 21 \\ \hline \end{array}$

d. $\begin{array}{r} 354 \\ \times\ 79 \\ \hline \end{array}$

Part 4 Complete the equations.

a. $9 = \dfrac{\boxed{}}{3}$

b. $\dfrac{8}{4} = \boxed{}$

c. $\dfrac{\boxed{}}{3} = 21$

d. $\dfrac{96}{3} = \boxed{}$

e.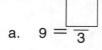
$5 = \dfrac{\boxed{}}{1} = \dfrac{\boxed{}}{4} = \dfrac{\boxed{}}{10}$

Part 5 Write the fraction to complete each equation.

a. $\dfrac{14}{5} - \dfrac{14}{5} = \boxed{}$

b. $\dfrac{7}{3} + \dfrac{2}{3} = \boxed{}$

c. $\dfrac{8}{2} \times \dfrac{3}{5} = \boxed{}$

d. $\dfrac{15}{10} - \dfrac{5}{10} = \boxed{}$

e. $\dfrac{1}{4} \times \dfrac{9}{8} = \boxed{}$

f. $\dfrac{7}{3} - 2 = \boxed{}$

g. $4 \times \dfrac{3}{5} = \boxed{}$

h. $9 + \dfrac{4}{3} = \boxed{}$

© SRA/McGraw-Hill. Permission is granted to reproduce for school use.

Part 6 Complete the equations to show the equivalent fractions.

a. $\dfrac{2}{5} = \dfrac{4}{}$

b. $\dfrac{7}{3} = \dfrac{}{12}$

c. $\dfrac{2}{5} = \dfrac{62}{}$

Part 7 For each item, circle the larger value.

a. $\dfrac{7}{4}$ $\dfrac{5}{4}$

b. 3 $\dfrac{6}{9}$

c. $\dfrac{4}{5}$ $\dfrac{3}{2}$

d. $\dfrac{2}{3}$ $\dfrac{4}{4}$

e. $\dfrac{8}{7}$ $\dfrac{8}{3}$

f. $\dfrac{10}{10}$ $\dfrac{6}{3}$

g. $\dfrac{16}{5}$ 3

h. 8.00 100

i. $\dfrac{16}{20}$ $\dfrac{3}{4}$

j. $.44$ $\dfrac{4}{9}$

Part 8 Write the decimal number for each value.

a. $\dfrac{8}{100} =$

b. $6 + \dfrac{9}{100} =$

c. $\dfrac{15}{10} =$

d. $2\dfrac{46}{100} =$

e. $\dfrac{3}{4} =$

Part 9 Write the mixed number for each item.

a. $\dfrac{37}{5} =$

b. $1.03 =$

c. $\dfrac{85}{2} =$

d. $4\overline{)49} =$

Part 10 Write the fraction to complete each equation.

a. $7\dfrac{2}{10} = \boxed{}$

b. $.49 = \boxed{}$

c. $8\overline{)67} = \boxed{}$

d. $5.00 = \boxed{}$

© SRA/McGraw-Hill. Permission is granted to reproduce for school use.

Part 11 Write the fraction for each item.

a.

b.

c.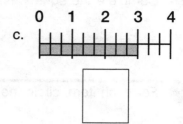

Part 12 Each item tells about a fraction. Write the fraction for each item.

a. A picture shows 7 parts in each unit. 14 parts are shaded.

b. The numbers for this fraction are 17 and 25.
   The fraction is greater than 1.

c. The fraction is less than 1.
   The numbers for this fraction are 2 and 5.

Part 13 Each item tells about a fraction. Write the fraction for each item.

a. The numbers for the fraction are 18 and 7.
   The numerator is 18.

b. The denominator of a fraction is 20. The other number is 25.

© SRA/McGraw-Hill. Permission is granted to reproduce for school use.

Part 14 The price tags show the cost of a mug, a cookbook, a pot, and a bowl. For each item, use the information to write a column problem and answer the question.

 $4.03    $2.38 $2.48 $2.63

a.   How much more is the cost of the bowl than the cost of the cookbook? _____

b.   Jim has $6.34 more than the cost of the mug. How much money does Jim have? _____

c.   Which item costs $1.55 less than the mug? _____

Part 15   Write the fourth value for each sequence.

a. 15, 12, 9, _____

b. 1, 3, 9, _____

c. 3, 7, 11, _____

d. 2, $\frac{2}{3}$, $\frac{2}{9}$, _____

© SRA/McGraw-Hill. Permission is granted to reproduce for school use.

Part 16 The table shows *x* and *y* values for three points on a line. Under the word **function,** write the linear function for the line.

x	function	y
2		4
12		14
3		5

Part 17 Each item shows two line segments. In the box next to each item, write **P** if the line segments are parallel. Write **I** if the line segments intersect. Do not write anything if the line segments are not parallel and do not intersect.

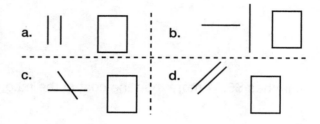

Part 18 The table shows a function and x and y values for three points. On the coordinate grid, plot the points and draw the line for the function.

x	function	y
	x − 3	
4	4 − 3	1
10	10 − 3	7
3	3 − 3	0

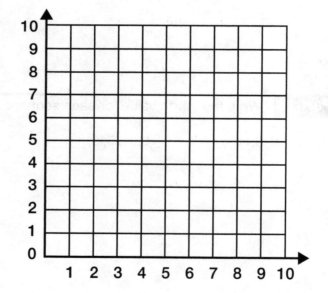

© SRA/McGraw-Hill. Permission is granted to reproduce for school use.

Part 19 Write the *x* and *y* values for each point in the table.

	x	*y*
A		
B		
C		

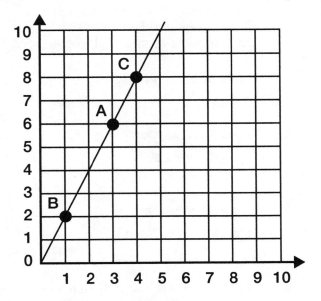

Part 20 Write a number in the table for each fact. Figure out the missing numbers.

	Rowe stream	Columbia stream	Total for both streams
Salmon			
Fish that are not salmon			
Total fish			

There are two streams: Rowe stream and Columbia stream.

In each stream, there are salmon and fish that are not salmon.

Facts:

a. The total number of salmon in the two streams is 85.

b. There are 46 fish that are not salmon in Columbia stream.

c. 72 fish that are not salmon are in Rowe stream.

d. 51 salmon are in Columbia stream.

© SRA/McGraw-Hill. Permission is granted to reproduce for school use.

Part 21 This table shows the trout and fish that are not trout in two creeks: Clear Creek and Rush Creek. Use the table to answer the questions.

	Rush Creek	Clear Creek	Total
Trout	187	394	**581**
Fish that are not trout	451	386	**837**
Total Fish	**638**	**780**	**1418**

a. How many trout are in Rush Creek? _____

b. What's the total number of fish in both creeks?

_____

c. How many more fish are in Clear Creek than in Rush Creek? _____

d. In Clear Creek, there are only rainbow trout and brown trout. There are 147 rainbow trout. How many brown trout are in Clear Creek? _____

© SRA/McGraw-Hill. Permission is granted to reproduce for school use.

Part 22 For each item, write the problem and answer the question. Write the unit name in each answer.

a.
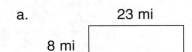
23 mi

8 mi

What is the area of rectangle A?

AREA = _____

b.

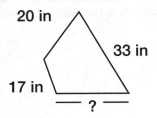
20 in

33 in

17 in

?

The perimeter of figure B is 91 inches. What is the length of the missing side?

LENGTH = _____

c.
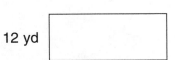
29 yd

12 yd

What is the perimeter of rectangle C?

PERIMETER = _____

d.
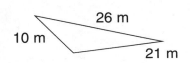
26 m

10 m

21 m

What is the perimeter of figure D?

PERIMETER = _____

e.
9 ft

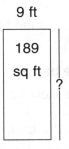
189 sq ft

?

What is the height of the rectangle?

HEIGHT = _____

f.
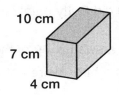
10 cm

7 cm

4 cm

What is the volume of rectangular solid F?

VOLUME = _____

g. A rectangle is 16 feet wide. The rectangle is 24 feet high. What is the area of the rectangle?

_____

© SRA/McGraw-Hill. Permission is granted to reproduce for school use.

Part 23 The picture shows the stars, circles, boxes, and **X**s in a bag. Use the picture to answer the questions.

a. What fraction of objects in the bag are stars?

b. What fraction of objects in the bag are boxes?

c. If you reached into the bag and drew out 1 object, would the object most likely be a star, a circle, a box, or an **X**? _____

d. 1 object is drawn from the bag. Write the fraction that shows the chances that the object is an **X**.

Part 24 For each item, write the number problem and the answer. Then answer the question.

a. Buffy and Jim painted a wall. Jim painted $\frac{2}{7}$ of the wall. What fraction of the wall did Buffy paint?

b. There were 178 birds in a swamp. 69 of the birds were ducks. What fraction of the birds were not ducks?

c. 24 people were on a boat. At the first port, 37 more people got on the boat, and 15 people got off the boat. At the second port, 8 people got on the boat. At the third port, 26 people got off the boat. How many people were left on the boat? _____

d. Dave had some money. He went to the store and bought a watch for $11.74. He bought some gum for $.30. He bought a hat for $7.06. Jim ended up with $8.21 after purchasing the items. How much money did Jim have to a start with? _____

© SRA/McGraw-Hill. Permission is granted to reproduce for school use.

Part 25   For each item, write the number problem and the answer. Then answer the question.

a.   There were hawks and crows in the forest. The ratio of hawks to crows was 2 to 7. There were
56 hawks. How many crows were in the forest? _____

b.   Betty earned $9.42 for every 3 hours she worked. Betty worked 36 hours. How much money did
Betty earn? _____

c.   Each hat costs $6. How many hats could you buy with $366? _____

© SRA/McGraw-Hill. Permission is granted to reproduce for school use.

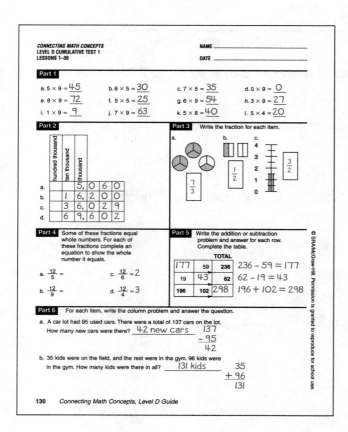

Part 1

a. $5 \times 9 = 45$ b. $6 \times 5 = 30$ c. $7 \times 5 = 35$ d. $0 \times 9 = 0$
e. $8 \times 9 = 72$ f. $5 \times 5 = 25$ g. $6 \times 9 = 54$ h. $3 \times 9 = 27$
i. $1 \times 9 = 9$ j. $7 \times 9 = 63$ k. $5 \times 8 = 40$ l. $5 \times 4 = 20$

Part 2

	hundred thousand	ten thousand	thousand			
a.			5	0	6	0
b.		1	6	2	0	0
c.	3	6	0	2	9	
d.	6	9	6	0	2	

Part 3 Write the fraction for each item.

a. $\frac{7}{3}$ b. $\frac{1}{2}$ c. $\frac{3}{2}$

Part 4 Some of these fractions equal whole numbers. For each of these fractions complete an equation to show the whole number it equals.

a. $\frac{12}{5} =$ c. $\frac{12}{6} = 2$
b. $\frac{12}{9} =$ d. $\frac{12}{4} = 3$

Part 5 Write the addition or subtraction problem and answer for each row. Complete the table.

		TOTAL	
177	59	236	$236 - 59 = 177$
19	43	62	$62 - 19 = 43$
196	102	298	$196 + 102 = 298$

Part 6 For each item, write the column problem and answer the question.

a. A car lot had 95 used cars. There were a total of 137 cars on the lot. How many new cars were there? __42 new cars__
$$\begin{array}{r} 137 \\ -\ 95 \\ \hline 42 \end{array}$$

b. 35 kids were on the field, and the rest were in the gym. 96 kids were in the gym. How many kids were there in all? __131 kids__
$$\begin{array}{r} 35 \\ +\ 96 \\ \hline 131 \end{array}$$

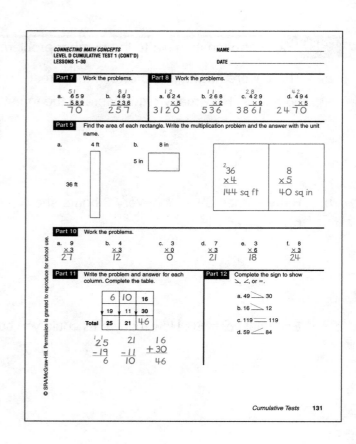

Part 7 Work the problems.

a. $\begin{array}{r} \overset{5\ 1}{6\ 5\ 9} \\ -\ 5\ 8\ 9 \\ \hline 7\ 0 \end{array}$ b. $\begin{array}{r} \overset{8\ 1}{4\ 9\ 3} \\ -\ 2\ 3\ 6 \\ \hline 2\ 5\ 7 \end{array}$

Part 8 Work the problems.

a. $\begin{array}{r} \overset{1\ 2}{6\ 2\ 4} \\ \times\ \ \ 5 \\ \hline 3\ 1\ 2\ 0 \end{array}$ b. $\begin{array}{r} \overset{1\ 1}{2\ 6\ 8} \\ \times\ \ \ 2 \\ \hline 5\ 3\ 6 \end{array}$ c. $\begin{array}{r} \overset{2\ 8}{4\ 2\ 9} \\ \times\ \ \ 9 \\ \hline 3\ 8\ 6\ 1 \end{array}$ d. $\begin{array}{r} \overset{4\ 2}{4\ 9\ 4} \\ \times\ \ \ 5 \\ \hline 2\ 4\ 7\ 0 \end{array}$

Part 9 Find the area of each rectangle. Write the multiplication problem and the answer with the unit name.

a. 4 ft, 36 ft: $\begin{array}{r} \overset{2}{3\ 6} \\ \times\ 4 \\ \hline 144 \text{ sq ft} \end{array}$

b. 8 in, 5 in: $\begin{array}{r} 8 \\ \times\ 5 \\ \hline 40 \text{ sq in} \end{array}$

Part 10 Work the problems.

a. $\begin{array}{r} 9 \\ \times\ 3 \\ \hline 27 \end{array}$ b. $\begin{array}{r} 4 \\ \times\ 3 \\ \hline 12 \end{array}$ c. $\begin{array}{r} 3 \\ \times\ 0 \\ \hline 0 \end{array}$ d. $\begin{array}{r} 7 \\ \times\ 3 \\ \hline 21 \end{array}$ e. $\begin{array}{r} 3 \\ \times\ 6 \\ \hline 18 \end{array}$ f. $\begin{array}{r} 8 \\ \times\ 3 \\ \hline 24 \end{array}$

Part 11 Write the problem and answer for each column. Complete the table.

	6	10	16
	19	11	30
Total	25	21	46

$\begin{array}{r} \overset{1\ 1}{2\ 5} \\ -\ 1\ 9 \\ \hline 6 \end{array}$ $\begin{array}{r} 21 \\ -\ 11 \\ \hline 10 \end{array}$ $\begin{array}{r} 16 \\ +\ 30 \\ \hline 46 \end{array}$

Part 12 Complete the sign to show >, <, or =.

a. $49 > 30$
b. $16 > 12$
c. $119 = 119$
d. $59 < 84$

© SRA/McGraw-Hill. Permission is granted to reproduce for school use.

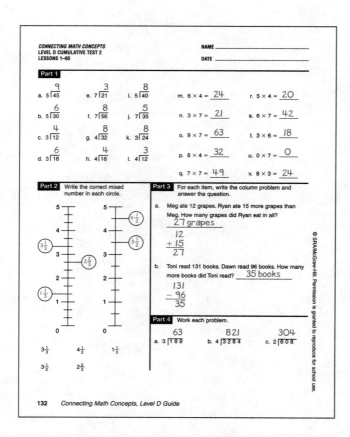

Part 1

a. $5\overline{)45} = 9$ e. $7\overline{)21} = 3$ i. $5\overline{)40} = 8$ m. $6 \times 4 = 24$ r. $5 \times 4 = 20$
b. $5\overline{)30} = 6$ f. $7\overline{)56} = 8$ j. $7\overline{)35} = 5$ n. $3 \times 7 = 21$ s. $6 \times 7 = 42$
c. $3\overline{)12} = 4$ g. $4\overline{)32} = 8$ k. $3\overline{)24} = 8$ o. $9 \times 7 = 63$ t. $3 \times 6 = 18$
d. $3\overline{)18} = 6$ h. $4\overline{)16} = 4$ l. $4\overline{)12} = 3$ p. $8 \times 4 = 32$ u. $0 \times 7 = 0$
        q. $7 \times 7 = 49$ v. $8 \times 3 = 24$

Part 2 Write the correct mixed number in each circle.

(number line circles) $3\frac{1}{3}$, $2\frac{2}{3}$, $1\frac{1}{3}$, $4\frac{1}{2}$, $3\frac{1}{2}$

$3\frac{1}{3}$ $4\frac{1}{2}$ $1\frac{1}{3}$
$3\frac{1}{2}$ $2\frac{2}{3}$

Part 3 For each item, write the column problem and answer the question.

a. Meg ate 12 grapes. Ryan ate 15 more grapes than Meg. How many grapes did Ryan eat in all? __27 grapes__
$$\begin{array}{r} 12 \\ +\ 15 \\ \hline 27 \end{array}$$

b. Toni read 131 books. Dawn read 96 books. How many more books did Toni read? __35 books__
$$\begin{array}{r} 131 \\ -\ 96 \\ \hline 35 \end{array}$$

Part 4 Work each problem.

a. $3\overline{)189} = 63$ b. $4\overline{)3284} = 821$ c. $2\overline{)608} = 304$

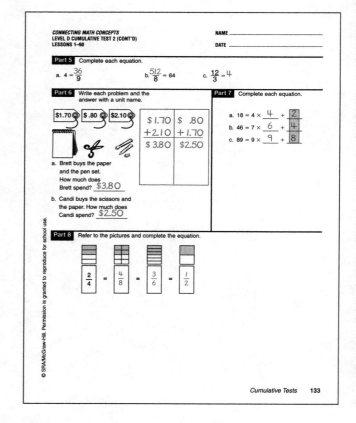

Part 5 Complete each equation.

a. $4 = \frac{36}{9}$ b. $\frac{512}{8} = 64$ c. $\frac{12}{3} = 4$

Part 6 Write each problem and the answer with a unit name.

$1.70 $.80 $2.10

$\begin{array}{r} \$1.70 \\ +2.10 \\ \hline \$3.80 \end{array}$ $\begin{array}{r} \$\ .80 \\ +1.70 \\ \hline \$2.50 \end{array}$

a. Brett buys the paper and the pen set. How much does Brett spend? __$3.80__

b. Candi buys the scissors and the paper. How much does Candi spend? __$2.50__

Part 7 Complete each equation.

a. $18 = 4 \times 4 + 2$
b. $46 = 7 \times 6 + 4$
c. $89 = 9 \times 9 + 8$

Part 8 Refer to the pictures and complete the equation.

$\frac{2}{4} = \frac{4}{8} = \frac{3}{6} = \frac{1}{2}$

© SRA/McGraw-Hill. Permission is granted to reproduce for school use.

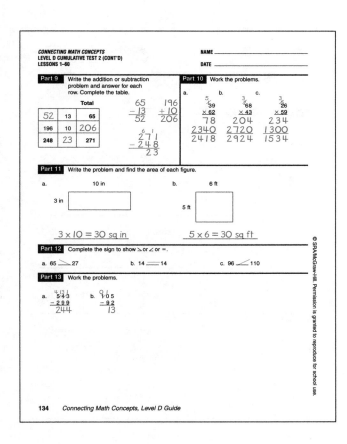

CONNECTING MATH CONCEPTS
LEVEL D CUMULATIVE TEST 2 (CONT'D)
LESSONS 1–60

NAME
DATE

Part 9 Write the addition or subtraction problem and answer for each row. Complete the table.

		Total
52	13	65
196	10	206
248	23	271

$$65 - 13 = 52$$
$$196 + 10 = 206$$
$$271 - 248 = 23$$

Part 10 Work the problems.

a.
$$39 \times 62 = 78,\ 2340,\ 2418$$
b.
$$68 \times 43 = 204,\ 2720,\ 2924$$
c.
$$26 \times 59 = 234,\ 1300,\ 1534$$

Part 11 Write the problem and find the area of each figure.

a. 10 in, 3 in
$$3 \times 10 = 30 \text{ sq in}$$
b. 6 ft, 5 ft
$$5 \times 6 = 30 \text{ sq ft}$$

Part 12 Complete the sign to show $>$ or $<$ or $=$.

a. $65 > 27$ b. $14 = 14$ c. $96 < 110$

Part 13 Work the problems.

a. $543 - 299 = 244$ b. $105 - 92 = 13$

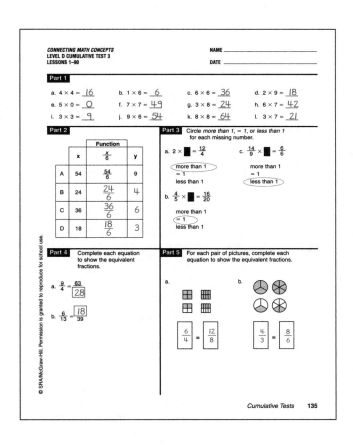

CONNECTING MATH CONCEPTS
LEVEL D CUMULATIVE TEST 3
LESSONS 1–90

NAME
DATE

Part 1

a. $4 \times 4 = 16$ b. $1 \times 6 = 6$ c. $6 \times 6 = 36$ d. $2 \times 9 = 18$
e. $5 \times 0 = 0$ f. $7 \times 7 = 49$ g. $3 \times 8 = 24$ h. $6 \times 7 = 42$
i. $3 \times 3 = 9$ j. $9 \times 6 = 54$ k. $8 \times 8 = 64$ l. $3 \times 7 = 21$

Part 2

	Function	
x	$\frac{x}{6}$	**y**
A	54	$\frac{54}{6}$ = 9
B	24	$\frac{24}{6}$ = 4
C	36	$\frac{36}{6}$ = 6
D	18	$\frac{18}{6}$ = 3

Part 3 Circle *more than 1*, *= 1*, or *less than 1* for each missing number.

a. $2 \times \blacksquare = \frac{12}{4}$ — (more than 1 / = 1) circled
c. $\frac{14}{9} \times \blacksquare = \frac{6}{6}$ — (less than 1) circled
b. $\frac{4}{5} \times \blacksquare = \frac{16}{20}$ — (= 1) circled

Part 4 Complete each equation to show the equivalent fractions.

$$\frac{9}{4} = \frac{63}{28}$$
$$\frac{6}{13} = \frac{18}{39}$$

Part 5 For each pair of pictures, complete each equation to show the equivalent fractions.

a. $\frac{6}{4} = \frac{12}{8}$ b. $\frac{4}{3} = \frac{8}{6}$

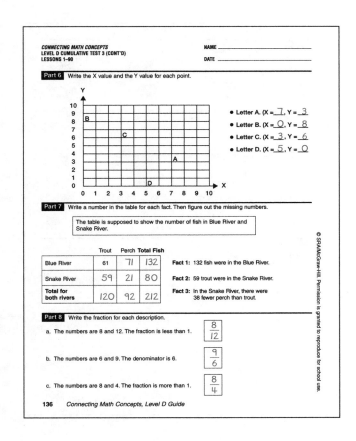

CONNECTING MATH CONCEPTS
LEVEL D CUMULATIVE TEST 3 (CONT'D)
LESSONS 1–90

NAME
DATE

Part 6 Write the X value and the Y value for each point.

Letter A. (X = 7, Y = 3)
Letter B. (X = 0, Y = 8)
Letter C. (X = 3, Y = 6)
Letter D. (X = 5, Y = 0)

Part 7 Write a number in the table for each fact. Then figure out the missing numbers.

The table is supposed to show the number of fish in Blue River and Snake River.

	Trout	Perch	Total Fish
Blue River	61	71	132
Snake River	59	21	80
Total for both rivers	120	92	212

Fact 1: 132 fish were in the Blue River.
Fact 2: 59 trout were in the Snake River.
Fact 3: In the Snake River, there were 38 fewer perch than trout.

Part 8 Write the fraction for each description.

a. The numbers are 8 and 12. The fraction is less than 1. $\frac{8}{12}$

b. The numbers are 6 and 9. The denominator is 6. $\frac{9}{6}$

c. The numbers are 8 and 4. The fraction is more than 1. $\frac{8}{4}$

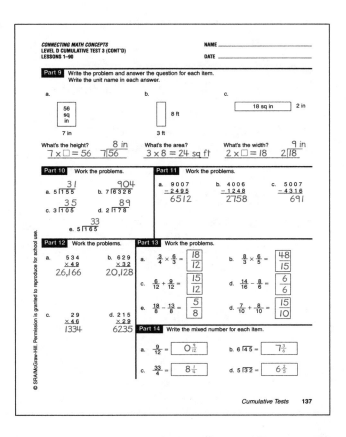

CONNECTING MATH CONCEPTS
LEVEL D CUMULATIVE TEST 3 (CONT'D)
LESSONS 1–90

NAME
DATE

Part 9 Write the problem and answer the question for each item. Write the unit name in each answer.

a. 56 sq in, 7 in. What's the height? 8 in
$$7 \times \square = 56, \quad 7\overline{)56} = 8$$
b. 8 ft, 3 ft. What's the area?
$$3 \times 8 = 24 \text{ sq ft}$$
c. 18 sq in, 2 in. What's the width? 9 in
$$2 \times \square = 18, \quad 2\overline{)18} = 9$$

Part 10 Work the problems.

a. $5\overline{)155} = 31$ b. $7\overline{)6328} = 904$
c. $3\overline{)105} = 35$ d. $2\overline{)178} = 89$
e. $5\overline{)165} = 33$

Part 11 Work the problems.

a. $9007 - 2495 = 6512$ b. $4006 - 1248 = 2758$ c. $5007 - 4316 = 691$

Part 12 Work the problems.

a. $534 \times 49 = 26,166$ b. $629 \times 32 = 20,128$
c. $29 \times 46 = 1334$ d. $215 \times 29 = 6235$

Part 13 Work the problems.

a. $\frac{3}{4} \times \frac{6}{3} = \frac{18}{12}$ b. $\frac{8}{3} \times \frac{6}{5} = \frac{48}{15}$
c. $\frac{6}{12} + \frac{9}{12} = \frac{15}{12}$ d. $\frac{14}{16} - \frac{8}{16} = \frac{6}{6}$
e. $\frac{18}{8} - \frac{13}{8} = \frac{5}{8}$ d. $\frac{7}{10} + \frac{8}{10} = \frac{15}{10}$

Part 14 Write the mixed number for each item.

a. $\frac{9}{12} = 0\frac{9}{12}$ b. $6\overline{)45} = 7\frac{3}{6}$
c. $\frac{33}{4} = 8\frac{1}{4}$ d. $5\overline{)32} = 6\frac{2}{5}$

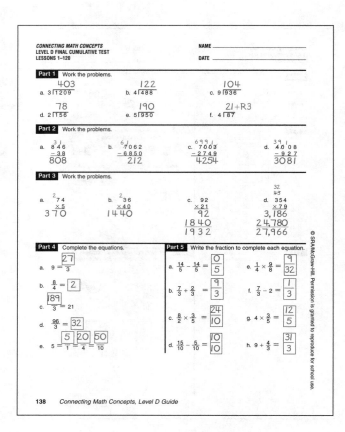

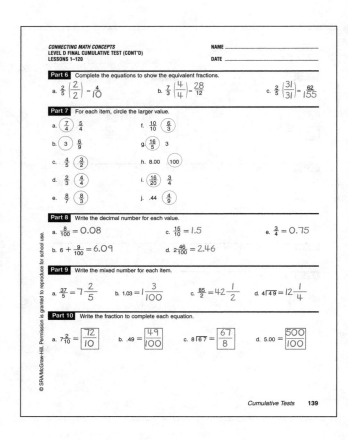

Page 140

Part 11 Write the fraction for each item.

a. [circles] $\dfrac{7}{4}$ b. [bars] $\dfrac{3}{5}$ c. [number line 0 1 2 3 4] $\dfrac{9}{3}$

Part 12 Each item tells about a fraction. Write the fraction for each item.

a. A picture shows 7 parts in each unit. 14 parts are shaded. $\dfrac{14}{7}$

b. The numbers for this fraction are 17 and 25. The fraction is greater than 1. $\dfrac{25}{17}$

c. The fraction is less than 1. The numbers for this fraction are 2 and 5. $\dfrac{2}{5}$

Part 13 Each item tells about a fraction. Write the fraction for each item.

a. The numbers for the fraction are 18 and 7. The numerator is 18. $\dfrac{18}{7}$

b. The denominator of a fraction is 20. The other number is 25. $\dfrac{25}{20}$

© SRA/McGraw-Hill. Permission is granted to reproduce for school use.

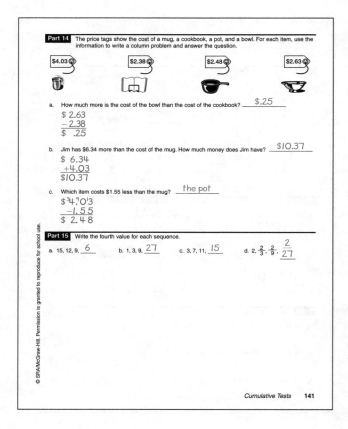

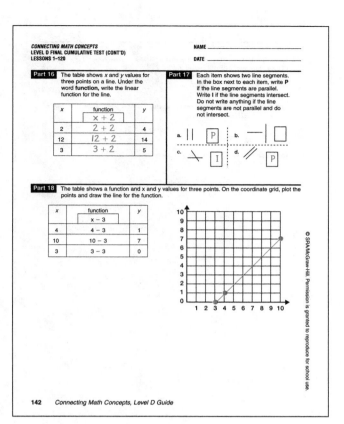

Part 16 The table shows *x* and *y* values for three points on a line. Under the word **function**, write the linear function for the line.

x	function $x + 2$	y
2	2 + 2	4
12	12 + 2	14
3	3 + 2	5

Part 17 Each item shows two line segments. In the box next to each item, write **P** if the line segments are parallel. Write **I** if the line segments intersect. Do not write anything if the line segments are not parallel and do not intersect.

a. ‖ **P**   b. — ▢

c. ✕ **I**   d. ⫽ **P**

Part 18 The table shows a function and *x* and *y* values for three points. On the coordinate grid, plot the points and draw the line for the function.

x	function $x - 3$	y
4	4 − 3	1
10	10 − 3	7
3	3 − 3	0

© SRA/McGraw-Hill. Permission is granted to reproduce for school use.

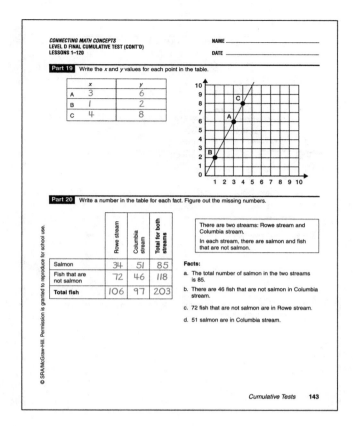

Part 19 Write the *x* and *y* values for each point in the table.

	x	y
A	3	6
B	1	2
C	4	8

Part 20 Write a number in the table for each fact. Figure out the missing numbers.

	Rowe stream	Columbia stream	Total for both streams
Salmon	34	51	85
Fish that are not salmon	72	46	118
Total fish	106	97	203

There are two streams: Rowe stream and Columbia stream.

In each stream, there are salmon and fish that are not salmon.

Facts:

a. The total number of salmon in the two streams is 85.

b. There are 46 fish that are not salmon in Columbia stream.

c. 72 fish that are not salmon are in Rowe stream.

d. 51 salmon are in Columbia stream.

© SRA/McGraw-Hill. Permission is granted to reproduce for school use.

Part 21 This table shows the trout and fish that are not trout in two creeks: Clear Creek and Rush Creek. Use the table to answer the questions.

	Rush Creek	Clear Creek	Total
Trout	187	394	581
Fish that are not trout	451	386	837
Total Fish	638	780	1418

a. How many trout are in Rush Creek? ___187___

b. What's the total number of fish in both creeks? 1418

c. How many more fish are in Clear Creek than in Rush Creek? 142

d. In Clear Creek, there are only rainbow trout and brown trout. There are 147 rainbow trout. How many brown trout are in Clear Creek? ___247___

© SRA/McGraw-Hill. Permission is granted to reproduce for school use.

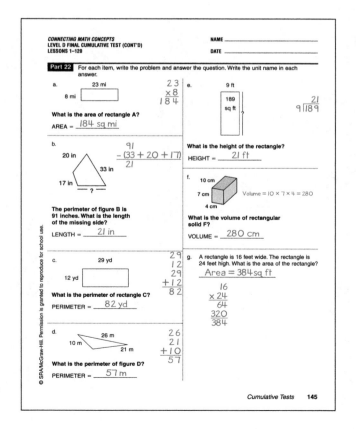

Part 22 For each item, write the problem and answer the question. Write the unit name in each answer.

a. 23 mi, 8 mi

$$\begin{array}{r} 23 \\ \times 8 \\ \hline 184 \end{array}$$

What is the area of rectangle A?

AREA = ___184 sq mi___

b. 20 in, 33 in, 17 in, ?

$$\begin{array}{r} 91 \\ -(33 + 20 + 17) \\ \hline 21 \end{array}$$

The perimeter of figure B is 91 inches. What is the length of the missing side?

LENGTH = ___21 in___

c. 29 yd, 12 yd

$$\begin{array}{r} 29 \\ 12 \\ 29 \\ +12 \\ \hline 82 \end{array}$$

What is the perimeter of rectangle C?

PERIMETER = ___82 yd___

d. 26 m, 10 m, 21 m

$$\begin{array}{r} 26 \\ 21 \\ +10 \\ \hline 57 \end{array}$$

What is the perimeter of figure D?

PERIMETER = ___57 m___

e. 9 ft, 189 sq ft, ?

$$\begin{array}{r} 21 \\ 9\overline{)189} \end{array}$$

What is the height of the rectangle?

HEIGHT = ___21 ft___

f. 10 cm, 7 cm, 4 cm

Volume = $10 \times 7 \times 4 = 280$

What is the volume of rectangular solid F?

VOLUME = ___280 cm___

g. A rectangle is 16 feet wide. The rectangle is 24 feet high. What is the area of the rectangle?

Area = 384 sq ft

$$\begin{array}{r} 16 \\ \times 24 \\ \hline 64 \\ 320 \\ \hline 384 \end{array}$$

© SRA/McGraw-Hill. Permission is granted to reproduce for school use.

© SRA/McGraw-Hill. Permission is granted to reproduce for school use.

Part 23 The picture shows the stars, circles, boxes, and **X**s in a bag. Use the picture to answer the questions.

a. What fraction of objects in the bag are stars? $\dfrac{3}{10}$

b. What fraction of objects in the bag are boxes? $\dfrac{1}{10}$

c. If you reached into the bag and drew out 1 object, would the object most likely be a star, a circle, a box, or an **X**? _Circle_

d. 1 object is drawn from the bag. Write the fraction that shows the chances that the object is an **X**. $\dfrac{2}{10}$

Part 24 For each item, write the number problem and the answer. Then answer the question.

a. Buffy and Jim painted a wall. Jim painted $\frac{2}{7}$ of the wall. What fraction of the wall did Buffy paint?

$$\frac{7}{7} - \frac{2}{7} = \frac{5}{7}$$

b. There were 178 birds in a swamp. 69 of the birds were ducks. What fraction of the birds were not ducks?

$$\frac{178}{178} - \frac{69}{178} = \frac{109}{178}$$

c. 24 people were on a boat. At the first port, 37 more people got on the boat, and 15 people got off the boat. At the second port, 8 people got on the boat. At the third port, 26 people got off the boat. How many people were left on the boat? _28 people_

$$\begin{array}{r} 24 \\ +37 \\ \hline 61 \\ -15 \\ \hline 46 \end{array} \qquad \begin{array}{r} 46 \\ +8 \\ \hline 54 \\ -26 \\ \hline 28 \end{array}$$

d. Dave had some money. He went to the store and bought a watch for $11.74. He bought some gum for $.30. He bought a hat for $7.06. Jim ended up with $8.21 after purchasing the items. How much money did Jim have to a start with? _$27.31_

$$\begin{array}{r} \$11.47 \\ .30 \\ +7.06 \\ \hline \$19.10 \end{array} \qquad \begin{array}{r} \$19.10 \\ +8.21 \\ \hline \$27.31 \end{array}$$

© SRA/McGraw-Hill. Permission is granted to reproduce for school use.

Part 25 For each item, write the number problem and the answer. Then answer the question.

a. There were hawks and crows in the forest. The ratio of hawks to crows was 2 to 7. There were 56 hawks. How many crows were in the forest? _196 crows_

$$\frac{h}{c} = \frac{2}{7} = \frac{56}{x} = 2x = 56(7) \quad x = \frac{56(7)}{2} \quad x = 28(7) \quad x = \underset{\text{crows}}{196}$$

b. Betty earned $9.42 for every 3 hours she worked. Betty worked 36 hours. How much money did Betty earn? _$113.04_

$$\frac{9.42}{3} = \frac{x}{36} = 3x = 9.42(36) = x = \frac{9.42(36)}{3} \quad x = 9.42(12) \quad x = 113.04$$

c. Each hat costs $6. How many hats could you buy with $366? _61 hats_

$$\frac{366}{6} = x \qquad 6 \overline{)366} \;\; \begin{array}{r} 61 \\ \underline{36} \\ 6 \\ \underline{6} \\ 0 \end{array}$$

Remedy Summary CMC D

Name	Cumulative Test 1 Check parts not passed											
	1	2	3	4	5	6	7	8	9	10	11	12
1.												
2.												
3.												
4.												
5.												
6.												
7.												
8.												
9.												
10.												
11.												
12.												
13.												
14.												
15.												
16.												
17.												
18.												
19.												
20.												
21.												
22.												
23.												
24.												
25.												
26.												
27.												
28.												
29.												
30.												

Copyright © SRA/McGraw-Hill. Permission is granted to reproduce for school use.

Remedy Summary CMC D

Name	Cumulative Test 2 Check parts not passed												
	1	2	3	4	5	6	7	8	9	10	11	12	13
1.													
2.													
3.													
4.													
5.													
6.													
7.													
8.													
9.													
10.													
11.													
12.													
13.													
14.													
15.													
16.													
17.													
18.													
19.													
20.													
21.													
22.													
23.													
24.													
25.													
26.													
27.													
28.													
29.													
30.													

Copyright © SRA/McGraw-Hill. Permission is granted to reproduce for school use.

Name	Cumulative Test 3													
	Check parts not passed													
	1	2	3	4	5	6	7	8	9	10	11	12	13	14
1.														
2.														
3.														
4.														
5.														
6.														
7.														
8.														
9.														
10.														
11.														
12.														
13.														
14.														
15.														
16.														
17.														
18.														
19.														
20.														
21.														
22.														
23.														
24.														
25.														
26.														
27.														
28.														
29.														
30.														

Copyright © SRA/McGraw-Hill. Permission is granted to reproduce for school use.

Remedy Summary CMC D

Name	Final Cumulative Test Check parts not passed																								
	1	2	3	4	5	6	7	8	9	10	11	12	13	14	15	16	17	18	19	20	21	22	23	24	25
1.																									
2.																									
3.																									
4.																									
5.																									
6.																									
7.																									
8.																									
9.																									
10.																									
11.																									
12.																									
13.																									
14.																									
15.																									
16.																									
17.																									
18.																									
19.																									
20.																									
21.																									
22.																									
23.																									
24.																									
25.																									
26.																									
27.																									
28.																									
29.																									
30.																									

Copyright © SRA/McGraw-Hill. Permission is granted to reproduce for school use.

Appendix B

Objectives Facts

Multiplication	Objectives	Lessons
	Use a number map to organize the multiplication facts that involve 5.	1, 4–8, 10
	Use a number map to organize the multiplication facts that involve 9.	5–7, 9
	Write answers to multiplication problems that involve 9.	8, 13
	Write answers to multiplication facts, some of which have a 1 or a zero.	9
	Complete numbers in a number map for threes.	11, 12
	Use number maps to organize multiplication facts that involve 3.	13–17, 19
	Say and work multiplication problems that have a missing middle number or a missing last number.	14–16, 18
	Write answers to multiplication facts that involve 3.	18
	Figure out the missing middle number for multiplication problems that have 9.	23–25
	Figure out the missing middle number or the missing first number for multiplication problems that involve 9.	26
	Use number maps to organize the multiplication facts that involve 4.	28
	Complete a number map for fours and use the map to write answers to multiplication problems that involve 4.	29, 31
	Write answers to multiplication facts that involve 4.	32, 36, 37, 56
	Complete a number map for multiplying by 7.	48, 50
	Use a number map to organize multiplication facts that involve 7.	49–52
	Write answers to multiplication facts that involve 7.	55–57
	Work with "square" facts for multiplying.	58, 59
	Complete a number map for multiplying by 6.	63, 64, 66
	Write answers to multiplication problems that involve 6.	65, 67, 68

	Objectives	Lessons
Division	Write algebra multiplication problems as division problems.	21–24, 64, 71–73
	Write division problems from statements that tell about "times."	25–27
	Write answers to division fact problems.	28, 31, 34, 37–39, 48
	Apply division rule for 5 to numerals that end in zero or 5.	31, 32
	Work a set of problems that divide by 5 and 9.	33
	Solve division problems that divide by 3.	34–36, 38
	Work division problems that have zero as a dividend.	35
	Solve division problems that involve 4.	42–45, 56
	Write and solve dictated division-fact problems.	55, 56
	Use a number map to organize division facts that involve 7.	58–60
	Write answers to division problems that divide by 6.	76, 77, 86
	Work a set of division problems that divide by 7, 6, 4 and 3.	87

CALCULATOR SKILLS

Objective	Lessons
Use a calculator to check answers to problems.	4, 5, 8
Use a calculator to check addition problems that have more than two addends.	6
Solve column subtraction problems. Then check answers with a calculator.	12, 17
Write and solve column subtraction problems from row problems. Then check answers with a calculator.	13, 14
Solve column multiplication problems. Then check answers with a calculator.	38

WHOLE NUMBER OPERATIONS

Objective	Lessons
Write and solve column addition problems.	1
Work a set of problems that calls for different operations: addition, subtraction, multiplication.	5
Solve multiplication problems that involve a money amount and a whole number.	89, 91
Estimate the sums of addition problems involving hundreds or thousands numbers.	97, 98

	Objectives	Lessons
MENTAL ARITHMETIC		

	Objectives	Lessons
	Write answers to orally presented addition problems that have a 2-digit and a 1-digit addend.	49
	Work mental addition problems that require renaming.	55, 57
	Solve mental addition problems of the form: 56 plus what number equals 60?	62–64
	Solve problems of the form: Some number plus 1 equals 600.	78, 79, 81, 82

COLUMN MULTIPLICATION

	Objectives	Lessons
Times 1 Digit	Solve column multiplication problems that multiply 2-digit numerals by 1-digit numerals.	1–3, 5
	Solve column multiplication problems that multiply 3-digit numerals by 1-digit numerals.	6, 8
	Solve column multiplication problems that have a zero.	15, 16
	Solve multiplication problems that have a 5-digit value times a 1-digit value.	23
Times 2 Digits	Solve row problems that multiply a 1-digit value by a tens number.	32, 33
	Solve column problems that multiply a 1-digit value by a tens number.	34, 35
	Solve column problems that multiply a 2-digit value by a tens value.	36
	Solve column multiplication problems. Then check answers with a calculator.	38
	Solve 2-digit-times-2-digit multiplication problems that require no carrying or carrying for the tens only.	41–44
	Solve 2-digit-times-2-digit multiplication problems that require carrying for the ones and carrying for the tens.	45–48
	Solve column problems that multiply a 3-digit value by a 2-digit value.	49, 51
Expanded Notation	Write statements of "expanded notation" for 2-digit values.	37–39

COLUMN SUBTRACTION

	Objectives	Lessons
	Write and solve subtraction problems that require one renaming.	1–4
	Write and solve column subtraction problems that require more than one renaming.	8, 9, 11

Objectives	Lessons
Solve column subtraction problems. Then check answers with a calculator.	12, 17
Write and solve column subtraction problems from row problems. Then check answers with a calculator.	13, 14
Solve subtraction problems that involve zero(s) and require renaming.	82–87

DIVISION

	Objectives	Lessons
No Remainder	Solve division problems that have a 3-digit dividend and a 3-digit answer.	33–35
	Solve division problems that have a 3-digit dividend and a 2-digit answer.	36, 37
	Work division problems by first underlining the first digit or the first two digits of the dividend to determine where to write the first digit of the answer.	38, 39, 41, 42
	Solve division problems, some of which have 4-digit dividends.	44
	Solve division problems that have zero(s) in the dividend.	45, 49, 51, 53
	Identify answers to division problems that do not have a sufficient number of digits in the answer.	45
	Work division problems that have 3-digit, 4-digit or 5-digit dividends.	50–52, 54–56
	Correct wrong answers to division problems.	57, 58
	Complete division equations of the form: 24 ÷ 6.	97, 98
Remainders	Complete equations that involve both multiplication and addition.	45–49, 52, 53, 56, 58, 63
	Work division problems in which the first digit of the answer has a remainder.	68–76
	Work division problems in which the last digit of the answer has a remainder.	106–110

EQUATIONS AND RELATIONSHIPS

Objectives	Lessons
Complete equations that have a missing sign or a missing number.	10, 14, 15
Say and work multiplication problems that have a missing middle number or a missing last number.	14–16, 18

Objectives	Lessons
Complete equations for fractions that equal whole numbers.	16–22
Write and complete equations with a missing number from verbal descriptions.	19–22, 26
Write multiplication and addition problems from descriptions that tell about what number.	20–22, 26
Write algebra multiplication problems as division problems.	21–24, 64, 65, 71–73
Complete inequalities for whole numbers.	21, 22
Copy fractions that equal whole numbers and write the equations for these fractions.	23–26, 28, 34
Write addition or multiplication equations using three compatible numbers.	27, 29, 31, 32
Complete equations to show the fraction that equals a whole number.	35, 36, 39–41, 43, 60
Rewrite equations of the form: number = number, sign, number.	37, 38
Write the missing operation sign in equations.	46
Write division problems and answers for fractions that equal whole numbers.	56–59, 61, 62, 88
Complete a table that has division problems and equations involving fractions and whole numbers.	63, 65
Complete a table that has rows for multiplication problems and corresponding division problems.	66, 67, 69
Complete equations that tell about the multiplication and addition needed to reach a number.	68, 69
Complete a table that shows corresponding multiplication facts, division facts and fraction-to-whole-number equations.	78
Write equations that show the fraction that equals a hundredth decimal number.	89–91
Write mixed numbers equal to decimals or decimals equal to mixed numbers.	91–93
Write fractions for division problems that use the sign: ÷.	95
Complete an equation that shows a division problem, the equivalent fraction and the equivalent whole number.	96

Objectives	Lessons
Complete a table with columns for decimal values, mixed numbers and fractions.	96, 97
Rewrite fractions as equivalent decimal values.	98, 99, 105

PLACE VALUE

	Objectives	Lessons
Whole Numbers	Read 4-digit thousands numerals.	1, 2
	Write 4-digit thousands numerals.	3–5
	Read thousands numerals that have more than 4 digits.	7, 9
	Read thousands numerals that have 4, 5 or 6 digits.	12
	Write 5-digit thousands numerals.	13
	Write 4- and 5-digit thousands numerals.	14
	Write 4-, 5- and 6-digit thousands numerals.	15, 17
	Write 4-, 5- and 6-digit thousands numerals from verbal descriptions.	16, 17, 21
	Round thousands numerals to the nearest thousand.	91
	Round thousands numerals to the nearest hundred.	92–95
Decimals	Write dollar-and-cents amounts from written descriptions.	8, 9, 13
	Align and compute dollar-and-cents amounts.	24, 26
	Write hundredths decimal values from descriptions.	87, 88
	Write equations that show the fraction that equals a hundredth decimal number.	89–91
	Order whole numbers, some of which have a decimal point and zeros after the decimal.	92–95
	Complete a table with columns for decimal values, mixed numbers and fractions.	96, 97
	Rewrite fractions as equivalent decimal values.	98, 99, 105

FRACTIONS

	Objectives	Lessons
Representation	Write fractions for pictures of fractions.	1, 2, 34
	Write fractions from pictures, then indicate which fractions are more than 1.	3–5
	Write fractions for separate groups and for number lines.	6–9
	Write fractions from descriptions that tell about the numbers or that tell about the picture.	7–11, 13, 15, 16, 34

	Objectives	Lessons
	Write equations for pictures of fractions that show whole numbers.	11–15
	Write fractions for whole numbers on a number line.	22–24
	Write fractions for zero on number lines.	25
	Write fractions that have a denominator of 1 for a "whole number" number line.	27
	Indicate verbally whether fractions equal 1 or do not equal 1.	33, 34
	Complete fractions for whole numbers on number lines that show no fractional divisions.	37–39, 41
	Indicate where fractions that do not equal whole numbers go on a number line.	46–48
	Identify numerators and denominators of fractions.	81
	Compare fractions with like numerators.	99–101
Equivalent Fractions	Complete equations for fractions that equal whole numbers.	16–22
	Complete equations to show various fractions that equal whole numbers.	29–34, 36, 43
	Identify pictures that show equivalent fractions and write the equation.	42–44
	Complete equations that show a whole number and an equivalent fraction.	55, 56
	Solve problems that multiply by a fraction, then write a simple equation for problems that multiply by 1.	56–58
	Complete equations that involve multiplying fractions, then write simple equations for problems that multiply by 1.	59–61, 63, 64
	Write equations for pairs of pictures of equivalent fractions, then identify the fractions that equal 1.	65–70, 73
	Complete equations involving equivalent fractions by indicating the fraction that equals 1 and completing the fraction after the equal sign.	66–69, 75
	Use division to figure out the missing fraction that equals 1.	73
	Write = or ≠ between pairs of fractions.	80–82, 96

Objectives		Lessons
	Solve equivalent-fraction problems to determine whether a decimal number or a fraction is larger.	106, 107
Fraction Addition/ Subtraction	Identify and work fraction addition and subtraction problems that can be worked without rewriting.	27–30, 32, 34
	Work a set of fraction problems that require addition, subtraction and multiplication.	51, 52, 61–63
Fraction Multiplication	Solve problems that multiply a fraction by a fraction.	46–49
	Work a set of fraction problems that require addition, subtraction and multiplication.	51, 52, 61–63
	Solve multiplication problems that have a fraction and a whole number.	53–55
	Solve multiplication problems that have a whole number and a fraction that equals 1.	54, 55
	Complete equations by figuring out the fraction the first value is multiplied by.	59–61
	Determine parts of two different fractions to complete equations that multiply fractions.	62
Mixed Numbers	Indicate where mixed numbers go on a number line for fifths.	34
	Indicate the appropriate number line for mixed numbers.	35–37
	Write addition equations for mixed numbers.	38, 39, 40, 41, 70
	Add or subtract to work problems that involve either a whole number and a fraction or two fractions.	42, 44, 45, 47
	Add or subtract to work problems that involve a whole number and a fraction.	43, 45, 47
	Write equations that show mixed numbers for fractions on a number line.	49, 52–54
	Write fractions for mixed numbers with 2-digit whole numbers or denominators.	52
	Complete equations to show the mixed numbers that equal fractions.	57–59
	Write equations that show the mixed numbers improper fractions equal.	61–65
	Write the whole number or mixed number a fraction equals.	66, 67

Objectives	Lessons
Fraction Comparison	
Follow instructions involving the word **denominator** to work mixed-number problems.	74
Write fractions for mixed numbers of the form: 4 + 36/100.	95
Write fractions that equal mixed numbers written without a plus sign.	100
Indicate whether fractions are more, less or equal to 1 from verbal descriptions.	35, 57
Identify whether a value is multiplied by more than 1 or less than 1.	71–73
Compare fractions with unlike denominators to determine which is larger.	72
Compare fractions with like or unlike denominators to determine which is larger.	74
Identify whether a fraction is multiplied by more than 1 or less than 1.	74, 75, 77–80
Indicate whether the answer to a fraction-multiplication problem is more than or less than the starting fraction.	81, 82
Identify whether a value is multiplied by more than 1, less than 1 or 1.	83, 84
Use equivalent-fraction equations to compare fractions.	101–103

RATIOS AND PROPORTIONS

Objectives	Lessons
Word Problems	
Write names and fractions for sentences that give ratio information.	64, 65
Write names and fractions for sentences that tell about **each** or **every.**	68, 69
Work complete ratio word problems.	71–78
Write names and fractions for sentences that use the wording: The ratio of . . .	81
Measurement Review of measurements for time and units of length.	3–41
Solve ratio problems involving length by using the table of measurement facts.	83, 84
Solve ratio problems involving units of time by referring to the table of measurement facts.	85
Solve ratio problems involving capacity by using the table of measurement facts.	86

Objectives	Lessons
Work a mixed set of ratio problems involving units of time, weight and capacity.	87, 88
Solve ratio problems involving metric units of length by using the table of measurement facts.	89
Work ratio problems involving time.	94
Work ratio problems that involve dollar amounts.	95–97
Write fractions for sentences that refer to **per.**	99
Compare two or three ratios.	102–105

NUMBER FAMILIES

	Objectives	Lessons
Families With Whole Numbers	Construct addition and subtraction problems from number families that have one missing number.	1–5
	Write and solve addition and subtraction problems from vertical number families.	6, 7
	Solve number-family problems based on data.	39, 41, 42
Fraction Number Families	Complete number families that show two fractions.	66
	Complete number families that show a fraction and a whole number.	67–69, 71
	Complete number families that show a fraction with a 2-digit or 3-digit denominator and the whole number 1.	76
	Write fraction number-families for different diagrams of fractions.	77, 78
Number-Family Tables	Compute the missing number in each row of a 3-by-3 table.	6, 7
	Compute the missing number in each column of a 3-by-3 table.	9
	Complete two number-family tables, one by working rows, the other by working columns.	11–14
	Figure out all the missing numbers in a table by first working all the columns that have two numbers, then working all the rows that have two numbers.	17–19, 21
	Answer questions by referring to a completed number-family table.	18, 19, 21, 23

Objectives	Lessons
Use number-family analysis to figure out all the missing numbers in a table.	22, 23, 25
Answer comparison questions by referring to a completed number-family table.	24–26
Write missing numbers in a table, then answer questions.	27–29
Complete a number-family table that gives only four numbers.	48
Complete a table that involves times for when a person leaves, how long the trip takes and when the person arrives.	51, 52
Use facts to put needed numbers in a 3-by-3 table.	53–57, 59
Use comparative information and number-family analysis to put a number in a 3-by-3 table.	61–65
Use facts including comparative information to put numbers in a 3-by-3 table.	66, 67
Use information displayed in a bar graph to generate numbers for a 3-by-3 table.	98, 99

WORD PROBLEMS

	Objectives	Lessons
Money Problems	Write addition problems to determine the cost of specified items that are displayed with price tags.	29, 31
	Solve multiplication word problems that tell about a dollar amount and the number of items purchased.	92
	Solve subtraction problems that involve items with price tags.	32, 33, 46
Comparison	Make number families with two names to show comparison.	24
	Make families with three names and a difference number from comparison sentences.	25–27
	Solve comparison word problems.	28, 29, 31
	Solve word problems that ask about the difference.	43, 44
	Solve word problems, some of which ask about the difference and some of which tell about the difference.	45, 46
	Solve price-tag problems that ask about the difference.	47, 48

	Objectives	Lessons
	Solve price-tag problems, some of which ask about the difference and some of which tell about the difference.	52, 60
	Use numerical answers to price-tag problems to identify "mystery items."	53
	Use price-tag information to work a set of comparison problems that ask about the name of objects or the difference number.	54, 59
	Make number families for price-tag comparison sentences.	61
	Work variations of comparison problems involving price tags.	62, 63
Classification	Solve word problems that require classification inferences.	16–19, 22
Discrimination	Make number families for sentences, some of which compare and some of which classify.	33–35
	Solve number-family problems, some of which compare and some of which classify.	36, 37
	Work a mixed set of number-family word problems.	88, 89
	Work a mixed set of word problems involving dollar amounts.	93, 94
Fractions	Write fraction number-families from word problems.	79
	Make fraction number-families to solve word problems.	81–83
	Solve fraction number-family word problems that give numbers, not fractions.	84–86
	Work a mixed set of fraction number-family word problems.	87
	Solve fraction number-family word problems that ask questions about **numbers** and about **fractions.**	88, 89
Multi-Step	Work problems that involve given information about amounts **in,** amounts **out** and amounts **ended up** with.	74–78
	Work "stacking" problems that give more than one value for in or for out.	79, 81–87

GEOMETRY

	Objectives	Lessons
Area	Compute the area of rectangles, first by repeated addition, then by multiplication.	9, 12

	Objectives	Lessons
Perimeter	Compute the area of rectangles by multiplication.	13
	Compute the area of rectangles and write abbreviations for the appropriate unit names in the answers.	14–16, 18
	Draw diagrams from descriptions of rectangles and compute the area.	19, 21, 22
	Work area-of-rectangle problems that require multiplication or division.	79, 81, 83, 84
	Compute the perimeter of rectangles by addition.	85
	Compute both the perimeter and area of rectangles.	86, 87
	Compute perimeters of figures that are not rectangles.	88, 89
	Figure out the length of a side by using a number family.	90–92
	Work a set of problems that ask about the length of an unmarked side or about the perimeter.	93
	Work a mixed set of area word problems, some of which ask about the length of a side, some of which ask about the number of square units.	96, 97
Volume	Compute the volume of a box.	98, 99
Parallel & Intersect	Identify pairs of lines that intersect and that are parallel.	99, 100

FUNCTIONS

	Objectives	Lessons
Coordinate System	Use information about X and Y coordinates to identify points.	72–74
	Write X and Y values for points on a coordinate grid.	75, 76
	Complete a function table that gives values for X and the function rule.	77–79, 81, 82
	Use information about X and Y values to plot points and draw a line on a coordinate grid.	83, 84
	Complete a function table and graph the function.	85–87
	Write two functions for specified X and Y values.	88, 89, 91, 92
	Select the appropriate function rule and complete a function table.	93–96

Objectives	Lessons
Complete a function table and determine a function rule given a graph of the function.	97, 98
Plot equivalent fractions on a coordinate system.	105
Plot equivalent ratios on a coordinate system.	106
Use a graph of equivalent ratios on a coordinate grid to answer questions.	107, 108
Sequence Write a function to express the pattern in a sequence.	100–105

PROBABILITY

Objectives	Lessons
Rank fractions for the probability of picking a winner.	91–93
Translate fractions into statements of probability involving winners and losers.	93, 94
Conduct an experiment that compares probability predictions with actual outcomes.	94
Make a fraction number-family based on a description of winners and losers in a set.	95–97
Solve problems that ask about the probability of winners or expected trials.	98, 99, 101, 102

PROJECTS

Objectives	Lessons
Project: Conduct an experiment to test a prediction of the number of trials needed to get 20 winners when flipping one coin.	101
Project: Conduct an experiment to test a prediction of the number of needed trials to get 20 winners flipping two coins simultaneously.	102
Project: Conduct an experiment to determine the number of cards that are winners.	103–105
Project: Conduct an experiment to verify whether the probability of three coins being all heads is 1 out of 6 or 1 out of 8.	106
Project: Determine the probability of 4 out of 4 coins being heads and 5 out of 5 coins being heads.	107
Project: Determine the ratio of winners to total possibilities of a die; then conduct experiments to confirm the fraction 1-sixth.	108
Project: Predict the probability of two dice both showing 1 and conduct an experiment to verify or refute the prediction.	109

Objectives	Lessons
Project: Conduct an experiment to determine the number of cards that are winners; then plot the ratios on a coordinate grid and answer questions.	110
Project: Verify that the area of a triangle is 1-half the area of a rectangle with the same base and height.	111
Project: Verify that the equation for the area of a triangle works for right triangles of different shapes.	112
Project: Demonstrate that the equation for the area of a triangle works for triangles that do not have a 90-degree angle.	113
Project: Figure the area and perimeter of a room; then compute the cost of carpeting the room and installing baseboard molding.	114
Project: Figure out the "rules" for the relationship between perimeter and area of a square.	115
Project: Demonstrate that the equation for the area of a triangle works for a range of triangles that have the same base and same height.	116
Project: Figure out the dimensions of a "mystery" rectangle by using clues that tell about the (a) relationship of its width and height; (b) range of its area; (c) relationship between its area and perimeter.	117
Project: Conduct a sighting experiment to arrange cards of different heights so they appear to be the same height; then use ratio equations to confirm the distances between cards and spotter.	118
Project: Graph data from the experiment in lesson 118 to show the general function for the relationship between the height of an object and its distance from the spotter.	119
Project: Create a function table for converting a cake recipe that serves 4 into a recipe that serves 12.	120
Project: (This exercise is optional.) Conduct a survey; use the results as a basis for projecting the results of a survey that involves a larger number of respondents; then combine data with those from other small-scale surveys on the same topic.	120

Skills Profile

Student's name _____ Grade or year in school _____

Teacher's name _____

Starting lesson _____ Date _____

Last lesson Completed _____ Date _____ Number of days absent _____

Summary of In-program Test Performance

Workbook   **Textbook**

	Part 1	Part 2	Part 3	Part 4	Part 5	Part 6	Part 7			
Test 1	+ −	+ −	+ −	Part 4	Part 5					
Test 2	+ −	+ −	+ −	+ −	+ −	+ −	+ −			
Test 3	+ −	+ −	+ −	+ −	+ −	+ −	+ −			
Test 4	+ −	+ −	+ −	+ −	+ −	+ −	+ −	Part 1 + −	Part 2 + −	
Test 5	+ −	+ −	+ −	+ −	+ −	Part 1 + −	Part 2 + −	Part 3 + −		
Test 6	+ −	+ −	+ −	+ −	+ −	+ −	Part 7a, b, c + −	Part 7 d, e + −	Part 8 + −	
Test 7	+ −	+ −	+ −	+ −	Part 1 + −	Part 2 + −	Part 3 + −	Part 4 + −		
Test 8	+ −	+ −	+ −	+ −	Part 1 + −	Part 2 + −	Part 3 + −	Part 4 + −	Part 5 + −	
Test 9	+ −	+ −	+ −	+ −	Part 1 + −	Part 2 + −	Part 3 + −	Part 4 + −	Part 5 + −	Part 6 + −
Test 10	+ −	+ −	+ −	Part 1 + −	Part 2 + −	Part 3 + −	Part 4 + −	Part 5 + −		

The charts on pages 174 to 183 may be reproduced to make a skills profile for each student. The charts summarize the skills presented in *Connecting Math Concepts D* and provide space for indicating the date on which the student completes the lessons in which the skills are taught.

© SRA/McGraw-Hill. Permission is granted to reproduce for school use.

Skills	Taught in these Lessons	Date Lessons Completed
FACTS **Multiplication**		
Uses a number map to organize the multiplication facts that involve 5.	1–10	
Uses a number map to organize the multiplication facts that involve 9.	5–9	
Writes answers to multiplication problems that involve 9.	8–13	
Writes answers to multiplication facts, some of which have a 1 or a zero.	9	
Completes numbers in a number map for threes.	11, 12	
Uses number maps to organize multiplication facts that involve 3.	13–19	
Says and works multiplication problems that have a missing middle number or a missing last number.	14–18	
Writes answers to multiplication facts that involve 3.	18	
Figures out the missing middle number for multiplication problems that have 9.	23–25	
Figures out the missing middle number or the missing first number for multiplication problems that involve 9.	26	
Uses number maps to organize the multiplication facts that involve 4.	28	
Completes a number map for fours and uses the map to write answers to multiplication problems that involve 4.	29–31	
Writes answers to multiplication facts that involve 4.	32–56	
Completes a number map for multiplying by 7.	48–50	
Uses a number map to organize multiplication facts that involve 7.	49–52	
Writes answers to multiplication facts that involve 7.	55–57	
Works with "square" facts for multiplying.	58, 59	

Skills	Taught in these Lessons	Date Lessons Completed
Completes a number map for multiplying by 6.	63–66	
Writes answers to multiplication problems that involve 6.	65–68	
Division		
Writes algebra multiplication problems as division problems.	21–73	
Writes division problems from statements that tell about "times."	25–27	
Writes answers to division fact problems.	28–48	
Applies division rule for 5 to numerals that end in zero or 5.	31, 32	
Works a set of problems that divide by 5 and 9.	33	
Solves division problems that divide by 3.	34–38	
Works division problems that have zero as a dividend.	35	
Solves division problems that involve 4.	42–56	
Writes and solves dictated division-fact problems.	55, 56	
Uses a number map to organize division facts that involve 7.	58–60	
Writes answers to division problems that divide by 6.	76–86	
Works a set of division problems that divide by 7, 6, 4 and 3.	87	
CALCULATOR SKILLS		
Uses a calculator to check answers to problems.	4–8	
Uses a calculator to check addition problems that have more than two addends.	6	
Solves column subtraction problems. Then checks answers with a calculator.	12–17	

© SRA/McGraw-Hill. Permission is granted to reproduce for school use.

Skills	Taught in these Lessons	Date Lessons Completed
Writes and solves column subtraction problems from row problems. Then checks answers with a calculator.	13, 14	
Solves column multiplication problems. Then checks answers with a calculator.	38	
WHOLE NUMBER OPERATIONS		
Writes and solves column addition problems.	1	
Works a set of problems that calls for different operations: addition, subtraction, multiplication.	5	
Solves multiplication problems that involve a money amount and a whole number.	89–91	
Estimates the sums of addition problems involving hundreds or thousands numbers.	97, 98	
MENTAL ARITHMETIC		
Writes answers to orally presented addition problems that have a 2-digit and a 1-digit addend.	49	
Works mental addition problems that require renaming.	55–57	
Solves mental addition problems of the form: 56 plus what number equals 60?	62–64	
Solves problems of the form: Some number plus 1 equals 600.	78–82	
COLUMN MULTIPLICATION **Times 1 Digit**		
Solves column multiplication problems that multiply 2-digit numerals by 1-digit numerals.	1–5	
Solves column multiplication problems that multiply 3-digit numerals by 1-digit numerals.	6–8	
Solves column multiplication problems that have a zero.	15, 16	
Solves multiplication problems that have a 5-digit value times a 1-digit value.	23	

Skills	Taught in these Lessons	Date Lessons Completed
Times 2 Digits		
Solves row problems that multiply a 1-digit value by a tens number.	32, 33	
Solves column problems that multiply a 1-digit value by a tens number.	34, 35	
Solves column problems that multiply a 2-digit value by a tens value.	36	
Solves column multiplication problems. Then checks answers with a calculator.	38	
Solves 2-digit-times-2-digit multiplication problems that require no carrying or carrying for the tens only.	41–44	
Solves 2-digit-times-2-digit multiplication problems that require carrying for the ones and carrying for the tens.	45–48	
Solves column problems that multiply a 3-digit value by a 2-digit value.	49–51	
Expanded Notation		
Writes statements of "expanded notation" for 2-digit values.	37–39	
COLUMN SUBTRACTION		
Writes and solves subtraction problems that require one renaming.	1–4	
Writes and solves column subtraction problems that require more than one renaming.	8–11	
Solves column subtraction problems. Then checks answers with a calculator.	12–17	
Writes and solves column subtraction problems from row problems. Then checks answers with a calculator.	13, 14	
Solves subtraction problems that involve items with price tags.	32–46	
Solves subtraction problems that involve zero(s) and require renaming.	82–87	

© SRA/McGraw-Hill. Permission is granted to reproduce for school use. *Skills Profile* **175**

Skills	Taught in these Lessons	Date Lessons Completed
DIVISION **No Remainder**		
Solves division problems that have a 3-digit dividend and a 3-digit answer.	33–35	
Solves division problems that have a 3-digit dividend and a 2-digit answer.	36, 37	
Works division problems by first underlining the first digit or the first two digits of the dividend to determine where to write the first digit of the answer.	38–42	
Solves division problems, some of which have 4-digit dividends.	44	
Solves division problems that have zero(s) in the dividend.	45–53	
Identifies answers to division problems that do not have a sufficient number of digits in the answer.	45	
Works division problems that have 3-digit, 4-digit or 5-digit dividends.	50–56	
Corrects wrong answers to division problems.	57, 58	
Completes division equations of the form: 24 ÷ 6.	97, 98	
Remainders		
Completes equations that involve both multiplication and addition.	45–63	
Works division problems in which the first digit of the answer has a remainder.	68–76	
Works division problems in which the last digit of the answer has a remainder.	106–110	
EQUATIONS AND RELATIONSHIPS		
Completes equations that have a missing sign or a missing number.	10–15	
Says and works multiplication problems that have a missing middle number or a missing last number.	14–18	
Completes equations for fractions that equal whole numbers.	16–22	

Skills	Taught in these Lessons	Date Lessons Completed
Writes and completes equations with a missing number from verbal descriptions.	19–26	
Writes multiplication and addition problems from descriptions that tell about what number.	20–26	
Write algebra multiplication problems as division problems.	21–73	
Completes inequalities for whole numbers.	21, 22	
Copies fractions that equal whole numbers and writes the equations for these fractions.	23–34	
Writes addition or multiplication equations using three compatible numbers.	27–32	
Completes equations to show the fraction that equals a whole number.	35–60	
Rewrites equations of the form: number = number, sign, number.	37, 38	
Writes the missing operation sign in equations.	46	
Writes division problems and answers for fractions that equal whole numbers.	56–88	
Completes a table that has division problems and equations involving fractions and whole numbers.	63–65	
Completes a table that has rows for multiplication problems and corresponding division problems.	66–69	
Completes equations that tell about the multiplication and addition needed to reach a number.	68, 69	
Completes a table that shows corresponding multiplication facts, division facts and fraction-to-whole-number equations.	78	
Writes equations that show the fraction that equals a hundredth decimal number.	89–91	
Writes mixed numbers equal to decimals or decimals equal to mixed numbers.	91–93	

 © SRA/McGraw-Hill. Permission is granted to reproduce for school use.

Name _____

Skills	Taught in these Lessons	Date Lessons Completed
Writes fractions for division problems that use the sign: ÷.	95	
Completes an equation that shows a division problem, the equivalent fraction and the equivalent whole number.	96	
Completes a table with columns for decimal values, mixed numbers and fractions.	96, 97	
Rewrites fractions as equivalent decimal values.	98–105	
PLACE VALUE **Whole Numbers**		
Reads 4-digit thousands numerals.	1, 2	
Writes 4-digit thousands numerals.	3–5	
Reads thousands numerals that have more than 4 digits.	7–9	
Reads thousands numerals that have 4, 5 or 6 digits.	12	
Writes 5-digit thousands numerals.	13	
Writes 4- and 5-digit thousands numerals.	14	
Writes 4-, 5- and 6-digit thousands numerals.	15–17	
Writes 4-, 5- and 6-digit thousands numerals from verbal descriptions.	16–21	
Rounds thousands numerals to the nearest thousand.	91	
Rounds thousands numerals to the nearest hundred.	92–95	
Decimals		
Writes dollar-and-cents amounts from written descriptions.	8–13	
Aligns and computes dollar-and-cents amounts.	24–26	
Writes hundredths decimal values from descriptions.	87, 88	
Writes equations that show the fraction that equals a hundredth decimal number.	89–91	

Skills	Taught in these Lessons	Date Lessons Completed
Orders whole numbers, some of which have a decimal point and zeros after the decimal.	92–95	
Completes a table with columns for decimal values, mixed numbers and fractions.	96, 97	
Rewrites fractions as equivalent decimal values.	98–105	
FRACTIONS **Representation**		
Writes fractions for pictures of fractions.	1–34	
Writes fractions from pictures, then indicates which fractions are more than 1.	3–5	
Writes fractions for separate groups and for number lines.	6–9	
Writes fractions from descriptions that tell about the numbers or that tell about the picture.	7–34	
Writes equations for pictures of fractions that show whole numbers.	11–15	
Writes fractions for whole numbers on a number line.	22–24	
Writes fractions for zero on number lines.	25	
Writes fractions that have a denominator of 1 for a "whole number" number line.	27	
Indicates verbally whether fractions equal 1 or do not equal 1.	33, 34	
Completes fractions for whole numbers on number lines that show no fractional divisions.	37–41	
Indicates where fractions that do not equal whole numbers go on a number line.	46–48	
Identifies numerators and denominators of fractions.	81	
Compares fractions with like numerators.	99–101	

© SRA/McGraw-Hill. Permission is granted to reproduce for school use. *Skills Profile*

Skills	Taught in these Lessons	Date Lessons Completed
Equivalent Fractions		
Completes equations for fractions that equal whole numbers.	16–22	
Completes equations to show various fractions that equal whole numbers.	29–43	
Identifies pictures that show equivalent fractions and write the equation.	42–44	
Completes equations that show a whole number and an equivalent fraction.	55, 56	
Solves problems that multiply by a fraction, then writes a simple equation for problems that multiply by 1.	56–58	
Completes equations that involve multiplying fractions, then writes simple equations for problems that multiply by 1.	59–64	
Writes equations for pairs of pictures of equivalent fractions, then identifies the fractions that equal 1.	65–73	
Completes equations involving equivalent fractions by indicating the fraction that equals 1 and completing the fraction after the equal sign.	66–75	
Uses division to figure out the missing fraction that equals 1.	73	
Writes = or ≠ between pairs of fractions.	80–96	
Solves equivalent-fraction problems to determine whether a decimal number or a fraction is larger.	106, 107	
Fraction Addition/Subtraction		
Identifies and works fraction addition and subtraction problems that can be worked without rewriting.	27–34	
Works a set of fraction problems that require addition, subtraction and multiplication.	51–63	
Fraction Multiplication		
Solves problems that multiply a fraction by a fraction.	46–49	

Skills	Taught in these Lessons	Date Lessons Completed
Works a set of fraction problems that require addition, subtraction and multiplication.	51–63	
Solves multiplication problems that have a fraction and a whole number.	53–55	
Solves multiplication problems that have a whole number and a fraction that equals 1.	54, 55	
Completes equations by figuring out the fraction the first value is multiplied by.	59–61	
Determines parts of two different fractions to complete equations that multiply fractions.	62	
Mixed Numbers		
Indicates where mixed numbers go on a number line for fifths.	34	
Indicates the appropriate number line for mixed numbers.	35–37	
Writes addition equations for mixed numbers.	38–70	
Adds or subtracts to work problems that involve either a whole number and a fraction or two fractions.	42–47	
Adds or subtracts to work problems that involve a whole number and a fraction.	43–47	
Writes equations that show mixed numbers for fractions on a number line.	49–54	
Writes fractions for mixed numbers with 2-digit whole numbers or denominators.	52	
Completes equations to show the mixed numbers that equal fractions.	57–59	
Writes equations that show the mixed numbers improper fractions equal.	61–65	
Writes the whole number or mixed number a fraction equals.	66, 67	
Follows instructions involving the word **denominator** to work mixed-number problems.	74	

© SRA/McGraw-Hill. Permission is granted to reproduce for school use.

Name _____

Skills	Taught in these Lessons	Date Lessons Completed
Writes fractions for mixed numbers of the form: 4 + 36/100.	95	
Writes fractions that equal mixed numbers written without a plus sign.	100	
Fraction Comparison		
Indicates whether fractions are more, less or equal to 1 from verbal descriptions.	35–57	
Identifies whether a value is multiplied by more than 1 or less than 1.	71–73	
Compares fractions with unlike denominators to determine which is larger.	72	
Compares fractions with like or unlike denominators to determine which is larger.	74	
Identifies whether a fraction is multiplied by more than 1 or less than 1.	74–80	
Indicates whether the answer to a fraction-multiplication problem is more than or less than the starting fraction.	81, 82	
Identifies whether a value is multiplied by more than 1, less than 1 or 1.	83, 84	
Uses equivalent-fraction equations to compare fractions.	101–103	
RATIOS AND PROPORTIONS **Word Problems**		
Writes names and fractions for sentences that give ratio information.	64, 65	
Writes names and fractions for sentences that tell about **each** or **every**.	68, 69	
Works complete ratio word problems.	71–78	
Writes names and fractions for sentences that use the wording: The ratio of . . .	81	
Measurement		
Solves ratio problems involving length by using the table of measurement facts.	83, 84	

Skills	Taught in these Lessons	Date Lessons Completed
Solves ratio problems involving units of time by referring to the table of measurement facts.	85	
Solves ratio problems involving capacity by using the table of measurement facts.	86	
Works a mixed set of ratio problems involving units of time, weight and capacity.	87, 88	
Solves ratio problems involving metric units of length by using the table of measurement facts.	89	
Works ratio problems involving time.	94	
Works ratio problems that involve dollar amounts.	95–97	
Writes fractions for sentences that refer to **per**.	99	
Compares two or three ratios.	102–105	
NUMBER FAMILIES **Families with Whole Numbers**		
Constructs addition and subtraction problems from number families that have one missing number.	1–5	
Writes and solves addition and subtraction problems from vertical number families.	6, 7	
Solves number-family problems based on data.	39–42	
Fraction Number Families		
Completes number families that show two fractions.	66	
Completes number families that show a fraction and a whole number.	67–71	
Completes number families that show a fraction with a 2-digit or 3-digit denominator and the whole number 1.	76	
Writes fraction number-families for different diagrams of fractions.	77, 78	

© SRA/McGraw-Hill. Permission is granted to reproduce for school use. *Skills Profile* **179**

Skills	Taught in these Lessons	Date Lessons Completed
Number-Family Tables		
Computes the missing number in each row of a 3-by-3 table.	6, 7	
Computes the missing number in each column of a 3-by-3 table.	9	
Completes two number-family tables, one by working rows, the other by working columns.	11–14	
Figures out all the missing numbers in a table by first working all the columns that have two numbers, then working all the rows that have two numbers.	17–21	
Answers questions by referring to a completed number-family table.	18–23	
Uses number-family analysis to figure out all the missing numbers in a table.	22–25	
Answers comparison questions by referring to a completed number-family table.	24–26	
Writes missing numbers in a table, then answers questions.	27–29	
Completes a number-family table that gives only four numbers.	48	
Completes a table that involves times for when a person leaves, how long the trip takes and when the person arrives.	51, 52	
Uses facts to put needed numbers in a 3-by-3 table.	53–59	
Uses comparative information and number-family analysis to put a number in a 3-by-3 table.	61–65	
Uses facts including comparative information to put numbers in a 3-by-3 table.	66, 67	
Uses information displayed in a bar graph to generate numbers for a 3-by-3 table.	98, 99	

Skills	Taught in these Lessons	Date Lessons Completed
WORD PROBLEMS **Money Problems**		
Writes addition problems to determine the cost of specified items that are displayed with price tags.	29–31	
Solves multiplication word problems that tell about a dollar amount and the number of items purchased.	92	
Comparison		
Makes number families with two names to show comparison.	24	
Makes families with three names and a difference number from comparison sentences.	25–27	
Solves comparison word problems.	28–31	
Solves word problems that ask about the difference.	43, 44	
Solves word problems, some of which ask about the difference and some of which tell about the difference.	45, 46	
Solves price-tag problems that ask about the difference.	47, 48	
Solves price-tag problems, some of which ask about the difference and some of which tell about the difference.	52–60	
Uses numberical answers to price-tag problems to identify "mystery items."	53	
Uses price-tag information to work a set of comparison problems that ask about the name of objects or the difference number.	54–59	
Makes number families for price-tag comparison sentences.	61	
Works variations of comparison problems involving price tags.	62, 63	
Classification		
Solves word problems that require classification inferences.	16–22	

Connecting Math Concepts, Level D Guide   © SRA/McGraw-Hill. Permission is granted to reproduce for school use.

Name _____

Skills	Taught in these Lessons	Date Lessons Completed
Discrimination		
Makes number families for sentences, some of which compare and some of which classify.	33–35	
Solves number-family problems, some of which compare and some of which classify.	36, 37	
Works a mixed set of number-family word problems.	88, 89	
Works a mixed set of word problems involving dollar amounts.	93, 94	
Fractions		
Writes fraction number-families from word problems.	79	
Makes fraction number-families to solve word problems.	81–83	
Solves fraction number-family word problems that give numbers, not fractions.	84–86	
Works a mixed set of fraction number-family word problems.	87	
Solves fraction number-family word problems that ask questions about **numbers** and about **fractions.**	88, 89	
Multi-Step		
Works problems that involve given information about amounts **in,** amounts **out** and amounts **ended up** with.	74–78	
Works "stacking" problems that give more than one value for in or for out.	79–87	
GEOMETRY **Area**		
Computes the area of rectangles, first by repeated addition, then by multiplication.	9–12	
Computes the area of rectangles by multiplication.	13	
Computes the area of rectangles and write abbreviations for the appropriate unit names in the answers.	14–18	

Skills	Taught in these Lessons	Date Lessons Completed
Draws diagrams from descriptions of rectangles and computes the area.	19–22	
Works area-of-rectangle problems that require multiplication or division.	79–84	
Perimeter		
Computes the perimeter of rectangles by addition.	85	
Computes both the perimeter and area of rectangles.	86, 87	
Computes perimeters of figures that are not rectangles.	88, 89	
Figures out the length of a side by using a number family.	90–92	
Works a set of problems that ask about the length of an unmarked side or about the perimeter.	93	
Works a mixed set of area word problems, some of which ask about the length of a side, some of which ask about the number of square units.	96, 97	
Volume		
Computes the volume of a box.	98, 99	
Parallel & Intersect		
Identifies pairs of lines that intersect and that are parallel.	99, 100	
FUNCTIONS		
Coordinate System		
Uses information about X and Y coordinates to identify points.	72–74	
Writes X and Y values for points on a coordinate grid.	75, 76	
Completes a function table that gives values for X and the function rule.	77–82	
Uses information about X and Y values to plot points and draws a line on a coordinate grid.	83, 84	
Completes a function table and graphs the function.	85–87	

Skills	Taught in these Lessons	Date Lessons Completed	Skills	Taught in these Lessons	Date Lessons Completed
Writes two functions for specified X and Y values.	88–92		Project: Conducts an experiment to determine the number of cards that are winners.	103–105	
Selects the appropriate function rule and completes a function table.	93–96		Project: Conducts an experiment to verify whether the probability of three coins being all heads is 1 out of 6 or 1 out of 8.	106	
Completes a function table and determines a function rule given a graph of the function.	97, 98		Project: Determines the probability of 4 out of 4 coins being heads and 5 out of 5 coins being heads.	107	
Plots equivalent fractions on a coordinate system.	105		Project: Determines the ratio of winners to total possibilities of a die; then conducts experiments to confirm the fraction 1-sixth.	108	
Plots equivalent ratios on a coordinate system.	106		Project: Predicts the probability of two dice both showing 1 and conducts an experiment to verify or refute the prediction.	109	
Uses a graph of equivalent ratios on a coordinate grid to answer questions.	107, 108		Project: Conducts an experiment to determine the number of cards that are winners; then plots the ratios on a coordinate grid and answers questions.	110	
Sequence			Project: Verifies that the area of a triangle is 1-half the area of a rectangle with the same base and height.	111	
Writes a function to express the pattern in a sequence.	100–105		Project: Verifies that the equation for the area of a triangle works for right triangles of different shapes.	112	
PROBABILITY			Project: Demonstrates that the equation for the area of a triangle works for triangles that do not have a 90-degree angle.	113	
Ranks fractions for the probability of picking a winner.	91–93		Project: Figures the area and perimeter of a room; then computes the cost of carpeting the room and installing baseboard molding.	114	
Translates fractions into statements of probability involving winners and losers.	93, 94		Project: Figures out the "rules" for the relationship between perimeter and area of a square.	115	
Conducts an experiment that compares probability predictions with actual outcomes.	94		Project: Demonstrates that the equation for the area of a triangle works for a range of triangles that have the same base and same height.	116	
Makes a fraction number-family based on a description of winners and losers in a set.	95–97				
Solves problems that ask about the probability of winners or expected trials.	98–102				
PROJECTS					
Project: Conducts an experiment to test a prediction of the number of trials needed to get 20 winners when flipping one coin.	101				
Project: Conducts an experiment to test a prediction of the number of needed trials to get 20 winners flipping two coins simultaneously.	102				

© SRA/McGraw-Hill. Permission is granted to reproduce for school use.

Skills	Taught in these Lessons	Date Lessons Completed
Project: Figure out the dimensions of a "mystery" rectangle by using clues that tell about the (a) relationship of its width and height; (b) range of its area; (c) relationship between its area and perimeter.	117	
Project: Conducts a sighting experiment to arrange cards of different heights so they appear to be the same height; then uses ratio equations to confirm the distances between cards and spotter.	118	
Project: Graphs data from the experiment in lesson 118 to show the general function for the relationship between the height of an object and its distance from the spotter.	119	

Skills	Taught in these Lessons	Date Lessons Completed
Project: Creates a function table for converting a cake recipe that serves 4 into a recipe that serves 12.	120	
Project: (This exercise is optional.) Conducts a survey; uses the results as a basis for projecting the results of a survey that involves a larger number of respondents; then combines data with those from other small-scale surveys on the same topic.	120	

© SRA/McGraw-Hill. Permission is granted to reproduce for school use. *Skills Profile* **183**

Remedy Summary—Group Summary of Test Performance

Note: Test remedies are specified in the *Answer Key.* Percent Summary is also specified in the *Answer Key.*

Name	Test 1 Check parts not passed 1	2	3	4	5	Total %	Test 2 Check parts not passed 1	2	3	4	5	6	7	Total %
1.														
2.														
3.														
4.														
5.														
6.														
7.														
8.														
9.														
10.														
11.														
12.														
13.														
14.														
15.														
16.														
17.														
18.														
19.														
20.														
21.														
22.														
23.														
24.														
25.														
26.														
27.														
28.														
29.														
30.														
Number of Students Not Passed = NP														
Total number of students = T														
Remedy needed if NP/T = 25% or more														

Copyright © SRA/McGraw-Hill. Permission is granted to reproduce for school use.

Remedy Summary—Group Summary of Test Performance

	Test 3								Test 4									
	Check parts not passed							Total %	Check parts not passed									Total %
Name	1	2	3	4	5	6	7		1	2	3	4	5	6	7	8	9	
1.																		
2.																		
3.																		
4.																		
5.																		
6.																		
7.																		
8.																		
9.																		
10.																		
11.																		
12.																		
13.																		
14.																		
15.																		
16.																		
17.																		
18.																		
19.																		
20.																		
21.																		
22.																		
23.																		
24.																		
25.																		
26.																		
27.																		
28.																		
29.																		
30.																		
Number of Students Not Passed = NP																		
Total number of students = T																		
Remedy needed if NP/T = 25% or more																		

Copyright © SRA/McGraw-Hill. Permission is granted to reproduce for school use.

Remedy Summary—Group Summary of Test Performance

Name	Test 5 Check parts not passed 1	2	3	4	5	6	7	8	Total %	Test 6 Check parts not passed 1	2	3	4	5	6	7 a,b,c	7 d,e	8	Total %
1.																			
2.																			
3.																			
4.																			
5.																			
6.																			
7.																			
8.																			
9.																			
10.																			
11.																			
12.																			
13.																			
14.																			
15.																			
16.																			
17.																			
18.																			
19.																			
20.																			
21.																			
22.																			
23.																			
24.																			
25.																			
26.																			
27.																			
28.																			
29.																			
30.																			
Number of Students Not Passed = NP																			
Total number of students = T																			
Remedy needed if NP/T = 25% or more																			

Copyright © SRA/McGraw-Hill. Permission is granted to reproduce for school use.

Remedy Summary—Group Summary of Test Performance

Name	Test 7 Check parts not passed								Total %	Test 8 Check parts not passed									Total %
	1	2	3	4	5	6	7	8		1	2	3	4	5	6	7	8	9	
1.																			
2.																			
3.																			
4.																			
5.																			
6.																			
7.																			
8.																			
9.																			
10.																			
11.																			
12.																			
13.																			
14.																			
15.																			
16.																			
17.																			
18.																			
19.																			
20.																			
21.																			
22.																			
23.																			
24.																			
25.																			
26.																			
27.																			
28.																			
29.																			
30.																			
Number of Students Not Passed = NP																			
Total number of students = T																			
Remedy needed if NP/T = 25% or more																			

Copyright © SRA/McGraw-Hill. Permission is granted to reproduce for school use.

Remedy Summary—Group Summary of Test Performance

Name	Test 9 Check parts not passed										Total %	Test 10 Check parts not passed								Total %
	1	2	3	4	5	6	7	8	9	10		1	2	3	4	5	6	7	8	
1.																				
2.																				
3.																				
4.																				
5.																				
6.																				
7.																				
8.																				
9.																				
10.																				
11.																				
12.																				
13.																				
14.																				
15.																				
16.																				
17.																				
18.																				
19.																				
20.																				
21.																				
22.																				
23.																				
24.																				
25.																				
26.																				
27.																				
28.																				
29.																				
30.																				
Number of Students Not Passed = NP																				
Total number of students = T																				
Remedy needed if NP/T = 25% or more																				

Copyright © SRA/McGraw-Hill. Permission is granted to reproduce for school use.